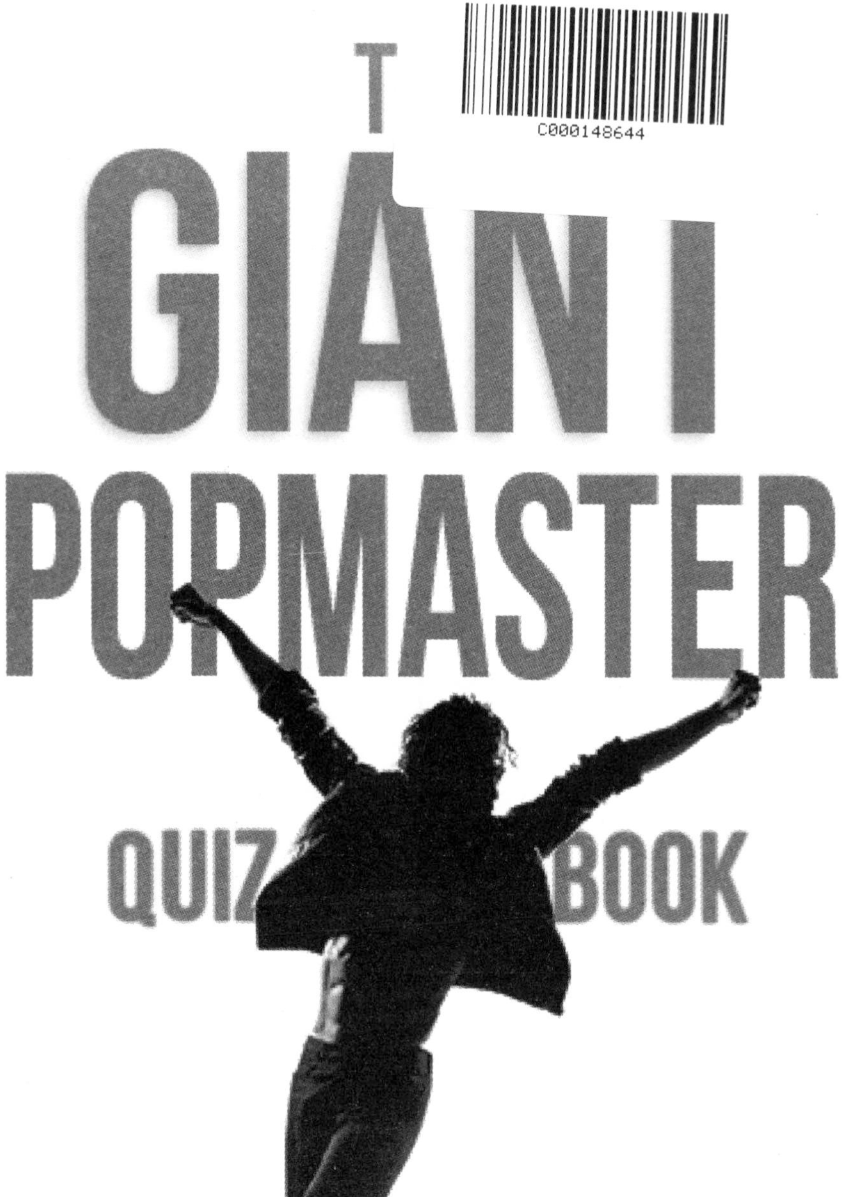

BBC RADIO 2

First published in this edition October 2017
by Red Planet Publishing Ltd

Paperback ISBN: 978 1 911346 80 7

Printed in the UK by CPI Group

For more information about our music books visit:
www.musicbookclub.co.uk

BBC Radio 2 logo used by permission
PopMaster Logo © Red Planet Publishing Ltd

Red Planet is an imprint of Red Planet Publishing Ltd

Contains questions published in previous PopMaster Quiz books

BBC RADIO 2

Welcome

In 1996, my daily mid-morning show on BBC Radio 2 was given a refresh and some old features taken out and new ones substituted. One of the ideas I wanted to include was a daily pop quiz so I invited my producer at the time, Colin Martin and quiz setter and colleague Phil Swern out to lunch to discuss a format that could work on a daily basis. After two bottles of rather expensive red wine, we had virtually developed the concept of PopMaster which, after a few dry runs, was introduced into the programme a few weeks later. It has now become one of the high spots of the morning with many thousands of listeners taking their tea break at 10.30 in order to catch the quiz.

We have now asked over 90.000 questions to more than 5,000 contestants since the inception of the quiz-but despite that, current question setters Phil Swern and Neil Myners have come up with some new and even more intriguing head-scratchers for what I hope will prove to be an entertaining quiz book.

In 2013 I presented a live version of PopMaster in Manchester to raise money for the charity Children In Need that was filled to capacity and BBC Radio 2 decided to repeat the event on a somewhat larger scale in 2015 and again in 2016 in Glasgow.

I'm also happy to be able to announce that this year we began taking PopMaster on the road to selective venues and plan to continue to hold even more live events in 2018 to a live audience in selected towns across the UK.

I hope you enjoy answering the questions posed and if you score well, then perhaps you'll be brave enough to apply to join me live one morning on Radio 2 as a contestant!

Ken Bruce
BBC Radio 2

IMPORTANT

The *answers to all questions are cunningly printed on the outside column of the page directly after the quiz page you're looking at. The answers are therefore always two pages after the quiz – so the answers to this quiz are on page 8. Stop! Don't turn and look until you've done the quiz – they are there, we promise you!*

QUIZ 001 POPMASTER

THE 2 TONE ERA

Questions on the bands and artists from the 2 Tone and ska-revival era of the late Seventies and early Eighties

QUESTION 1
The Specials had their first hit with the song 'Gangsters' – but under what name did they release this song?

QUESTION 2
Bad Manners had a Top 3 instrumental hit in 1981 with a ska-flavoured version of which music hall dance?

QUESTION 3
Who was the female singer with The Selecter?

QUESTION 4
The first and last Top 40 hits by The Beat were both cover versions – name either of them.

QUESTION 5
...and after the break-up of The Beat, Dave Wakeling and Ranking Roger went on to form which group?

QUESTION 6
The 1979 chart debut by Madness was the band's only hit on the 2 Tone label – what was it called?

QUESTION 7
The 1980 single 'Let's Do Rock Steady' was the title of the only Top 40 hit for an all-female group on the 2 Tone label – what were they called?

QUESTION 8
Bad Manners' final Top 10 single in 1982 was a retitled version of song that had been a hit for Millie in 1964 – what was it called?

QUESTION 9
Which of Terry Hall's groups had a hit in 1985 with the song 'Thinking of You'?

QUESTION 10
Elvis Costello and the Attractions only single for 2 Tone was due for release in 1980 but couldn't be sold due to an injunction, but it became their first hit single for F-Beat that same year. What was it called?

POPMASTER QUIZ 002

ACROSS THE POND

Questions about the most influential chart in the world – the American Hot 100 and the Billboard 200

QUESTION 1
Simple Minds had their biggest American hit when they had a 1985 No 1 song from the film 'The Breakfast Club' – what was it called?

QUESTION 2
The albums 'Late Registration', 'Graduation', '808s & Heartbreak', 'My Beautiful Dark Twisted Fantasy' and 'Yeezus' have all been American No 1 albums in the 21st century for which artist?

QUESTION 3
Which 1984 album by Prince and the Revolution spent a total of 24 weeks at No 1 on the American albums chart?

QUESTION 4
America's first No 1 of the 1970s was 'Raindrops Keep Fallin' On My Head' – but this four week chart topper wasn't sung by Sacha Distel who had the main UK hit. Who recorded it?

QUESTION 5
Which Black Eyed Peas song was the first to top 8 million downloads in the USA?

QUESTION 6
...and which British artist became the second in 2013, with a song she released over two years earlier? Name both artist and song.

QUESTION 7
The band Fun. spent six weeks at No 1 in America in 2012 with the song 'We Are Young', but which female singer also features on the song?

QUESTION 8
KC & The Sunshine Band had five American No 1s – 'That's The Way (I Like It)' was one of them, but their UK No 1 'Give It Up' wasn't. Name one of their four other No 1s.

QUESTION 9
When it was released in 1995, a song called 'Missing' by an English duo became what was, at the time, the longest-charting record in America, notching up 55 weeks – which duo recorded it?

QUESTION 10
Name both the British group and the album that has spent the most number of weeks on the American albums chart

IMPORTANT

The *answers to all questions are cunningly printed on the outside column of the page directly after the quiz page you're looking at. The answers are therefore always two pages after the quiz – so the answers to this quiz are on page 9. Stop! Don't turn and look until you've done the quiz – they are there, we promise you!*

QUIZ 001

Q1 *The Special A.K.A.*

Q2 *Can Can*

Q3 *Pauline Black*

Q4 *'Tears of a Clown' (double 'A' side with 'Ranking Full Stop'), 'Can't Get Used To Losing You'*

Q5 *General Public*

Q6 *The Prince*

Q7 *The Bodysnatchers*

Q8 *'My Girl Lollipop' ('My Boy Lollipop')*

Q9 *Neville Staple, Lynval Golding*

Q10 *'I Can't Stand Up for Falling Down'*

QUIZ 003 POPMASTER

ALL AT SEA

QUESTION 1
In 1988, Erasure reached the Top 10 singing about a 'Ship Of…' what?

QUESTION 2
'The Boat That I Row' was a Top 10 single in 1967 for which singer?

QUESTION 3
In 1980 Madness took the 'Night Boat To…' where?

QUESTION 4
'Martha's Harbour' was the only Top 10 hit for which group?

QUESTION 5
What 'Drive' did the Lighthouse Family sing about in the mid-Nineties?

QUESTION 6
'Sail On Sailor' was the opening track on the 1973 album, 'Holland', recorded by which successful American group?

QUESTION 7
Released in 1974, what was the title of the first and biggest hit for The Hues Corporation?

QUESTION 8
The songs 'Silence Is Easy', 'Alcoholic', 'Good Souls', 'Four To The Floor' and 'Fever' were all hits in the Noughties for which group?

QUESTION 9
In 1977, Canadian singer-songwriter Gordon Lightfoot reached the chart with a song about a shipping disaster in 1975 – what was it called?

QUESTION 10
Neil Arthur and Stephen Luscombe were the duo that had a hit in 1983 called 'Waves' – under what name did they record this song?

POPMASTER QUIZ 004

ALL CREATURES GREAT AND SMALL

QUESTION 1
In 1972, what type of creature was featured in Elton John's 'Rock' hit?

QUESTION 2
Can you name the male rapper who was featured on Dr Dre's 2001 Top 5 hit 'The Next Episode'?

QUESTION 3
Who wrote Ugly Kid Joe's 1993 Top 10 hit 'Cat's In The Cradle'?

QUESTION 4
From 1981, which group achieved their first No 1 single with 'Stand And Deliver'?

QUESTION 5
Who had a Top 5 hit in 2014 with the song 'Dark Horse' featuring Juicy J?

QUESTION 6
In 1987, which group found a 'Rat In Mi Kitchen?'

QUESTION 7
Can you name the group that achieved a Top 5 hit in 1991 with 'The Size Of A Cow'?

QUESTION 8
Which group of singers accompanied Paul McCartney on his 1984 Top 10 hit 'We All Stand Together'?

QUESTION 9
Can you name the performer who made the Top 20 in 2013 with a song called 'Wings'?

QUESTION 10
What was the name of the legendary soul singer who achieved his only UK hit in 1970 with 'The Funky Chicken'?

A answers

QUIZ 002

Q1 *'Don't You (Forget About Me)'*

Q2 *Kanye West (also had a No 1 album with Jay-Z called Watch The Throne)*

Q3 *Purple Rain*

Q4 *B.J. Thomas*

Q5 *'I Gotta Feeling'*

Q6 *Adele – 'Rolling In The Deep'*

Q7 *Janelle Monáe*

Q8 *'Get Down Tonight ('Shake, Shake, Shake'), ' Shake Your Booty', 'I'm Your Boogie Man', 'Please Don't Go'*

Q9 *Everything But The Girl (reached its peak of No.2 in its 28th week on chart)*

Q10 *Pink Floyd – Dark Side Of The Moon (has topped 800 weeks)*

QUIZ 003

Q1
Fools

Q2
Lulu

Q3
Cairo (lead track on their Top 10 'Work Rest and Play' EP)

Q4
All About Eve

Q5
'Ocean Drive'

Q6
The Beach Boys

Q7
'Rock the Boat'

Q8
Starsailor

Q9
'The Wreck of the Edmund Fitzgerald'

Q10
Blancmange

QUIZ 005 POPMASTER

ARMED FORCES

QUESTION 1
What was the title of The Village People's Top 3 follow-up to their No 1 'Y.M.C.A'?

QUESTION 2
'Soldier' was the title of a Top 5 single in 2005 for an American female vocal group that featured guest appearances by TI and Lil Wayne – name the female group

QUESTION 3
What was the title of the love theme from the film 'Top Gun' and which group recorded it?

QUESTION 4
Which singer's first Top 10 single was her 1995 hit "Army Of Me"?

QUESTION 5
Name the 2002 No 1 by Sugababes that samples a portion of Tubeway Army's 1979 No 1 'Are 'Friends' Electric'?

QUESTION 6
The group Pilot had four hit singles – the No 1 song 'January' was one, name one of the other three?

QUESTION 7
Which male singer had a Top 10 cover version of The White Stripe's '7 Nation Army' in 2012?

QUESTION 8
'Sailing' by Rod Stewart reached No 1 in 1975 but was a Top 3 hit again in 1976 when it was used as the theme song to a BBC documentary series about life on board which naval ship?

QUESTION 9
Name the drummer with Nirvana who formed the band Foo Fighters in 1994?

QUESTION 10
'Oliver's Army' was a Top 3 single for Elvis Costello and the Attractions in 1979 – but what was the title of the Top 3 album from which it was taken?

POPMASTER QUIZ 006

AROUND THE WORLD

QUIZ 004

QUESTION 1
'Hong Kong Garden' was the title of the 1978 chart debut by which group?

QUESTION 2
'Somebody That I Used To Know' was a worldwide No 1 for a Belgian-Australian singer born Wouter "Wally" De Backer – under what name does he record?

QUESTION 3
Which Beatles song has the subtitle '(This Bird Has Flown)'?

QUESTION 4
Which one of these chart artists was not born in Canada – Justin Beiber, Carly Rae Jepsen, Avril Lavigne, Robin Thicke?

QUESTION 5
The 1980 Top 3 song by The Vapors was called 'Turning… what?

QUESTION 6
'Im Nin'Alu' was a hit in 1988 for which Israeli singer?

QUESTION 7
The Dutch group Focus are best known for their two instrumental hits from 1973 – name either of them

QUESTION 8
'Gangnam Style' was an international hit for PSY – which country does he come from?

QUESTION 9
The Holly Valance song 'Kiss Kiss' is a remake of a song originally called 'Simarik' and recorded by a male singer called Tarkan – but did this song originate in India, Turkey or Russia?

QUESTION 10
'The Final Countdown' was a No 1 in 1986 for a Swedish rock band – name the band.

Q1 *Crocodile*

Q2 *Snoop Dogg*

Q3 *Harry Chapin*

Q4 *Adam and the Ants*

Q5 *Katy Perry*

Q6 *UB40*

Q7 *The Wonder Stuff*

Q8 *The Frog Chorus*

Q9 *Birdy*

Q10 *Rufus Thomas*

QUIZ 005

Q1
'In the Navy'

Q2
Destiny's Child

Q3
'Take My Breath Away' – Berlin

Q4
Bjork

Q5
'Freak Like Me'

Q6
'Magic', 'Call Me Round', 'Just a Smile'

Q7
Marcus Collins

Q8
HMS Ark Royal

Q9
Dave Grohl

Q10
Armed Forces

QUIZ 007 POPMASTER

AT THE ZOO (1)

QUESTION 1
Who had a No 1 hit in 2013 with a song called 'Roar'?

QUESTION 2
What was the name of the German rock band that scored a Top 5 hit in 1991 with 'Wind of Change'?

QUESTION 3
Which Welsh singer-songwriter achieved his only UK Top 40 hit in 1992 with 'Dolphins Make Me Cry'?

QUESTION 4
Can you name the group that achieved Top 20 hits in the Eighties with 'Digging Your Scene' and 'It Doesn't Have to Be this Way'?

QUESTION 5
With which successful Californian band were Bernie Leadon and Randy Meisner both members?

QUESTION 6
Which American group had their one and only Top 20 hit in 1968 with 'Gimme Gimme Good Lovin'?

QUESTION 7
Which musician wrote and produced all of the hit singles by The Wombles?

QUESTION 8
What was the name of the French singer who achieved his only UK hit single in 1971 with 'Butterfly'?

QUESTION 9
In 1959, Neil Sedaka achieved his first UK Top 10 hit. Can you name it?

QUESTION 10
What was the title of the 1984 Top 5 hit by Paul McCartney and The Frog Chorus?

POPMASTER QUIZ 008

AT THE ZOO (2)

QUESTION 1
Which group topped the chart for three weeks in 1966 with 'Pretty Flamingo'?

QUESTION 2
What's the name of the rock band that achieved Top 10 hits with 'Animal', 'Let's Get Rocked' and 'When Love and Hate Collide'?

QUESTION 3
Can you name the trio that had a Top 20 hit in 1999 with 'King of the Snake'?

QUESTION 4
What album title is shared by Ziggy Marley, Jefferson Starship and The Strawbs?

QUESTION 5
Which rock and roll legend had a Top 3 hit in 1957 with '(Let Me Be Your) Teddy Bear', as featured in his movie "Loving You"?

QUESTION 6
In 1982 which group achieved their second Top 10 hit with 'Hungry Like The Wolf'?

QUESTION 7
What was the title of the 1983 financial Top 10 hit single for The Flying Lizards?

QUESTION 8
In 1974, which singer who was once married to Bobbie Gentry claimed that he didn't like 'Spiders And Snakes'?

QUESTION 9
Which group had a Top 5 hit in 1970 with a song called 'Apeman'?

QUESTION 10
From 1984, can you name the only hit achieved by Sunderland group, The Toy Dolls?

QUIZ 006

Q1 *Siouxsie & The Banshees*

Q2 *Gotye*

Q3 *Norwegian Wood*

Q4 *Robin Thicke (He has a Canadian father, but American mother and was born in Los Angeles)*

Q5 *Japanese*

Q6 *Ofra Haza*

Q7 *Sylvia, Hocus Pocus*

Q8 *South Korea*

Q9 *Turkey*

Q10 *Europe*

QUIZ 007

Q1
Katy Perry

Q2
Scorpions

Q3
Martyn Joseph

Q4
The Blow Monkeys

Q5
Eagles

Q6
Crazy Elephant

Q7
Mike Batt

Q8
Danyel Gerard

Q9
'I Go Ape'

Q10
'We All Stand Together'

QUIZ 009 POPMASTER

ATLANTIC RECORDS

Ten questions about the American record label that through the years has been home to some of the biggest and most influential artists

QUESTION 1
Which song by Chic became the biggest-selling single in Atlantic Records history when it was released in 1978?

QUESTION 2
Nicknamed 'The Queen of Soul', who had her first UK hit in 1967 with the song 'Respect'?

QUESTION 3
Doo-Wops & Hooligans was the title of Bruno Mars' first No 1 album in the UK – what is the title of his second?

QUESTION 4
Which American singer had Top 10 hits in 1988 with the songs 'Shake Your Love' and 'Foolish Beat'?

QUESTION 5
What year did James Blunt sing about in the title of his 2007 Top 5 single?

QUESTION 6
Name the jazz vocal group whose hits on the label included 'Tuxedo Junction', 'On a Little Street in Singapore' and 'Spice of Life'?

QUESTION 7
What was the title of the Average White Band instrumental that was a UK Top 10 hit and American No 1 in 1975?

QUESTION 8
Which band had a No 1 album in 1980 called Back in Black?

QUESTION 9
Released in 2008, what was the title of Kid Rock's only UK No 1?

QUESTION 10
During the Seventies, which band had No 1 albums on the label called In Through the Out Door, Presence and The Song Remains the Same?

POPMASTER QUIZ 010

AUTOBAHN

QUESTION 1
What was the title of the 1977 chart debut by the Tom Robinson Band?

QUESTION 2
Featuring fellow rapper Krayzie Bone, 'Ridin'' was a Top 3 single in 2006 for which American artist?

QUESTION 3
Queen's 1978 hit 'Bicycle Race' was a double A side with which other song?

QUESTION 4
According to the title of his 1989 single and album, which singer and guitarist took 'The Road to Hell'?

QUESTION 5
'Drive' was one of four songs to reach the Top 40 for Cars. Name one of the other three.

QUESTION 6
The song 'Born to Be Wild' was a hit in both 1969 and 1999 for which group?

QUESTION 7
What colour was the 'Little Corvette' in the 1983 song by Prince and the Revolution?

QUESTION 8
What type of 'Emptiness' did Manic Street Preachers sing about on their 1992 Top 20 single?

QUESTION 9
The song 'I Drove All Night' has been a hit both for Roy Orbison and also for which female singer?

QUESTION 10
Rose Royce made their chart debut in 1976 with the theme song to an American comedy film starring Richard Pryor, Antonio Fargas, George Carlin and The Pointer Sisters – what was it called?

QUIZ 008

Q1 *Manfred Mann*

Q2 *Def Leppard*

Q3 *Underworld*

Q4 *Dragonfly (NB the Jefferson Starship album was listed as two words, "Dragon Fly").*

Q5 *Elvis Presley*

Q6 *Duran Duran*

Q7 *'Money'*

Q8 *Jim Stafford*

Q9 *The Kinks*

Q10 *'Nellie the Elephant'*

QUIZ 009

Q1 *'Le Freak' (No. 1 in America and Top 10 in UK – sold a reported 7 million copies)*

Q2 *Aretha Franklin*

Q3 *Unorthodox Jukebox*

Q4 *Debbie Gibson*

Q5 *'1973'*

Q6 *Manhattan Transfer*

Q7 *'Pick Up the Pieces'*

Q8 *AC/DC*

Q9 *'All Summer Long'*

Q10 *Led Zeppelin*

QUIZ 011 POPMASTER

THE BEACH BOYS

QUESTION 1
What was the title of The Beach Boys hit that Lonnie Donegan had previously recorded under the title of 'I Wanna Go Home'?

QUESTION 2
Can you name the Top 5 hit from 1987 on which The Beach Boys appeared with The Fat Boys?

QUESTION 3
On which Beach Boys album did the tracks 'Vegetables', 'Heroes and Villains' and 'Gettin' Hungry' first appear?

QUESTION 4
In 1964, Brian Wilson wrote and produced a single by Sharon Marie titled 'Thinkin' 'Bout You Baby' that he re-wrote four years later to become a Top 20 hit for The Beach Boys under what title?

QUESTION 5
What was the title of the first Beach Boys single to reach the Top 10 in America?

QUESTION 6
Under what name did they record prior to naming themselves The Beach Boys, that would subsequently become the title of one of their albums?

QUESTION 7
What was the name of the label set up by The Beach Boys at the beginning of the Seventies after they had left Capitol?

QUESTION 8
What was the title of their 1988 American No 1 that was featured in the movie "Cocktail'"?

QUESTION 9
Which American Sixties Beach Boys Top 10 hit did they revive in 1996 with the help of Status Quo?

QUESTION 10
What was the title of the first Beach Boys single to make the Top 10 in the UK?

POPMASTER QUIZ 012

BIG MAC

QUESTION 1
In 2008, which DJ and producer made the Top 20 with his record 'Paddy's Revenge'?

QUESTION 2
Can you name the Irish singer whose only UK hit was the 1967 Top 20 hit 'Five Little Fingers'?

QUESTION 3
In 1981, the late Kirsty MacColl achieved her first hit single with the somewhat long title. Can you name it?

QUESTION 4
Can you name the singer who made a name for herself whilst appearing in the TV series "The Cruise", and as a result achieved a Top 10 hit in 1998 with 'Cruise into Christmas Medley'?

QUESTION 5
Which Sixties group achieved their only UK Top 40 hit in 1965 with 'Hang on Sloopy'?

QUESTION 6
In 1977, singer Billy Davis, Jr achieved a Top 10 hit duet with another former member of The Fifth Dimension. Their hit was 'You Don't Have to Be a Star (To Be in My Show).' Can you name the female singer?

QUESTION 7
Can you name the group that had a double A side in 2007 with 'Baby's Coming Back' and 'Transylvania'?

QUESTION 8
Don McLean reached No 2 in the UK in 1972 with his song 'American Pie', but which female singer topped the chart with the same song in the year 2000?

QUESTION 9
Under what name did Colin Blunstone release his 1969 Top 40 hit 'She's Not There'?

QUESTION 10
Can you name the singer from Westlife who achieved solo success in 2004 with his chart-topping hit 'Real to Me'?

QUIZ 010

Q1
'2-4-6-8 Motorway'

Q2
Chamillionaire

Q3
'Fat Bottomed Girls'

Q4
Chris Rea (the single's full title was 'The Road to Hell (Part 2)'

Q5
'My Best Friend's Girl', 'Just What I Needed', 'Since You're Gone'

Q6
Steppenwolf

Q7 *Red (reached the UK Top 40 in 1985 when re-released as a double A side with '1999')*

Q8
'Motorcycle Emptiness'

Q9
Cyndi Lauper

Q10
'Car Wash'

QUIZ 013 POPMASTER

BIG STARS, LITTLE HITS (1)

Not all releases by successful acts make the Top 10 – can you name the famous artists or bands from the titles of three of their smaller Top 40 hits?

QUESTION 1
'Another Part of Me' in 1988, 'Jam' in 1992, 'Cry' in 2001.

QUESTION 2
'Don't Let Me Be the Last to Know' in 2001, 'If U Seek Amy' in 2009, 'Till the World Ends' in 2011.

QUESTION 3
'Once Upon a Time' in 1965, 'Letter to Lucille' in 1973, 'If I Only Knew' in 1994.

QUESTION 4
'I Found Heaven' in 1992, I'd Wait for Life' in 2007, 'Kidz' in 2011.

QUESTION 5
'Never Say Never' in 2011, 'As Long As You Love Me' in 2012, 'Confident' in 2013.

QUESTION 6
'Sorry Doesn't Always Make It Right' in 1975, 'Muscles' in 1982, 'The Force Behind the Power' in 1992.

QUESTION 7
'She's So Cold' in 1980, 'I Go Wild' in 1995, 'Rain Fall Down' in 2005.

QUESTION 8
'Butterfly' in 1997, 'Don't Forget About Us' in 2005, 'Beautiful' in 2013.

QUESTION 9
'Cover Me' in 1984, 'Better Days' in 1992, 'Lonesome Day' in 2002.

QUESTION 10
'Tomorrow, Tomorrow' in 1969, 'My World' in 1972, 'Paying the Price of Love' in 1993.

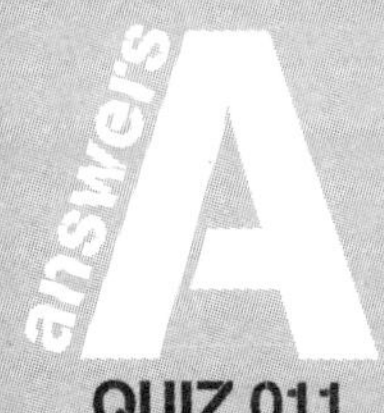

QUIZ 011

Q1
'Sloop John B'

Q2
'Wipe Out'

Q3
Smiley Smile

Q4
'Darlin''

Q5
Surfin' U.S.A

Q6
Carl & The Passions

Q7
Brother

Q8
'Kokomo'

Q9
'Fun Fun Fun'

Q10
'I Get Around'

POPMASTER QUIZ 014

BIG STARS, LITTLE HITS (2)

Not all releases by successful acts make the Top 10 – can you name the famous artists or bands from the titles of three of their smaller Top 40 hits?

QUESTION 1
'Two Hearts Beat as One' in 1983, 'If God Will Send His Angels' in 1997, 'I'll Go Crazy If I Don't Go Crazy Tonight' in 2009.

QUESTION 2
'Underground' in 1986, 'The Heart's Filthy Lesson' in 1995, 'Everyone Says 'Hi' in 2002.

QUESTION 3
'In My Chair' in 1970, 'Going Down Town Tonight' in 1984 and 'Jam Side Down' in 2002.

QUESTION 4
'Me, Myself and I' in 2004, 'Broken Hearted Girl' in 2009, 'XO' in 2014.

QUESTION 5
'Marianne' in 1968, 'Hey Mr Dream Maker' in 1976, 'She's So Beautiful' in 1985.

QUESTION 6
'Get Down (You're the One for Me)' in 1996, 'More than That' in 2001, 'Inconsolable' in 2007.

QUESTION 7
'Oh Father' in 1996, 'Love Profusion / Nothing Fails' in 2003, 'Miles Away' in 2008.

QUESTION 8
'Radio Song' in 1991, 'Lotus' in 1998, 'Wanderlust' in 2005.

QUESTION 9
'Take Me Home' in 1985, 'It's in Your Eyes' in 1996, 'Can't Stop Loving You' in 2002.

QUESTION 10
'Nice and Slow' in 1998, 'U Turn' in 2002, 'Moving Mountains' in 2008.

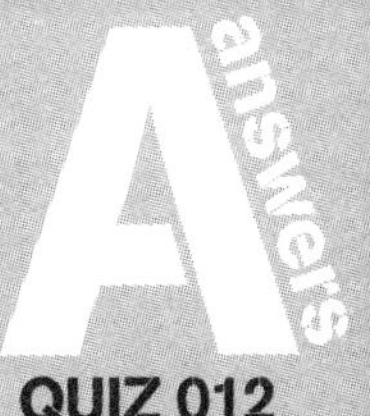

QUIZ 012

Q1
Steve Mac

Q2
Frankie McBride

Q3
'There's a Guy Works Down the Chip Shop Swears He's Elvis'

Q4
Jane McDonald

Q5
The McCoys

Q6
Marilyn McCoo

Q7
McFly

Q8
Madonna

Q9
Neil McArthur

Q10
Brian McFadden

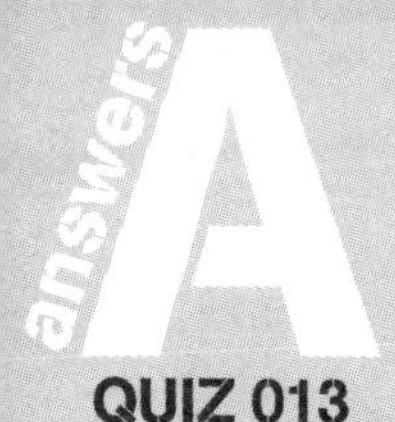

QUIZ 013

Q1
Michael Jackson (No. 15, No. 13, No. 25)

Q2
Britney Spears (No. 13, No. 20, No. 21)

Q3
Tom Jones (No. 32, No. 31, No. 11)

Q4
Take That (No. 15, No. 17, No. 28)

Q5
Justin Bieber (No. 34, No. 22, No. 33)

Q6
Diana Ross (No. 23, No. 15, No. 27)

Q7
The Rolling Stones (No. 33, No. 29, No. 33)

Q8
Mariah Carey (No. 22, No. 11, No. 22)

Q9
Bruce Springsteen (No. 16, No. 34, No. 39)

Q10
Bee Gees (No. 23, No. 16, No. 23)

QUIZ 015 POPMASTER

BIG STARS, LITTLE HITS (3)

Not all the releases by the most successful acts have been Top 10 singles – can you name these artists or bands from the titles of three of their smaller Top 40 hits?

QUESTION 1
'Ego' in 1978, 'I Don't Wanna Go on with You Like That' in 1988, 'Recover Your Soul' in 1998.

QUESTION 2
'Anyone Can Play Guitar' in 1993, 'Knives Out' in 2001, 'Nude' in 2008.

QUESTION 3
'Pleasure Principle' in 1987, 'Twenty Foreplay' in 1996, Someone to Call My Lover' in 2001.

QUESTION 4
'Beautiful' in 2009, 'Space Bound' in 2011, 'Survival' in 2013.

QUESTION 5
'Cardiac Arrest' in 1982, 'Uncle Sam' in 1985, 'Shame & Scandal' in 2005.

QUESTION 6
'We Ride' in 2006, 'Te Amo' in 2010, 'What Now' in 2013.

QUESTION 7
'Passion' in 1980, 'Ooh La La' in 1998, 'I Can't Deny It' in 2001.

QUESTION 8
'Typical Male' in 1986, 'Disco Inferno' in 1993, 'Whatever You Need' in 2000.

QUESTION 9
'Hot Dog' in 1980, 'Come See About Me' in 1987, 'I'll Be Home this Christmas' in 1991.

QUESTION 10
'Request Line' in 2001, 'Let's Get It Started' in 2004, 'Don't Stop the Party' in 2011.

POPMASTER QUIZ 016

BLINDED WITH SCIENCE

QUESTION 1
Which band made its chart debut in 1986 with the song 'E=MC2'?

QUESTION 2
Which No 1 single by Blondie is missing from this list – 'Heart of Glass', 'Sunday Girl', 'Call Me', 'The Tide Is High', 'Maria'?

QUESTION 3
Which girl group had a Top 5 hit in 2005 called 'Biology'?

QUESTION 4
What was the title of Diana Ross' 1986 No 1 written by the Bee Gees?

QUESTION 5
'Chemistry' was the title of a Top 20 hit in 1981 for which family group?

QUESTION 6
What was the title of the 1979 No 1 and only hit single by Tubeway Army?

QUESTION 7
Name the band that sang about a 'Chemical World' on their 1993 Top 30 single.

QUESTION 8
Which German physicist featured in the title of the first and biggest hit for the New Romantic group Landscape?

QUESTION 9
Albedo 0.39 was the title of a 1976 album by the Greek keyboard player and composer who went on to have hit singles with Jon Anderson and write award-winning film soundtracks – who is he?

QUESTION 10
The Chemical Brothers had two No 1 singles in the 1990s. Name either of them?

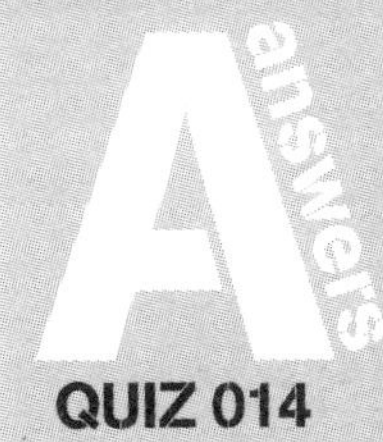

QUIZ 014

Q1
U2 (No.18, No.12, No.32)

Q2
David Bowie (No.21, No.35, No.20)

Q3
Status Quo (No.21, No.20, No.17)

Q4
Beyoncé (No.11, No.27, No.22)

Q5
Cliff Richard (No.22, No.31, No.17)

Q6
Backstreet Boys (No.14, No.12, No.24)

Q7
Madonna (No. 16, No. 11, No. 39)

Q8
R.E.M. (No.28, No.26, No.27)

Q9
Phil Collins (No.19, No.30, No.28)

Q10
Usher (No.24, No.16, No.25)

QUIZ 015

Q1
Elton John (No.34, No.30, No.16)

Q2
Radiohead (No.32, No.13, No.21)

Q3
Janet Jackson (No.24, No.22, No.11)

Q4
Eminem (No.12, No.34, No.22)

Q5
Madness (No.14, No.21, No.38)

Q6
Rihanna (No.17, No.14, No.21)

Q7
Rod Stewart (No.17, No.16, No.26)

Q8
Tina Turner (No.36, No.12, No.27)

Q9
Shakin Stevens (No.24, No.12, No.34)

Q10
Black Eyed Peas (No.31, No.11, No.17)

QUIZ 017 POPMASTER

BOY BANDS

All of these boy bands took a stab at being the next Bay City Rollers or Take That but didn't quite make it. Can you name them from their Top 40 hits?

QUESTION 1
'The Harder I Try', 'He Ain't No Competition' (both Top 10 in 1988), 'Be My Twin', 'Can You Keep a Secret' (both 1989).

QUESTION 2
'Sacred Trust' (Top 3 in 2002), 'Shakespeare's (Way with) Words' (Top 10 in 2003).

QUESTION 3
'It's Only Make Believe', 'When You Walk in the Room' (both 1978), 'Only You (And You Alone)' (1979).

QUESTION 4
'Let Me In', 'Forever Girl', 'All out of Love' (all 1997).

QUESTION 5
'Blame It on the Boogie', 'Can't Shake the Feeling' (both 1989), 'Handful of Promises' (1990).

QUESTION 6
'Change Your Mind', 'Every Time I Fall in Love', 'Never Found a Love Like This Before', 'If You Leave Me Now' (all 1996)?

QUESTION 7
'Could Have Told You So' (Top 10 in 1989).

QUESTION 8
'Speechless', 'Invisible' (both Top 10 in 2003), 'Real World', 'Pushin' Me Out' (both 2004).

QUESTION 9
'I'm a Man Not a Boy', 'Tarantino's New Star', 'Breathing' (all 1997).

QUESTION 10
'Dawn' (No.30 in 1976).

POPMASTER QUIZ 018

BRACKETS (1)

A collection of songs that have part of their titles included in brackets, can you fill in the missing words?

QUESTION 1
'(.........) Half as Nice' by Amen Corner

QUESTION 2
'Can't Give You Anything (.........)' by The Stylistics

QUESTION 3
'I Thought It Took a Little Time (.........)' by Diana Ross

QUESTION 4
'I Said Never Again (.........)' by Rachel Stevens

QUESTION 5
'It May Be Winter Outside (.........)' by Love Unlimited

QUESTION 6
'(.........) Rock Around the Clock' by Bill Haley & His Comets

QUESTION 7
'I Love to Love (.........)' by Tina Charles

QUESTION 8
'I'd Do Anything for Love (.........)' by Meat Loaf

QUESTION 9
'Do You Know (.........)' by Enrique Iglesias

QUESTION 10
'No More Tears (.........)' by Barbra Streisand and Donna Summer

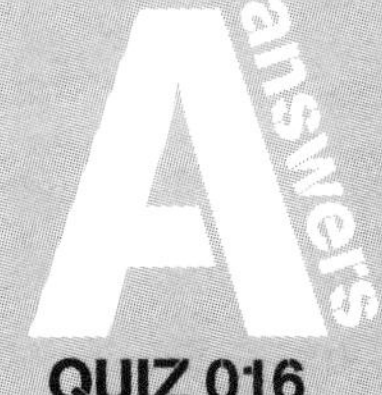

QUIZ 016

Q1
Big Audio Dynamite

Q2
'Atomic'

Q3
Girls Aloud

Q4
'Chain Reaction'

Q5
The Nolans

Q6
'Are 'Friends' Electric?'

Q7
Blur

Q8
Einstein ('Einstein a Go-Go' was a Top 5 single in 1981)

Q9
Vangelis

Q10
'Setting Sun' (1996), 'Block Rockin' Beats' (1997)

QUIZ 017

Q1
Brother Beyond

Q2
One True Voice (lost the Popstars: The Rivals battle to Girls Aloud)

Q3
Child

Q4
OTT

Q5
Big Fun

Q6
Upside Down (subject of a TV documentary about manufacturing a boy band)

Q7
Halo James

Q8
D-Side

Q9
North & South (featured in their own TV series called No Sweat)

Q10 *Flintlock (featured Mike Holoway on drums, who played Mike Bell in TV's The Tomorrow People!)*

QUIZ 019 POPMASTER

BRACKETS (2)

A collection of songs that have part of their titles included in brackets, can you fill in the missing words?

QUESTION 1
'Sha-La-La (.........)' by Al Green

QUESTION 2
'Hot Stuff (.........)' by Craig David

QUESTION 3
'Truck on (.........)' by T. Rex

QUESTION 4
'I'm Gonna Be (.........)' by The Proclaimers

QUESTION 5
'(.........) Cold Light Of Day' by Gene Pitney

QUESTION 6
'Sunset (.........)' by Fatboy Slim

QUESTION 7
'Thanks for the Memory (.........)' by Slade

QUESTION 8
'I'm Just a Singer (.........)' by The Moody Blues

QUESTION 9
'(.........) I Do It for You' by Bryan Adams

QUESTION 10
'What Kinda Boy You Looking for (.........)' by Hot Chocolate

POPMASTER QUIZ 020

BRACKETS (3)

A collection of songs that have part of their titles included in brackets, can you fill in the missing words?

QUESTION 1
'This Time (.........)' by England World Cup Squad

QUESTION 2
'Case of the Ex (.........)' by Mya

QUESTION 3
'(.........) I'm the One You Need' by Smokey Robinson & the Miracles

QUESTION 4
'It Keeps Rainin' (.........)' by Bitty McLean

QUESTION 5
'December '63 (.........)' by The Four Seasons

QUESTION 6
'Touch Me (.........)' by Cathy Dennis

QUESTION 7
'Caribbean Queen (.........)' by Billy Ocean

QUESTION 8
'Two Wrongs (.........)' by Wyclef Jean featuring Claudette Ortiz

QUESTION 9
'(.........) Maria' by Ricky Martin

QUESTION 10
'Big Girl (.........)' by Mika

A answers

QUIZ 018

Q1
If Paradise Is

Q2
But My Love

Q3
But Today I Fell in Love

Q4
But Here We Are

Q5
But in My Heart It's Spring

Q6
We're Gonna

Q7
But My Baby Loves to Dance

Q8
But I Won't Do That

Q9
The Ping Pong Song

Q10
Enough Is Enough

QUIZ 019

Q1 *Makes Me Happy*

Q2 *Let's Dance*

Q3 *Tyke*

Q4 *500 Miles*

Q5 *In the*

Q6 *Bird of Prey*

Q7 *Wham Bam Thank You Mam*

Q8 *In a Rock 'n' Roll Band*

Q9 *Everything I Do*

Q10 *Girl*

QUIZ 021 POPMASTER

QUESTION 1
Which of these singers had a Top 10 single in the mid-Eighties with 'Girlie Girlie' – was it Dawn Penn, Sophia George or Susan Cadogan?

QUESTION 2
The group formed by the winners of the 2001 reality show "Popstars" was called Hear'Say – but what are the first names of the two original male members of the group?

QUESTION 3
Which fashion model made her one and only Top 40 appearance as a singer in 1994 with the song 'Love and Tears'?

QUESTION 4
Brother and sister Sean and Sarah Smith featured on "The X Factor" in 2007 and made their chart debut the following year with the Top 20 single 'We R One' – under what name did they record this song?

QUESTION 5
Who released a debut solo album of cover versions in 1973 called These Foolish Things?

QUESTION 6
What was the surname of Victoria Beckham when the Spice Girls first reached the chart?

QUESTION 7
The Top 40 hits 'Love Is Everywhere' by Cicero and 'The Crying Game' by Boy George were released on Spaghetti Records – a label set up by which regular chart act?

QUESTION 8
These three songs are amongst the smaller Top 40 hits for one of the most successful chart acts – 'In My Chair', 'Accident Prone', 'Rock 'Til You Drop'. Name the group or artist?

QUESTION 9
Which one-time "EastEnders" actor had Top 20 singles in the 1990s with 'Good Day', 'Don't Pull Your Love' and 'Someone to Love'?

QUESTION 10
The 1983 Top 20 single 'Tantalise (Wo Wo Ee Yeh Yeh)' was the only hit for which British group?

POPMASTER QUIZ 022

QUIZ 20

QUESTION 1
Ron and Russell Mael had their first hit as Sparks in 1974 – what was the song?

QUESTION 2
Brothers Neil and Tim Finn have recorded together as The Finn Brothers, Finn, members of Crowded House and which other chart group?

QUESTION 3
Brothers Greg and Pat Kane had their biggest hit with their 1987 chart debut – what was the song called and under what name did they record it?

QUESTION 4
Kevin and Joe are two of the three Jonas Brothers – who is the third?

QUESTION 5
What was the first Oasis hit single to feature Noel Gallagher on lead vocal rather than Liam?

QUESTION 6
What was the name of the Bee Gees younger brother who had hits in the late 1970s with 'An Everlasting Love' and 'I Just Wanna Be Your Everything'?

QUESTION 7
Kings of Leon had both a No 1 single and another Top 3 hit in 2008 from the No 1 album 'Only By the Night' – name either of these songs.

QUESTION 8
What is the first name of actor Mark Wahlberg's older brother who is a member of New Kids on the Block?

QUESTION 9
The Jackson Five didn't have any UK No 1s, but they did reach No 1 in 1977 when they were known as The Jacksons – what was the title of this No 1?

QUESTION 10
The early hits for Bros were recorded as a trio – but who was the non-family member who left the group in 1989, leaving Matt and Luke Goss to continue as a duo?

Q1 *We'll Get It Right*

Q2 *Whatcha Gonna Do*

Q3 *Come 'Round Here*

Q4 *Tears from My Eyes*

Q5 *Oh What a Night*

Q6 *All Night Long*

Q7 *No More Love on the Run*

Q8 *Don't Make a Right*

Q9 *Un, Dos, Tres*

Q10 *You Are Beautiful*

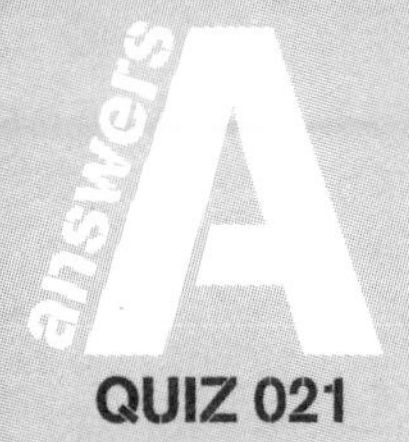

QUIZ 021

Q1 *Sophia George*

Q2 *Danny (Foster), Noel (Sullivan) (a third male member, Johnny Shentall, joined in 2002)*

Q3 *Naomi Campbell*

Q4 *Same Difference*

Q5 *Bryan Ferry*

Q6 *Adams*

Q7 *Pet Shop Boys (they produced both songs)*

Q8 *Status Quo (No.21 in 1970, No.36 in 1978, No.38 in 1992)*

Q9 *Sean Maguire*

Q10 *Jimmy the Hoover*

QUIZ 023 POPMASTER

CALL OF NATURE

QUESTION 1
Who is the lead singer with The Killers?

QUESTION 2
The 1966 Top 10 debut hit by Ike and Tina Turner was also a Top 20 hit in 1971 for the combined forces of The Supremes and The Temptations – what is the song?

QUESTION 3
Did Michael Jackson release his No 1 single 'Earth Song' in the Eighties, Nineties or Noughties?

QUESTION 4
'Fire and Rain' was the title of a 1970 single by which American singer songwriter?

QUESTION 5
Which Dutch pianist achieved his only hit in 1965 with 'A Walk in the Black Forest'?

QUESTION 6
Which band sang about 'Fake Plastic Trees' in 1995?

QUESTION 7
In 1985, guitarist Gary Moore and Phil Lynott from Thin Lizzy had a Top 10 duet called 'Out in the... what?

QUESTION 8
Which group had a hit in both 1985 and 1991 with The 'Whole of the Moon'?

QUESTION 9
Name the early Seventies song by Marvin Gaye about the state of the environment that was subtitled ('The Ecology')?

QUESTION 10
'Little Fluffy Clouds' was a Top 10 hit in 1993 for which instrumental and production duo?

POPMASTER QUIZ 024

CAN'T GET HER OUT OF MY HEAD

QUESTION 1
In which Australian soap did Kylie Minogue star in the late Eighties?

QUESTION 2
Name the production team behind her early hits.

QUESTION 3
Beginning with the earliest, put these three songs by Kylie Minogue in the order they were originally hits – 'Wow', 'Spinning Around', 'Step Back in Time'?

QUESTION 4
Name the American singer who had the original 1962 hit version of 'The Loco-Motion'?

QUESTION 5
Kylie featured on the 2010 Top 10 song 'Higher', released by which British singer?

QUESTION 6
What was the title of Kylie's Top 3 duet with Robbie Williams in 2000?

QUESTION 7
'Can't Get You out of My Head' was written and produced by Cathy Dennis along with Rob Davis, who had been guitarist in which 1970s band?

QUESTION 8
Which of her early singles has a French title?

QUESTION 9
'If You Were with Me Now' was a Top 5 duet in 1991 with which American R&B singer?

QUESTION 10
What is the title of Kylie's 2004 single co-written and produced by Jake Shears and Babydaddy of Scissor Sisters?

QUIZ 022

Q1 *'This Town Ain't Big Enough for Both of Us'*

Q2 *Split Enz*

Q3 *'Labour Of Love' – Hue and Cry*

Q4 *Nick*

Q5 *'Don't Look Back in Anger'*

Q6 *Andy Gibb*

Q7 *'Sex on Fire', 'Use Somebody'*

Q8 *Donnie (Donald Edmond "Donnie" Wahlberg, Jr)*

Q9 *'Show You the Way to Go'*

Q10 *Craig Logan*

QUIZ 023

Q1
Brandon Flowers

Q2
'River Deep – Mountain High'

Q3
Nineties (1995)

Q4
James Taylor

Q5
Horst Jankowski

Q6
Radiohead

Q7
Fields

Q8
The Waterboys

Q9
'Mercy Mercy Me'

Q10
The Orb

QUIZ 025 POPMASTER

CLASSIC ALBUMS

Three song titles – all from one classic album. One point for naming the artist and a total of three if you can also name the album

QUESTION 1
'Drawing Crazy Patterns', 'Polo Mint City' and 'Black Eyed Boy'.

QUESTION 2
'If It's Hurting You', 'Sing for the Lonely', and 'Let Love Be Your Energy'.

QUESTION 3
'She Said, She Said', 'Doctor Robert' and 'Good Day Sunshine'.

QUESTION 4
'Push the Button', 'Joy Division, and 'Ace Reject'.

QUESTION 5
'I Am a Lonesome Lobo', 'As I Went out One Morning' and 'All Along the Watchtower'.

QUESTION 6
'Summer Romance', 'Down in the Hole' and 'She's So Cold'.

QUESTION 7
'Is Your Mama Gonna Miss Ya?', 'Hey Honey-I'm Packin' You In!' and 'Thought I'd Died and Gone to Heaven'.

QUESTION 8
'The Song Remains the Same', 'Over The Hills And Far Away' and 'D'yer Mak'er'.

QUESTION 9
'I Take the Dice', 'The Seventh Stranger' and 'New Moon on Monday'.

QUESTION 10
'Planet Home', 'Soul Education' and 'Canned Heat'.

POPMASTER QUIZ 026

CLASSIC POP

QUESTION 1
Barry Manilow's song 'Could It Be Magic' is based on a piano prelude by which of these composers – Mozart, Chopin or Liszt?

QUESTION 2
'A Fifth of Beethoven', a UK Top 30 hit and American No 1 from "Saturday Night Fever" was recorded by Walter Murphy and the (.........) Band?

QUESTION 3
Which of Take That's No 1s begins with a trumpet fanfare from Verdi's 'Requiem'?

QUESTION 4
Which British producer had a Top 5 hit in 1999 with his version of Samuel Barber's 'Adagio for Strings'?

QUESTION 5
'Csárdás' by Vittorio Monti is the violin solo heard at the start of which 2010 Top 10 single by Lady Gaga?

QUESTION 6
'Roll over Beethoven' was a Top 10 single in 1973 for which group?

QUESTION 7
Which of these Top 3 hits from 2000 by S Club 7 was based on 'Pavane' by Gabriel Fauré – was it 'Reach', 'Natural' or 'Never Had a Dream Come True'?

QUESTION 8
Music from Prokofiev's 'Lieutenant Kijé' featured in the 1985 single 'Russians', recorded by which artist?

QUESTION 9
The Beach Boys had a Top 10 single in 1979 with a song based on Bach's 'Jesu, Joy of Man's Desiring' – was the song called 'Here Comes the Night', 'Lady Lynda' or 'Sumahama'?

QUESTION 10
Beethoven's 'Für Elise' features on the 2003 single 'I Can' by which rapper?

QUIZ 024

Q1 *"Neighbours"*

Q2 *Stock, Aitken & Waterman*

Q3 *'Step Back in Time' (1990), 'Spinning Around' (2000), 'Wow' (2008)*

Q4 *Little Eva*

Q5 *Taio Cruz*

Q6 *'Kids'*

Q7 *Mud*

Q8 *'Je Ne Sais Pas Pourquoi'*

Q9 *Keith Washington*

Q10 *'I Believe in You'*

QUIZ 025

Q1
White on Blonde – Texas (1997)

Q2
Sing When You're Winning – Robbie Williams (2000)

Q3
Revolver – The Beatles (1966)

Q4
Taller in More Ways – The Sugababes (2005)

Q5
John Wesley Harding – Bob Dylan (1968)

Q6
Emotional Rescue – The Rolling Stones (1980)

Q7
Waking Up the Neighbours – Bryan Adams (1991)

Q8
Houses of the Holy – Led Zeppelin (1973)

Q9
Seven and the Ragged Tiger – Duran Duran (1983)

Q10
Synkronized – Jamiroquai (1999)

QUIZ 027 POPMASTER

COLOUR CODING

QUESTION 1
What hit song title is shared by the late busker Don Partridge and Elton John?

QUESTION 2
Can you name the first solo Top 10 hit achieved by the singer Pink?

QUESTION 3
Written by Raymond Froggatt as 'Callow La Vita', under what title did The Dave Clark Five later record the song, taking it into the Top 10?

QUESTION 4
Which group had hits in the Nineties with 'We're in this Together and 'Ain't that a Lot of Love'?

QUESTION 5
Who wrote Natalie Cole's 1988 Top 10 hit 'Pink Cadillac'?

QUESTION 6
Country singer, Crystal Gayle achieved two UK Top 20 hits in the Seventies. The second was 'Talking In Your Sleep', what was the other?

QUESTION 7
What was the title of the follow up hit to Peter Sarstedt's 1969 No 1, 'Where Do You Go to My Lovely'?

QUESTION 8
Which English rock band achieved an American Top 10 hit in 1968 with Joe South's song 'Hush'?

QUESTION 9
What was the title of Barry White's only UK No 1 hit single?

QUESTION 10
Under what group name did singer Colin Vearncombe achieve several Top 40 hits in the Eighties?

POPMASTER QUIZ 028

COLOURFUL HITS

QUESTION 1
Can you name the singer who had hits in the Seventies with '(Dancing) On A Saturday Night' and 'Do You Wanna Dance'?

QUESTION 2
Can you name the first Top 20 hit achieved by Simply Red in 1985?

QUESTION 3
In 2011, 'Read All About It' was a No 1 single featuring Emeli Sandé and a rapper whose real name is Stephen Manderson. Under what name did he top the chart?

QUESTION 4
Howard Donald is one of only two original members of Take That not to have achieved a solo hit. Can you name the other?

QUESTION 5
The song 'Red Red Wine' has been recorded by many different performers, not least UB40, but who wrote the song?

QUESTION 6
Reggae singer Horace Faith achieved his one and only Top 10 hit in 1970. What was the title of the song?

QUESTION 7
In 2003, The Black Eyed Peas secured their first No 1 hit. Can you name it?

QUESTION 8
What was the title of the 1968 animated musical fantasy movie featuring the music of The Beatles and based in Pepperland?

QUESTION 9
Who achieved a 2008 Top 10 hit duet titled 'Another Way to Die' with Alicia Keys?

QUESTION 10
Actor Sheb Wooley, who appeared as Peter Nolan in the TV series "Rawhide", had a Top 20 hit in 1958. Can you name its title?

QUIZ 026

Q1
Chopin ('Prelude in C Minor')

Q2
Walter Murphy and the Big Apple Band

Q3
'Never Forget'

Q4
William Orbit

Q5
'Alejandro'

Q6
Electric Light Orchestra

Q7
'Natural'

Q8
Sting

Q9
'Lady Lynda'

Q10
Nas

QUIZ 027

Q1
'Blue Eyes'

Q2
'There You Go'

Q3
'The Red Balloon'

Q4
Simply Red

Q5
Bruce Springsteen

Q6
'Don't It Make My Brown Eyes Blue'

Q7
'Frozen Orange Juice'

Q8
Deep Purple

Q9
'You're the First, the Last, My Everything'

Q10
Black

QUIZ 029 POPMASTER

COVER VERSIONS

QUESTION 1
Name the 1960s Eddie Floyd song that went on to be a hit in a live version for David Bowie in 1974 and a 1979 Top 10 disco anthem for Amii Stewart.

QUESTION 2
One Direction's 2013 Comic Relief single was a medley of the songs 'One Way or Another' and 'Teenage Kicks' – name either of the groups that originally recorded these songs.

QUESTION 3
All Saints 1998 double A side No 1 consisted of cover versions of LaBelle's 'Lady Marmalade' and which Red Hot Chili Peppers song?

QUESTION 4
Name one of the four chart acts to reach No 1 in the UK with the song 'Unchained Melody'.

QUESTION 5
A cover of which George Michael song gave Robbie Williams his first hit as a solo artist, in 1996?

QUESTION 6
Which actor had a hit in 1987 with his version of The Drifters' 'Under the Boardwalk'?

QUESTION 7
Little Mix began their chart career in 2011 with a No 1 cover version of a song written and originally recorded by Irish singer-songwriter Damien Rice. What is it called?

QUESTION 8
The success of 'Don't Stop Believin' in the TV series "Glee" and a TV performance by Joe McElderry saw the song in the UK Top 10 for the first time, nearly 18 years after its release. Who recorded the original?

QUESTION 9
Which Dusty Springfield hit from 1963 has also reached the chart for Bay City Rollers, The Tourists and Samantha Fox?

QUESTION 10
Which female singer joined the rock band Counting Crows on their 2003 Top 20 hit, the revival of Joni Mitchell's 'Big Yellow Taxi'?

POPMASTER QUIZ 030

QUESTION 1
The Beat made their chart debut in 1979 with a double A side of 'Ranking Full Stop' and a cover of which Smokey Robinson and the Miracles hit?

QUESTION 2
Which "X Factor" winner reached No 1 in 2008 with Leonard Cohen's song 'Hallelujah'?

QUESTION 3
In 1991, Kate Bush reached the chart with her version of which Elton John song?

QUESTION 4
Soft Cell's No 1 'Tainted Love' had been a northern soul hit prior to 1981 for the girlfriend of Marc Bolan. Who is she?

QUESTION 5
Which R.E.M. song was recorded by various artists as a charity single for the Haiti Earthquake disaster in 2010?

QUESTION 6
Which group's run of 15 hit singles in the Seventies (including three No 1s) ended in 1976 with a Top 10 cover version of Bill Withers' 'Lean on Me'?

QUESTION 7
In 1991, Pet Shop Boys reached the Top 5 with a medley of two songs that had been hits for U2 and Andy Williams respectively – what are those two songs?

QUESTION 8
Which band recorded the original version of Johnny Cash's 2002 hit 'Hurt'?

QUESTION 9
The Australian band Pseudo Echo had its only UK hit in 1987 with a cover version of which song?

QUESTION 10
Joan Jett & the Blackhearts' biggest hit 'I Love Rock 'N Roll' was originally written and recorded by a group that had hits in the mid-Seventies with 'A Touch Too Much' and 'My Last Night with You'. Name the group.

QUIZ 028

Q1
Barry Blue

Q2
'Money's Too Tight to Mention'

Q3
Professor Green

Q4
Jason Orange

Q5
Neil Diamond

Q6
Black Pearl

Q7
'Where is the Love?'

Q8
"Yellow Submarine"

Q9
Jack White

Q10
'Purple People Eater'

QUIZ 029

Q1 *'Knock On Wood'*

Q2 *Blondie, The Undertones*

Q3 *'Under the Bridge'*

Q4 *Jimmy Young (1955), Righteous Brothers (1990), Robson & Jerome (1995), Gareth Gates (2002)*

Q5 *Freedom (George's solo song 'Freedom' Not the Wham song 'Freedom')*

Q6 *Bruce Willis*

Q7 *'Cannonball'*

Q8 *Journey*

Q9 *'I Only Want to Be with You' (some versions use 'Wanna')*

Q10 *Vanessa Carlton*

QUIZ 031 POPMASTER

CREEPY CRAWLIES

QUESTION 1
Which band reached No 1 in 1991 with 'The Fly'?

QUESTION 2
Who had a Top 20 hit in 1979 with the title song to his multi-million-selling album – 'Bat out of Hell?

QUESTION 3
'Chicken Payback' was the title of a hit single in 2005 for which group?

QUESTION 4
What was the title of Adam Ant's only No 1 as a solo artist?

QUESTION 5
Which band sang about 'The Caterpillar' in 1984?

QUESTION 6
What was the name of 'The Spider' in the 1966 song by The Who, written by bassist John Entwistle?

QUESTION 7
On which of these Genesis albums does the song 'The Carpet Crawlers' appear – is it "Selling England By the Pound", "The Lamb Lies Down on Broadway" or "A Trick of the Tail"?

QUESTION 8
Which American theatrical 'shock-rock' singer often featured a live boa constrictor in his stage act?

QUESTION 9
Released in 1993, what was the title of Radiohead's first Top 10 single?

QUESTION 10
What was the name of the female harmony group that provided backing vocals on "Top Of The Pops" between 1966 and 1978?

POPMASTER QUIZ 032

DAVID BOWIE

QUESTION 1
David Bowie had his first No 1 in 1975 with the re-release of a song from 1969 – what is it called?

QUESTION 2
Who played piano on the song 'Life on Mars'?

QUESTION 3
'Let's Dance' was one of three hit singles from his album of the same name, but can you name one of the other two?

QUESTION 4
Which successful duo provided the single remix of Bowie's 1996 hit 'Hallo Spaceboy'?

QUESTION 5
Released in January 2013, what was the title of Bowie's first Top 10 single for 20 years?

QUESTION 6
Bowie featured as guest vocalist on the title track of the 2013 album 'Reflektor', released by which Canadian group?

QUESTION 7
In which of these films did David Bowie star as Jack Celliers – "The Man Who Fell to Earth", "Merry Christmas Mr Lawrence" or "Absolute Beginners"?

QUESTION 8
How many No 1 duets has David Bowie had?

QUESTION 9
Apart from 'Space Oddity', which other single by David Bowie mentions the character Major Tom?

QUESTION 10
Only two of Bowie's hits in the 1970s were *not* songs written by him – name both the songs.

QUIZ 30

Q1 *'Tears of a Clown'*

Q2 *Alexandra Burke*

Q3 *'Rocket Man (I Think It's Going to Be a Long Long Time)'*

Q4 *Gloria Jones (recorded in the 1960s; a northern soul favourite in the 1970s*

Q5 *'Everybody Hurts'*

Q6 *Mud*

Q7 *'Where the Streets Have No Name/Can't Take My Eyes Off You'*

Q8 *Nine Inch Nails*

Q9 *'Funkytown' (original by Lipps Inc in 1980)*

Q10 *The Arrows 'I Love Rock 'n Roll' (written by band members Jake Hooker and Alan Merrill)*

QUIZ 031

Q1
U2

Q2
Meat Loaf

Q3
The Bees

Q4
'Goody Two Shoes'

Q5
The Cure

Q6
Boris

Q7
The Lamb Lies Down on Broadway

Q8
Alice Cooper

Q9
'Creep'

Q10
The Ladybirds

QUIZ 033 POPMASTER

DECK OF CARDS

QUESTION 1
What type of 'Face' did Lady Gaga sing about on her 2009 No 1?

QUESTION 2
Which group released the 1980 single 'Ace of Spades'?

QUESTION 3
What was the title of the Steve Miller Band's No 1 from 1990?

QUESTION 4
Released in 1973 and 1975 – name both the easy listening singer and the duo that both had hits with the song 'Solitaire'?

QUESTION 5
What was the title of Chris Cornell's Top 10 theme song for the 2006 James Bond film "Casino Royale"?

QUESTION 6
Dave Edmunds followed up his 1979 Top 10 hit 'Girls Talk' with the song 'Queen of'... what?

QUESTION 7
... and which American group made its chart debut in 1974 with the song 'Queen of Clubs'?

QUESTION 8
Which two footballers sang about 'Diamond Lights' in 1987?

QUESTION 9
The American record producer and orchestral leader Van McCoy had two Top 10 singles in the 1970s – one was called 'The Hustle', what was the other one called?

QUESTION 10
Producers Benito Benites and John Garrett Virgo III were behind a run of Top 10 dance hits in the early Nineties, including 'Exterminate', 'Rhythm is a Dancer' and 'The Power'. Under what name did they record?

POPMASTER QUIZ 034

DEJA VU

The following are singles that have been Top 10 hits in their original versions in two different decades. Name both of the decades in each instance

QUESTION 1
'My Sweet Lord' by George Harrison

QUESTION 2
'When A Man Loves A Woman' by Percy Sledge

QUESTION 3
'1999' by Prince and the Revolution

QUESTION 4
'You Sexy Thing' by Hot Chocolate

QUESTION 5
'Jailhouse Rock' by Elvis Presley

QUESTION 6
'Bohemian Rhapsody' by Queen

QUESTION 7
'He Ain't Heavy, He's My Brother' by The Hollies

QUESTION 8
'Man In the Mirror' by Michael Jackson

QUESTION 9
'You've Lost that Lovin' Feelin' by The Righteous Brothers

QUESTION 10
'I Heard It Through the Grapevine by Marvin Gaye

A answers

QUIZ 032

Q1 *'Space Oddity'*

Q2 *Rick Wakeman*

Q3 *'China Girl', 'Modern Love'*

Q4 *Pet Shop Boys*

Q5 *'Where Are We Now'*

Q6 *Arcade Fire*

Q7 *"Merry Christmas Mr Lawrence"*

Q8 *Two: 'Under Pressure' with Queen, 'Dancing In the Street 'with Mick Jagger.*

Q9 *'Ashes To Ashes'*

Q10 *'Sorrow '(made famous in 1966 by The Merseys) and 'Knock on Wood' (Eddie Floyd, 1967)*

QUIZ 033

Q1
'Poker Face'

Q2
Motörhead

Q3
'The Joker'

Q4
Andy Williams, The Carpenters

Q5
'You Know My Name'

Q6
Hearts

Q7
KC & the Sunshine Band

Q8
Glenn Hoddle and Chris Waddle (billed as Glenn and Chris)

Q9
'The Shuffle'

Q10
Snap!

QUIZ 035 POPMASTER

THE DEVIL'S RECORD COLLECTION

We've listed two hits from one particular year that might have been in the devil's record collection. What year were the records in the chart?

QUESTION 1
'Jilted John' by Jilted John and 'Ally's Tartan Army' by Andy Cameron.

QUESTION 2
'Wonderwall' by Mike Flowers Pop and 'We're Gonna do It Again' by Manchester United Football Squad.

QUESTION 3
'Stutter Rap (No Sleep 'Til Bedtime)' by Morris Minor & The Majors and 'Donald Where's Your Troosers' (re-issue) by Andy Stewart.

QUESTION 4
'Hole in the Ground' by Bernard Cribbins and 'That Noise' by Anthony Newley.

QUESTION 5
'The Funky Gibbon' by The Goodies and 'The Rochdale Cowboy' by Mike Harding.

QUESTION 6
'Pickin' a Chicken' by Eve Boswell and 'The Trouble With Harry' by Alfi and Harry.

QUESTION 7
'Can We Fix It?' by Bob the Builder and 'No. 1' by The Tweenies.

QUESTION 8
'The Sparrow' by The Ramblers (From The Abbey Hey Junior School) and 'Luton Airport' by Cats UK.

QUESTION 9
'The Chicken Song' by Spitting Image and 'Snooker Loopy' by The Matchroom Mob with Chas & Dave.

QUESTION 10
'Fog on the Tyne (Revisited)' by Gazza and Lindisfarne and 'Turtle Power' by Partners in Kryme.

POPMASTER QUIZ 036

DOUBLE 'A' SIDES (1)

You will be given the title and artist of a record in which both sides of the record shared the same chart placing. Name the other song.

QUESTION 1
'We Love You', The Rolling Stones

QUESTION 2
'Transylvania', McFly

QUESTION 3
'I Have a Dream', Westlife

QUESTION 4
'Eternity', Robbie Williams

QUESTION 5
'Come Together', The Beatles

QUESTION 6
'Mama', The Spice Girls

QUESTION 7
'Mama', Connie Francis

QUESTION 8
'Candle in the Wind '97', Elton John

QUESTION 9
'Brown Girl in the Ring', Boney M

QUESTION 10
'My Place, Nelly

A answers

QUIZ 034

Q1
1970s, 2000s

Q2
1960s, 1980s

Q3
1980, 1990s

Q4
1970s, 1990s (was also Top 10 in 1980s but as a remix)

Q5
1950s, 2000s

Q6
1970s, 1990s

Q7
1960s, 1980s

Q8
1980s, 2000s

Q9
1960s, 1990s

Q10
1960s, 1980s

QUIZ 035

Q1 *1978*

Q2 *1995*

Q3 *1987*

Q4 *1962*

Q5 *1975*

Q6 *1956*

Q7 *2000*

Q8 *1979*

Q9 *1986*

Q10 *1990*

QUIZ 037 POPMASTER

DOUBLE 'A' SIDES (2)

You are given the title and artist of a record in which both sides of the record shared the same chart placing. You need to name the other song.

QUESTION 1
'The Next Time', Cliff Richard.

QUESTION 2
'Heartbeat', Steps.

QUESTION 3
'Little Sister', Elvis Presley.

QUESTION 4
'Punky Reggae Party', Bob Marley & The Wailers.

QUESTION 5
'Under the Bridge', All Saints.

QUESTION 6
'Ghosts', Michael Jackson.

QUESTION 7
'The Power of Goodbye', Madonna.

QUESTION 8
'Angeleyes', Abba.

QUESTION 9
'Going Underground', The Jam.

QUESTION 10
'I'm Alive', Seal.

POPMASTER QUIZ 038

ELTON JOHN

QUESTION 1
Who recorded the 1976 No 1 'Don't Go Breaking My Heart' with Elton'?

QUESTION 2
Elton didn't have his first solo No 1 in the UK until 1990, with a double A side of two songs he'd released as singles in 1989 – name both songs.

QUESTION 3
Which singer and actor played a young Elton John in the video for his 2002 single 'This Train Don't Stop There Anymore'?

QUESTION 4
Which Elton song did Ellie Goulding cover and release in 2010?

QUESTION 5
Who is the lyricist who wrote the words to many of his hits, including 'Daniel', 'Rocket Man' and 'Goodbye Yellow Brick Road'?

QUESTION 6
What was the title of the 2005 No 1 by 2Pac (featuring Elton John)?

QUESTION 7
What is the name of the record label he co-founded in 1973, on which he released the majority of his singles and albums?

QUESTION 8
With which opera singer did he record the 1996 Top 10 duet 'Live Like Horses'?

QUESTION 9
For which musical did he win a Tony award for Best Original Music Score in 2000?

QUESTION 10
Kenneth was his middle name when he was called Reg Dwight – what is his middle name now he is Elton John?

QUIZ 036

Q1 *'Dandelion'*

Q2 *'Baby's Coming Back'*

Q3 *'Seasons in the Sun'*

Q4 *'The Road to Mandalay'*

Q5 *'Something'*

Q6 *'Who Do You Think You Are'*

Q7 *'Robot Man'*

Q8 *'Something About the Way You Look Tonight'*

Q9 *'Rivers of Babylon'*

Q10 *'Flap Your Wings'*

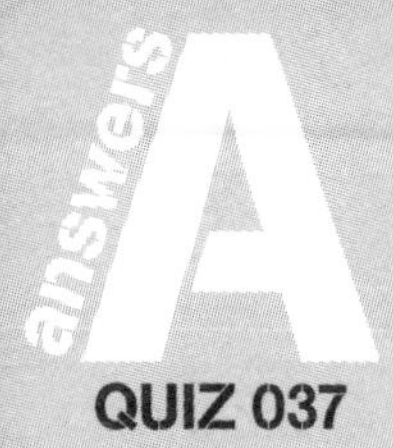

QUIZ 037

Q1
'Bachelor Boy'

Q2
'Tragedy'

Q3
'(Marie's the Name of) His Latest Flame'

Q4
'Jammin''

Q5
'Lady Marmalade'

Q6
'History'

Q7
'Little Star'

Q8
'Voulez-Vous'

Q9
'Dreams of Children'

Q10
'Kiss From a Rose'

QUIZ 039 POPMASTER

EUROPE AT EUROVISION

Simply name the winning country from the year, song, title and artist

QUESTION 1
2012 – 'Euphoria', Loreen.

QUESTION 2
1975 – 'Ding a Dong', Teach-In.

QUESTION 3
1965 – 'Poupée de Cire, Poupée de Son', France Gall.

QUESTION 4
1987– 'Hold Me Now', Johnny Logan.

QUESTION 5
2009 – 'Fairytale', Alexander Rybak.

QUESTION 6
1977 – 'L'Oiseau et L'Enfant', Marie Myriam.

QUESTION 7
1998 – 'Diva', Dana International.

QUESTION 8
1986 – 'J'Aime la Vie', Sandra Kim.

QUESTION 9
2006 – 'Hard Rock Hallelujah', Lordi.

QUESTION 10
1990 – 'Insieme:1992', Toto Cutugno.

POPMASTER QUIZ 040

EUROVISION SONG CONTEST

Love it or loathe it, we all talk about it, so how well do you remember the songs and the singers from years gone by?

QUESTION 1
The 2013 contest was held in Sweden and won by Emmelie de Forest with her song 'Only Teardrops'. What country did she represent?

QUESTION 2
Sandie Shaw was the first singer to win the contest for Great Britain, with a song written by Bill Martin and Phil Coulter. Can you name the song?

QUESTION 3
Can you name the title of the winning song from the 1971 contest held in Dublin and performed by Severine, representing Monaco?

QUESTION 4
In 1988, the winning song was Switzerland's entry 'Ne Partez Pas Sans Moi', performed by a singer who went on to achieve a string of international hits. Can you name her?

QUESTION 5
The final contest of the Nineties was held in Jerusalem and was won by Swedish singer, Charlotte Nilsson, but can you remember the title of her song?

QUESTION 6
In 1970, with the event travelling to Amsterdam in Holland, Ireland was represented by Dana, who was only the second artist to perform the winning song sitting down. Can you recall its title?

QUESTION 7
The fiftieth contest was held at the Palace of Sports in Kiev in Ukraine and was won by Elena Paparizou, representing Greece. In which year did this contest take place?

QUESTION 8
In 1977 when the contest was held in London, the UK entry was placed second and was performed by Lynsey De Paul and Mike Moran. Can you name the song?

QUESTION 9
And in 1995, when the contest was held in Ireland, the UK entry was performed by a group whose song had the same title as their name. What was it?

QUESTION 10
The UK's first entry was in 1959. Our song, 'Sing Little Birdie' came second, but can you remember the names of the two performers?

QUIZ 038

Q1 *Kiki Dee*

Q2 *'Sacrifice', 'Healing Hands'*

Q3 *Justin Timberlake*

Q4 *'Your Song'*

Q5 *Bernie Taupin*

Q6 *'Ghetto Gospel'*

Q7 *Rocket Records*

Q8 *Luciano Pavarotti*

Q9 *"Aida"*

Q10 *Hercules*

QUIZ 039

Q1
Sweden

Q2
Netherlands

Q3
Luxembourg

Q4
Ireland

Q5
Norway

Q6
France

Q7
Israel

Q8
Belgium

Q9
Finland

Q10
Italy

QUIZ 041 POPMASTER

EX-FACTOR

These questions are all linked to groups or artists that have a connection to TV talent shows

QUESTION 1
Which group was formed in 2001 by the singers who didn't make it into the "Popstars" group Hear'Say and what was their only No 1?

QUESTION 2
Showaddywaddy appeared on "New Faces" in 1973. What was the title of their 1974 debut hit?

QUESTION 3
What are the first names of the four members of JLS?

QUESTION 4
Mary Hopkin appeared on Opportunity Knocks in1968 and reached No 1 that year with 'Those Were The Days'. Who produced it?

QUESTION 5
Which group originally recorded Matt Cardle's 2010 No 1 'When We Collide' and what was its original title?

QUESTION 6
Peters and Lee reached No 1 in 1973 with which song?

QUESTION 7
'Cannonball' was the title of the first No 1 by Little Mix, but what was their second?

QUESTION 8
Who had a hit in 1981 with the song 'Star' which was used later that decade as the theme tune to the BBC's revival of "Opportunity Knocks"?

QUESTION 9
Which Snow Patrol song was a No 1 cover version for Leona Lewis in 2008?

QUESTION 10
"Pop Idol" ran for two series in the UK – Will Young won the first, who won the second and what was the title of her 2003 No 1 single?

POPMASTER QUIZ 042

THE EYES HAVE IT

QUESTION 1
Released in 1975 and 1979, name both of Art Garfunkel's UK No 1 singles

QUESTION 2
'See It In A Boy's Eyes' was a Top 5 single in 2004 for which singer?

QUESTION 3
What 1982 single by ABC shares the same title as a 1973 hit for Gladys Knight & The Pips and a 1987 song by Madonna?

QUESTION 4
Who was the uncredited vocalist on Rockwell's 1984 hit 'Somebody's Watching Me'?

QUESTION 5
What was the title of Elbow's 2008 album that included the singles 'Grounds for Divorce' and 'One Day Like This'?

QUESTION 6
Tony Christie was the guest vocalist on the 1999 Top 10 single 'Walk Like a Panther', by which group?

QUESTION 7
The band that sang the early Eighties Top 10 hit 'I Am The Beat' has the same name as the 1989 debut hit for Scandinavian duo Roxette – what is that shared band name and song title?

QUESTION 8
Born Jack Allsop, under what name did this artist have a Top 3 hit in 2007 with 'Starz In Their Eyes'?

QUESTION 9
Released in 1987, what was the title of Frankie Goes to Hollywood's last original hit single?

QUESTION 10
In the summer of 1979, two acts were in the chart at the same time with different songs called 'Angel Eyes' – name both of the acts.

QUIZ 040

Q1
Denmark

Q2
'Puppet on a String'

Q3
'Un Banc, Un Arbre, Une Rue'

Q4
Céline Dion

Q5
'Take Me to Your Heaven'

Q6
'All Kinds of Everything'

Q7
2005

Q8
'Rock Bottom'

Q9
'Love City Groove'

Q10
Pearl Carr and Teddy Johnson

QUIZ 041

Q1
Liberty X, 'Just A Little' (group called Liberty for their first two hits)

Q2
'Hey Rock 'n Roll'

Q3
Marvin, Aston, Oritsé JB (Jonathan Benjamin)

Q4
Paul Mccartney

Q5
Biffy Clyro, 'Many of Horror'

Q6
'Welcome Home'

Q7
'Wings'

Q8
Kiki Dee

Q9
'Run'

Q10
Michelle Mcmanus, 'All this Time'

QUIZ 043 POPMASTER

FASHION (1)

QUESTION 1
'She's in Fashion' was the title of a 1999 hit for the group whose lead singer is Brett Anderson. Name the group?

QUESTION 2
In 1974, Mungo Jerry sang about a 'Long Legged Woman Dressed In…' what?

QUESTION 3
Who wore a 'Suit & Tie', according to the title of his 2013 Top 3 hit?

QUESTION 4
Which song by The Smiths gave Sandie Shaw her first hit for 15 years in 1984?

QUESTION 5
Which Scottish singer-songwriter had a hit in 2007 with 'New Shoes', a song from his 2006 No 1 album 'These Streets'?

QUESTION 6
What was Neil Diamond wearing, according to the title of his final hit of the Seventies?

QUESTION 7
The song 'Paninaro' lists a number of designer clothing labels in its lyrics – which duo wrote and recorded the song?

QUESTION 8
What brand of trainers inspired Run-DMC's 1986 debut single?

QUESTION 9
Although not a hit single, who covered the song 'You Can Leave Your Hat On' for the film "The Full Monty"?

QUESTION 10
What type of 'Suit' did Paul Weller sing about on his 1996 Top 5 single?

POPMASTER QUIZ 044

FASHION (2)

QUESTION 1
What type of 'Shoes' provided a hit for both Carl Perkins and Elvis Presley?

QUESTION 2
Who recorded the 1990 No 1 version of 'Itsy Bitsy Teeny Weeny Yellow Polka Dot Bikini'?

QUESTION 3
Kraftwerk's No 1 'The Model' was a double A side with which other song?

QUESTION 4
'Up on the Catwalk' was a 1984 single by which Scottish band?

QUESTION 5
In 2005 and with a little help from a Shirley Bassey sample, Kanye West sang about 'Diamonds from…' where?

QUESTION 6
Which Welsh band reached the Top 5 in 2001 with a cover version of 'Handbags and Gladrags'?

QUESTION 7
Which 1992 Top 5 song by George Michael had an accompanying video that featured a number of supermodels of the day including Linda Evangelista, Tyra Banks and Emma Sjöberg?

QUESTION 8
'Hey There Delilah' was a Top 3 single in 2007 for which group?

QUESTION 9
What type of 'Beret' did Prince and the Revolution sing about in 1985?

QUESTION 10
Which two actors had a Top 5 hit in the early Nineties with the song 'Kinky Boots'?

QUIZ 042

Q1 *'I Only Have Eyes for You '(1975), 'Bright Eyes' (1979)*

Q2 *Jamelia*

Q3 *'The Look of Love'*

Q4 *Michael Jackson*

Q5 *The Seldom Seen Kid*

Q6 *'All Seeing I'*

Q7 *The Look*

Q8 *Just Jack*

Q9 *'Watching the Wildlife' (their biggest hits charted after this as remixes)*

Q10 *Abba, Roxy Music*

QUIZ 043

Q1
Suede

Q2
Black

Q3
Justin Timberlake (featuring Jay-Z)

Q4
'Hand in Glove'

Q5
Paulo Nutini

Q6
Blue Jeans ('Forever in Blue Jeans' was Top 20 hit 1979)

Q7
Pet Shop Boys (originally a B side to 'Suburbia', but re-recorded in 1995)

Q8
Adidas ('My Adidas')

Q9
Tom Jones

Q10
'Peacock Suit'

QUIZ 045 POPMASTER

FELINE GROOVY

QUESTION 1
Which glam-rock era group had a Top 3 single in 1974 called 'The Cat Crept In'?

QUESTION 2
What was the title of Survivor's 1982 No 1 theme song from the film "Rocky III"?

QUESTION 3
By what name was American singer and guitarist John Mellencamp known before he was just 'John Mellencamp'?

QUESTION 4
What was the title of Elton John and Tim Rice's 1994 Academy award-winning song from "The Lion King"?

QUESTION 5
Name the rockabilly group that had hits in the early 1980s called 'Runaway Boys' and 'Rock This Town'.

QUESTION 6
The Pussycat Dolls began their chart career in 2005 with two No 1 singles that year – name either of them.

QUESTION 7
With reported sales of 20 million worldwide, what is the title of the Def Leppard album that contains the hits 'Animal', 'Pour Some Sugar on Me', 'Love Bites' and 'Armageddon It'?

QUESTION 8
Although a popular album artist, can you name the singer-songwriter whose only hit single was 'Year of the Cat'?

QUESTION 9
Which of Atomic Kitten's three No 1 singles was not a cover version?

QUESTION 10
Who was the lead singer of the group Curiosity Killed the Cat?

POPMASTER QUIZ 046

FEMALE DUOS

QUESTION 1
On which Eurythmics' song did Aretha Franklin join Annie Lennox on lead vocals?

QUESTION 2
"X Factor" winner Leon Jackson's 2007 No 1 was 'When You Believe' – a cover version of a song that had been a hit in 1998, for which two American singers?

QUESTION 3
Barbara Dickson and Elaine Paige's 1985 No 1 'I Know Him So Well' was a song from which musical, written by Bjorn and Benny from ABBA and Tim Rice?

QUESTION 4
What was the title of the 2007 duet by Sugababes vs Girls Aloud released for Comic Relief?

QUESTION 5
The comedy duo French and Saunders with actress Kathy Burke adopted what name for their 1989 recording of The Beatles' 'Help' with Bananarama?

QUESTION 6
What was the title of the 1998 Top 3 hit and American No 1 sung by Brandy and Monica?

QUESTION 7
Who sang the 2007 No 1 duet 'Beautiful Liar' with Beyoncé?

QUESTION 8
By what collective name were duo Siobhan Fahey and Marcella Detroit better known?

QUESTION 9
The American vocal group En Vogue featured on the 1994 hit single 'Whatta Man', recorded by which female rap act?

QUESTION 10
What was the title of the 2003 Top 3 single by Britney Spears that featured Madonna?

QUIZ 044

Q1
'Blue Suede Shoes'

Q2
'Bombalurina' (the band fronted by TV presenter Timmy Mallett)

Q3
'Computer Love' ('The Model' received the majority of the airplay)

Q4
Simple Minds

Q5
Sierra Leone

Q6
Stereophonics

Q7
'Too Funky'

Q8
Plain White T's

Q9
'Raspberry Beret'

Q10
Patrick MacNee and Honor Blackman

QUIZ 045

Q1
Mud

Q2
'Eye of the Tiger'

Q3
John Cougar Mellencamp, before that John Cougar, and before that Johnny Cougar

Q4
'Can You Feel The Love Tonight'

Q5
Stray Cats

Q6
'Don't Cha', 'Stickwitu'

Q7
Hysteria

Q8
Al Stewart

Q9
'Whole Again' – the others were 'Eternal Flame' and 'The Tide Is High (Get The Feeling)'

Q10
Ben Volpeliere-Pierrot

QUIZ 047 POPMASTER

FIRST AND LAST (1)

Can you name the singer or group from the titles of their first and last Top 40 hits in the 20th century?

QUESTION 1
First – 'Planet Earth' in 1981; Last – 'Electric Barbarella' in 1999.

QUESTION 2
First – 'A Hard Rain's a-Gonna Fall' in 1973; Last – 'Will You Love Me Tomorrow' in 1993.

QUESTION 3
First – 'Betcha By Golly Wow' in 1972; Last '$7000 and You' in 1977.

QUESTION 4
First – 'That's the Way (I Like It)' in 1984; Last – 'Something in My House' in 1987.

QUESTION 5
First – 'All I Really Want To Do' in 1965; Last – 'Dove L'Amore' in 1999.

QUESTION 6
First – 'Peaches/Go Buddy Go' in 1977; Last – 'Always the Sun' in 1991.

QUESTION 7
First – 'Let's Stay Together' in 1983; Last – 'When The Heartache is Over' in 1999.

QUESTION 8
First – 'Keep on Dancing' in 1971; Last – 'You Made Me Believe in Magic' in 1977.

QUESTION 9
First – 'A Forest' in 1980; Last – 'Mint Car' in 1996.

QUESTION 10
First – 'Dignity' in 1988; Last – a re-issue of 'Dignity' in 1994.

POPMASTER QUIZ 048

FIRST AND LAST (2)

Can you name the singer or group from the titles of their first and last Top 40 hits in the 20th century?

QUESTION 1
First – 'Tears Are Not Enough' in 1981; Last – 'One Better World' in 1989.

QUESTION 2
First – '(There's) Always Something There to Remind Me' in 1964; Last – 'Hand in Glove' in 1984.

QUESTION 3
First – 'I Know What I Like (in Your Wardrobe)' in 1974; Last – 'Congo' in 1997.

QUESTION 4
First – 'Fire' in 1981; Last – 'Sweetest Thing' in 1998.

QUESTION 5
First – 'Love Resurrection' in 1984; Last – 'Whispering Your Name' in 1994.

QUESTION 6
First – 'Dreamer' in 1975; Last – 'It's Raining Again 'in 1982.

QUESTION 7
First – 'Love of the Loved' in 1963; Last – 'Baby We Can't Go Wrong' in 1974.

QUESTION 8
First – 'Spread a Little Happiness' in 1982; Last – 'Brand New Day' in 1997.

QUESTION 9
First – '10538 Overture' in 1972; Last – 'Calling America' in 1986.

QUESTION 10
First – 'Let Love Rule' in 1990; Last – 'Fly Away' in 1999.

A answers

QUIZ 046

Q1
'Sisters Are Doin' It for Themselves'

Q2
Mariah Carey & Whitney Houston

Q3
"Chess"

Q4
'Walk this Way'

Q5
'La Na Nee Nee Noo Noo' (separate words on the label, but one on the sleeve)

Q6
'The Boy Is Mine'

Q7
Shakira

Q8
Shakespear's Sister

Q9
Salt N' Pepa

Q10
'Me Against the Music'

QUIZ 047

Q1
Duran Duran

Q2
Bryan Ferry

Q3
The Stylistics

Q4
Dead Or Alive

Q5
Cher

Q6
The Stranglers

Q7
Tina Turner

Q8
Bay City Rollers

Q9
The Cure

Q10
Deacon Blue

QUIZ 049 POPMASTER

FIRST AND LAST (3)

Can you name the singer or group from the titles of their first and last Top 40 hits in the 20th century?

QUESTION 1
First – 'Money's Too Tight (To Mention)' in 1985; Last – 'Ain't That a Lot of Love' in 1999.

QUESTION 2
First – 'Spirit Body and Soul' in 1979; Last – 'Don't Love Me Too Hard' in 1982.

QUESTION 3
First – 'Reason to Believe' in 1971; Last – 'Ooh La La' in 1998.

QUESTION 4
First – 'Saving All My Love for You' in 1985; Last 'I Learned from the Best' in 1999.

QUESTION 5
First – 'Funny Funny' in 1971; Last – 'Love is Like Oxygen' in 1978.

QUESTION 6
First – 'Ocean Drive' in 1995; Last – 'Postcard from Heaven' in 1999.

QUESTION 7
First – 'Promised You f Miracle' in 1982; Last – 'Glitterball' in 1998.

QUESTION 8
First – 'I'm Leaving It (All) Up to You' in 1974; Last – 'Deep Purple' in 1976.

QUESTION 9
First – 'Times They Are A–Changin'' in 1965; Last – 'Dignity' in 1995?

QUESTION 10
First – 'I'm a Man' in 1970; Last – 'You're The Inspiration' in 1985.

POPMASTER QUIZ 050

FIRSTS AND LASTS (4)

Can you name the singer or group from the titles of their first and last Top 40 hits in the 20th century?

QUESTION 1
What was the first single to be issued in the UK on the Warner Brothers label, catalogue number, WB1?

QUESTION 2
What was the title of the last solo Top 10 hit achieved by Ringo Starr in the Seventies?

QUESTION 3
What was the first and only song to have been a hit three times in three different versions by the same artist?

QUESTION 4
What was the title of the fifth and final album of new material to be released by girl group Bananarama featuring Jacquie O' Sullivan, who had replaced Siobhan Fahey?

QUESTION 5
Who became the first British female singer to top the British chart with a self-composed song?

QUESTION 6
Can you name the group who set a new record when they became the first act to enter the chart at No 1 with their first seven releases?

QUESTION 7
During the Sixties, singer Eden Kane achieved five hit singles, all of which made the Top 10. What was the title of the last of those five hits?

QUESTION 8
What was the title of the first solo No 1 hit by Robbie Williams?

QUESTION 9
What was the first single to top the chart in two different decades in the same version?

QUESTION 10
Name the group who became the first act to have three singles enter the chart at No 1 in a single year.

QUIZ 048

Q1
ABC

Q2
Sandie Shaw

Q3
Genesis

Q4
U2

Q5
Alison Moyet

Q6
Supertramp

Q7
Cilla Black

Q8
Sting

Q9
Electric Light Orchestra

Q10
Lenny Kravitz

QUIZ 049

Q1
Simply Red

Q2
The Nolans (first hit billed as The Nolan Sisters)

Q3
Rod Stewart

Q4
Whitney Houston

Q5
The Sweet

Q6
Lighthouse Family

Q7
Simple Minds

Q8
Donny & Marie Osmond

Q9
Bob Dylan

Q10
Chicago

QUIZ 051 POPMASTER

FOOTLOOSE

QUESTION 1
According to the title of Snap!'s 1992 No 1, what '… is a Dancer'?

QUESTION 2
'The Twist (Yo Twist)' was a Top 3 single in 1988 by Chubby Checker and which American group?

QUESTION 3
What is the sub-title to Chic's 1977 UK debut hit 'Dance, Dance, Dance'?

QUESTION 4
Which group had Top 10 hits in the Seventies with 'Get Dancing' and 'I Wanna Dance wit Choo'?

QUESTION 5
David Bowie had hits in both 1972 and 1979 with two very different versions of the same song (with very slightly different title) – what is the song?

QUESTION 6
Which group had a hit in 2007 called 'Let's Dance Like Joy Division'?

QUESTION 7
Which song by The Gap Band was often 'danced' by a line of people sitting on the floor making 'rowing-boat' actions?

QUESTION 8
Released in 1994, who had a hit single with 'Riverdance', his music for the hugely successful dance production that made a star of Michael Flatley?

QUESTION 9
What dance craze did the group Kenny sing about on their debut Top 10 hit in the mid-Seventies?

QUESTION 10
The singer Maria Vidal had her only UK in 1985 with the title song to a film about a young man with a talent for break-dancing – what was the title of both the song and the film?

POPMASTER QUIZ 052

A FOREIGN AFFAIR

QUESTION 1
Nena's '99 Red Balloons' was No 1 in 1984. In America it reached the Top 3 in its original language What was that language?

QUESTION 2
'Moi...Lolita' was a Top 10 single in 2002 for which French singer?

QUESTION 3
The band Sigur Rós sing in their own made-up language called Vonlenska, but also occasionally in their native tongue. Where are they from?

QUESTION 4
Released in 1974, what was the title of Santana's first UK hit single?

QUESTION 5
'Dragostea Din Tei' was a Top 3 single in 2004 for O-Zone and the most successful UK hit sung in which language?

QUESTION 6
What was the title of the 1982 Top 3 single by the German band Trio?

QUESTION 7
What is the nationality of Plastic Bertrand who had a hit in 1978 with 'Ça Plane Pour Moi'?

QUESTION 8
What was the title of the 1963 Top 10 single and American No 1 by the Japanese singer Kyu Sakamoto?

QUESTION 9
'Yeke Yeke' was a Top 40 hit in 1988, 1995 and 1996 for which singer from Guinea?

QUESTION 10
What is the subtitle of the 2002 No 1 'The Ketchup Song', by Las Ketchup?

QUIZ 050

Q1
'Cathy's Clown 'by The Everly Brothers

Q2
'You're Sixteen'

Q3
'Candle In The Wind' by Elton John

Q4
Pop Life

Q5
Kate Bush with 'Wuthering Heights'

Q6
Westlife

Q7
'Boys Cry'

Q8
'Millennium'

Q9
'Bohemian Rhapsody' by Queen in 1975 and 1991

Q10
Slade (all in 1973)

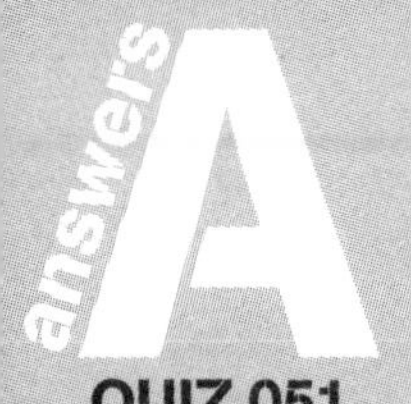

QUIZ 051

Q1
Rhythm ('Rhythm Is A Dancer' spent six weeks at No 1 in 1992)

Q2
Fat Boys (billed as Fat Boys and Chubby Checker)

Q3
'(Yowsah, Yowsah, Yowsah)'

Q4
Disco Tex And The Sex-O-Lettes

Q5
'John I'm Only Dancing' (1979 hit was 'John I'm Only Dancing (Again) (1975)'

Q6
The Wombats

Q7
'Oops Up Side Your Head'

Q8
Bill Whelan (billed as Bill Whelan and Anuna featuring the RTE Concert Orchestra)

Q9
'The Bump'

Q10
'Body Rock'

QUIZ 053 POPMASTER

FOUR SEASONS

QUESTION 1
The Four Seasons have only had one No 1 in the UK. What is it called?

QUESTION 2
Who is credited alongside The Fresh Prince on the 1991 Top 10 song 'Summertime'?

QUESTION 3
Which Paul Simon song was covered by The Bangles in 1988?

QUESTION 4
'Autumn Almanac' was a Top 3 song in 1967 for which group?

QUESTION 5
What is the subtitle to Love Unlimited's 1975 hit 'It May Be Winter Outside'?

QUESTION 6
Which Welsh band reached the Top 10 in 2007 with 'Autumnsong'?

QUESTION 7
Jacques Brel's song 'Le Moribund' was given English lyrics by Rod McKuen and became a No 1 for Terry Jacks in 1974 and Westlife in 1999 – what is the English version called?

QUESTION 8
What was the name of the Spanish DJ and producer who had a Top 3 hit in 2003 with a dance version of Don Henley's 'The Boys of Summer'?

QUESTION 9
What was the title of Justin Hayward's hit single from Jeff Wayne's version of "War of the Worlds"?

QUESTION 10
Which band recorded the 1992 single 'Four Seasons in One Day'?

POPMASTER QUIZ 054

FRENCH CONNECTION

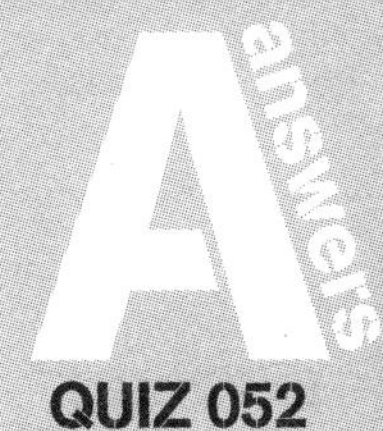

QUESTION 1
'Music Sounds Better with You' reached number 2 and spent nearly six months on the chart in 1998 for which group?

QUESTION 2
Modjo reached No 1 in 2000 with a song that sampled Chic's 'Soup For One' – what was the title of this No 1?

QUESTION 3
Which two singers are credited with the controversial 1969 hit 'Je T'Aime Moi Non Plus'?

QUESTION 4
What part of 'Oxygene' became Jean-Michel Jarre's hit single from the album 'Oxygene' – was it part I, II, III, IV, V or VI?

QUESTION 5
The singer Ryan Paris had his only hit in 1983 with a song that reached the Top 5. What was it called?

QUESTION 6
Who is the French house producer and DJ who had No 1s in 2009 with 'When Love Takes Over' featuring Kelly Rowland and 'Sexy Chick' featuring Akon?

QUESTION 7
Released in 1997, which of these singles was the UK chart debut by Daft Punk: 'One More Time', 'Harder Better Faster Stronger' or the double A side 'Da Funk / Musique'?

QUESTION 8
The group Voyage had its biggest hit with a 1978 single called 'From...what…to...what'?

QUESTION 9
Under what name did the French singer Claudie Fritsch have her 1988 Top 5 hit 'Voyage Voyage'?

QUESTION 10
In 1999, Elvis Costello had a hit with his version of a 1974 No 1 by Charles Aznavour. What is the song?

QUIZ 052

Q1 *German*

Q2 *Alizée*

Q3 *Iceland*

Q4 *'Samba Pa Ti'*

Q5 *Romanian*

Q6 *'Da Da Da'*

Q7 *Belgian*

Q8 *'Sukiyaki'*

Q9 *'Mory Kante' (1995 was re-issue of 1988 version, 1996 was a remix)*

Q10 *('Asereje')*

QUIZ 053

Q1
'December 1963 (Oh What a Night)'

Q2
DJ Jazzy Jeff

Q3
'Hazy Shade of Winter'

Q4
The Kinks

Q5
'(But in My Heart it's Spring)'

Q6
Manic Street Preachers

Q7
'Seasons in the Sun'

Q8
DJ Sammy

Q9
'Forever Autumn'

Q10
Crowded House

QUIZ 055 POPMASTER

FRUIT & VEG

QUESTION 1
With which group did Edwyn Collins have a 1983 hit called 'Rip It Up'?

QUESTION 2
Released in 1968, what is the title of the only No 1 by The Move?

QUESTION 3
The songs 'When Love Breaks Down', 'A Prisoner of the Past' and 'The King Of Rock 'n Roll' were Top 40 hits for which group?

QUESTION 4
The Black Eyed Peas had their first UK No 1 in 2003 – what was it called?

QUESTION 5
'Play that Funky Music' was a worldwide hit in 1976 for which American group?

QUESTION 6
Who is the lead singer of the group The Lemonheads?

QUESTION 7
What headwear provided Prince and the Revolution with the title of a 1985 single?

QUESTION 8
Which group's early albums include "Freaky Styley", "Mother's Milk" and "The Uplift Mofo Party Plan"?

QUESTION 9
'Strawberry Fields Forever' was a 1967 No 1 double A side for the Beatles with which other song?

QUESTION 10
D'Arcy Wretzky and James Iha are former members of which American alt-rock group?

POPMASTER QUIZ 056

GAMES PEOPLE PLAY

QUESTION 1
'Domino' was the title of a 2012 No 1 single by which female singer?

QUESTION 2
Which of these computer games provided the title of a 1992 Top 10 hit for Doctor Spin – was it 'Supermarioland', 'Tetris' or 'PAC-Man'?

QUESTION 3
Name the footballer who provided the rap on the 1990 No 1 'World In Motion' by Englandneworder?

QUESTION 4
Which Elton John and Bernie Taupin song from the mid-Seventies was written for tennis legend Billie Jean King?

QUESTION 5
Which of these games does Alice Cooper love to play – table tennis, croquet or golf?

QUESTION 6
The mid-Eighties hits 'I Know Him So Well' by Elaine Paige and Barbara Dickson and 'One Night in Bangkok' both come from which musical written by Tim Rice and Björn and Benny from ABBA?

QUESTION 7
Which David Bowie song was played both during the arrival of the Great Britain team at the 2012 Olympic and Paralympic Games and also at the medal ceremonies?

QUESTION 8
Which opera singer had a Top 5 hit in 1991 singing 'World in Union' – the anthem for the Rugby World Cup?

QUESTION 9
In 1983 Malcolm McLaren released a single about a skipping-rope craze. What was it called?

QUESTION 10
Born Joseph Alfred Souter, under what name did this American singer record his 1969 British hit 'Games People Play'?

QUIZ 054

Q1
Stardust

Q2
'Lady (Hear Me Tonight)'

Q3
Serge Gainsbourg, Jane Birkin

Q4
Part IV

Q5
'Dolce Vita'

Q6
David Guetta

Q7
'Da Funk / Musique' (Top 10 in 1997)

Q8 *'From East to West' (Top 20 in 1978, billed as a double A side with 'Scots Machine')*

Q9
Desireless

Q10
'She'

QUIZ 055

Q1
Orange Juice

Q2
'Blackberry Way'

Q3
Prefab Sprout

Q4
'Where is the Love?'

Q5
Wild Cherry

Q6
Evan Dando

Q7
'Raspberry Beret'

Q8
Red Hot Chili Peppers

Q9
'Penny Lane'

Q10
Smashing Pumpkins

QUIZ 057 POPMASTER

GET LUCKY (1)

(They're easy if you know them, they're not if you don't!)

QUESTION 1
The song 'Crazy' spent nine weeks at No 1 in 2006 for which group?

QUESTION 2
What type of 'Toy' did Roachford sing about, according to the title of his 1989 Top 10 single?

QUESTION 3
In which year did these three songs all reach No 1 – 'Saturday Night' by Whigfield, 'Sure' by Take That and 'Baby Come Back' by Pato Banton?

QUESTION 4
In 1973, the drummer Cozy Powell released a single that became a Top 3 hit early in 1974 called 'Dance with… what?

QUESTION 5
Released in 1984 and 1990, who's last Top 40 hit of the Eighties was 'Apollo 9' and first of the Nineties was 'Room At The Top'?

QUESTION 6
Which song has been No 1 for both Billy Joel and Westlife?

QUESTION 7
Who spent five weeks at No 1 in 2008 with her debut Top 40 hit called 'Mercy'?

QUESTION 8
Loudon Wainwright III has a son and a daughter who are both recording artists – what are they called?

QUESTION 9
Which of these songs was the 1993 Top 40 debut by Jamiroquai – 'Virtual Insanity', 'Too Young to Die' or 'Cosmic Girl'?

QUESTION 10
Which American singer-songwriter and guitarist had posthumous No 1 albums in the early Noughties with "Songbird", "Imagine" and "American Tune"?

POPMASTER QUIZ 058

GET LUCKY (2)

(They're easy if you know them, they're not if you don't!)

QUESTION 1
Who is the guitarist in U2?

QUESTION 2
The subtitle '(Mighty Real)' belongs to a 1978 disco hit recorded by Sylvester. What is the song's full title?

QUESTION 3
In which year did these three songs all reach No 1 – 'Viva La Vida' by Coldplay, 'The Promise' by Girls Aloud and 'Greatest Day' by Take That?

QUESTION 4
Which of these songs by The Rolling Stones gave the singer Melanie her first Top 10 hit in 1970 – was it 'As Tears Go By', 'Ruby Tuesday' or 'Out of Time'?

QUESTION 5
The Monkees consisted of Davy Jones, Micky Dolenz, Michael Nesmith and which other member?

QUESTION 6
What one word title is shared by a 1986 single by Human League and a 2008 single by The Killers?

QUESTION 7
Which British singer had hits in 1991 with her singles 'Change' and 'All Woman'?

QUESTION 8
The song 'In the City' was the 1977 Top 40 debut by which group?

QUESTION 9
Taio Cruz first reached No 1 in 2009 with a song he'd originally co-written for Cheryl Cole and in its remix version featured a guest appearance by American rapper Ludacris. What was it called?

QUESTION 10
Over the course of his career, which acclaimed singer-songwriter has released albums called "Astral Weeks", "Enlightenment", "The Healing Game" and "Too Long In Exile"?

QUIZ 056

Q1 *Jessie J*

Q2 *'Tetris' (Doctor Spin was a production duo that included Andrew Lloyd Webber!)*

Q3 *John Barnes*

Q4 *'Philadelphia Freedom'*

Q5 *Golf*

Q6 *'Chess'*

Q7 *'Heroes'*

Q8 *Kiri Te Kanawa*

Q9 *'Double Dutch'*

Q10 *Joe South*

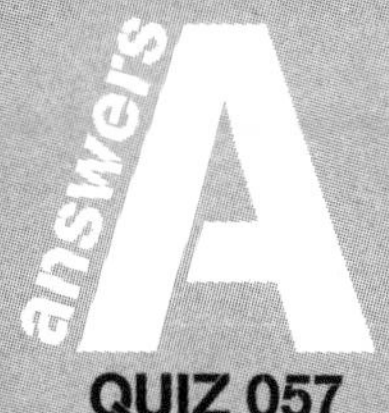

QUIZ 057

Q1
Gnarls Barkley

Q2
'Cuddly Toy'

Q3
1994

Q4
The Devil

Q5
Adam Ant

Q6
'Uptown Girl'

Q7
Duffy

Q8
Rufus, Martha

Q9
'Too Young to Die' (the other two were 1996)

Q10
Eva Cassidy

QUIZ 059 POPMASTER

HEARD IT ALL BEFORE

In each case name the group or artist to have a Top 40 hit with a cover version of a song by another successful act

QUESTION 1
Glam-rock-era band that took the Crickets' song 'Oh Boy' to No 1 in 1975.

QUESTION 2
Former Disney "Mousketeer" who had a 2002 hit with 'I Love Rock 'n Roll' by Joan Jett & The Blackhearts and The Arrows.

QUESTION 3
Former British folk group that had a No 1 in 1966 with The Beatles' 'Michelle'.

QUESTION 4
Late Eighties band that abbreviated its name to have a final Top 3 hit in 1992 with a cover of Johnny Bristol's 'Hang on in There Baby'.

QUESTION 5
Early gothic-rock band led by Peter Murphy whose biggest hit was with David Bowie's song 'Ziggy Stardust'.

QUESTION 6
American superstar who released her cover of Gloria Gaynor's 'I Will Survive' in 1996 under her first name only.

QUESTION 7
Band that had a 1986 hit with Bob and Earl's 1969 song 'Harlem Shuffle'.

QUESTION 8
The artists that reached No 1 and No 2 at Christmas 2008 with 'Hallelujah', by Leonard Cohen.

QUESTION 9
American country-pop singer who recorded the 1978 hit cover of 'Words' by the Bee Gees.

QUESTION 10
Veteran British band whose mid-Nineties version of 'Fun Fun Fun' featured the band that originally recorded the song.

POPMASTER QUIZ 060

HERE COME THE GIRLS

How much do you know about these successful female artists and groups

QUESTION 1
Name Motown's most successful girl group of the Sixties that featured Diana Ross.

QUESTION 2
'C'Est la Vie' was the first of four No 1, for B*Witched in the late Nineties. Name one of the other three.

QUESTION 3
Which vocal group had its only Top 40 hit in 1982 with the Top 10 song 'I Eat Cannibals Part 1'?

QUESTION 4
Which 2006 single by Rihanna contains elements of the song 'Tainted Love', made famous by Soft Cell?

QUESTION 5
Who recorded the 1977 Top 5 single 'Down Deep Inside', the theme song to the film "The Deep"?

QUESTION 6
The American singer Phyllis Nelson reached No 1 in 1985 with which song?

QUESTION 7
Which member of Girls Aloud had not released a solo album by the time the group performed their final concert in March 2013?

QUESTION 8
What David Bowie song gave Lulu her only Top 10 hit in the 1970s?

QUESTION 9
Who was the sixth and final singer to become a member of Sugababes before they split up?

QUESTION 10
Which song, written by Prince under the pseudonym Christopher Tracy, gave The Bangles their first UK hit?

Answers

QUIZ 058

Q1 *The Edge*

Q2 *'You Make Me Feel (Mighty Real)'*

Q3 *2008*

Q4 *'Ruby Tuesday'*

Q5 *Peter Tork*

Q6 *'Human'*

Q7 *Lisa Stansfield*

Q8 *The Jam*

Q9 *'Break Your Heart'*

Q10 *Van Morrison*

QUIZ 059

Q1
Mud

Q2
Britney Spears

Q3
The Overlanders

Q4
Curiosity (formerly Curiosity Killed the Cat)

Q5
Bauhaus

Q6
Diana (Diana Ross)

Q7
The Rolling Stones

Q8
Alexandra Burke, Jeff Buckley

Q9
Rita Coolidge

Q10
Status Quo (with the Beach Boys)

QUIZ 061 POPMASTER

HITS IN THE MOVIES

Can you name the movie in which these ten songs appeared?

QUESTION 1
'Hanky Panky' by Madonna

QUESTION 2
'Take My Breath Away' by Berlin

QUESTION 3
'When the Going Gets Tough, the Tough Get Going' by Billy Ocean

QUESTION 4
'I Don't Want to Miss a Thing' by Aerosmith

QUESTION 5
'Call Me' by Blondie

QUESTION 6
'Girls Just Want to Have Fun' by Cyndi Lauper

QUESTION 7
'It Must Have Been Love' by Roxette

QUESTION 8
'Waiting for a Star to Fall' by Boy Meets Girl

QUESTION 9
'Love Song for a Vampire' by Annie Lennox

QUESTION 10
'Take a Look Around' by Limp Bizkit

POPMASTER QUIZ 062

HITS OF THE EIGHTIES (1)

QUESTION 1
Can you name the last hit of the Eighties that also became the first hit of the Nineties?

QUESTION 2
In 1989, Simple Minds achieved their only No 1 of their career Can you name the song?

QUESTION 3
What are the first names of the two Mael brothers who make up the duo, Sparks?

QUESTION 4
What was the title of the Ben E. King hit from 1961 that topped the chart in 1987 when it was re-released?

QUESTION 5
Can you name the 1983 Top 5 hit by the Thompson Twins that was later featured in the 1998 movie, "The Wedding Singer"?

QUESTION 6
With which song, originally recorded by Marvin Gaye, did Paul Young take to No 1 in 1983?

QUESTION 7
Who performed on the hit duet, 'Easy Lover' with Phil Collins that topped the chart in 1985?

QUESTION 8
Can you name the musician who was credited for playing trumpet on the 1982 Top 20 hit by Modern Romance, 'Cherry Pink and Apple Blossom White'?

QUESTION 9
Although he achieved a string of hits in the Eighties, Chris Rea only managed one Top 10 entry. Can you name the song?

QUESTION 10
In what musical did the Elaine Paige and Barbara Dickson's 1985 chart topping hit 'I Know Him So Well' feature?

QUIZ 060

Q1
The Supremes

Q2
'Rollercoaster', 'To You I Belong', 'Blame It On The Weatherman'

Q3
Toto Coelo

Q4
SOS

Q5
Donna Summer

Q6
'Move Closer'

Q7
Sarah Harding

Q8
'The Man Who Sold The World' (No. 3 in 1974)

Q9
Jade Ewen

Q10
'Manic Monday'

QUIZ 061

Q1
"Dick Tracy"

Q2
"Top Gun"

Q3
"The Jewel of the Nile"

Q4
"Armageddon"

Q5
"American Gigalo"

Q6
"To Wong Foo, Thanks for Everything! Julie Newmar"

Q7
"Pretty Woman"

Q8
"Three Men and a Little Lady"

Q9
"Dracula"

Q10
"Mission Impossible 2"

QUIZ 063 POPMASTER

HITS OF THE EIGHTIES (2)

QUESTION 1
What was the title of the 1987 No 1 hit duet recorded by George Michael and Aretha Franklin?

QUESTION 2
In 1984 which group made the Top 10 with a song called 'Wood Beez (Pray Like Aretha Franklin)'?

QUESTION 3
One time lead singer with The Miracles, Smokey Robinson achieved his only solo No 1 hit in 1981. What was the title?

QUESTION 4
Which Madonna hit reached the Top 10 in 1984 when it was first released and again the following year when it was re-issued?

QUESTION 5
What was the only Pet Shop Boys hit of the Eighties that they didn't compose themselves?

QUESTION 6
In 1981, Human League achieved the only No 1 hit of their career. Can you name it?

QUESTION 7
What was the title of the only Top 10 hit achieved by Bette Midler in the Eighties?

QUESTION 8
In 1980, Blondie achieved three consecutive No 1 hits with 'Atomic', 'Call Me' and, what was the title of the third?

QUESTION 9
Surprisingly, Michael Jackson's first solo No 1 from 1981 was an old recording from his Seventies album, 'Forever Michael' that his previous record label issued as a single. What was the title?

QUESTION 10
What was the title of the 1987 Top 5 hit by A-ha that was the theme song to that year's James Bond movie?

POPMASTER QUIZ 064

HITS OF THE FIFTIES (1)

QUESTION 1
Can you name the only No 1 hit achieved by The Platters during the Fifties?

QUESTION 2
During the Fifties an American comedian achieved hits with parodies of 'Sh-Boom,' 'Rock Island Line' and 'Heartbreak Hotel.' Can you name him?

QUESTION 3
In 1953, Eddie Fisher achieve, two No 1 hits. The first was 'Outside Of Heaven,' what was the other?

QUESTION 4
Petula Clark made the UK chart for the first time in 1954 with a Top 10 hit that was a cover of an American recording by The Gaylords. Can you name the song?

QUESTION 5
Neil Sedaka's chart career began in 1959 with two Top 10 hits. One was 'Oh Carol', but what was the other?

QUESTION 6
Can you name the group that had hits in the Fifties with 'Searchin', 'Yakety Yak' and 'Charlie Brown'?

QUESTION 7
American singer and actress Vivian Blaine achieved a Top 20 hit in the Fifties with a song called 'A Bushel and a Peck' but can you name the successful musical from which it came and in which she starred?"

QUESTION 8
What was the title of Jerry Lee Lewis's first UK Top 10 hit?

QUESTION 9
Can you name Julie London's only hit of the Fifties that was successfully revived by Mari Wilson in 1983 and Michael Buble, in 2009?

QUESTION 10
In 1955, two versions of the instrumental 'Cherry Pink and Apple Blossom White' topped our chart. One was by American band leader Perez Prado, but who was the UK male trumpeter who did likewise?

QUIZ 062

Q1
'Do They Know It's Christmas' by Band Aid

Q2
'Belfast Child'

Q3
Ron and Russell

Q4
'Stand By Me'

Q5
'Hold Me Now'

Q6
'Wherever I Lay My Hat (That's My Home)'

Q7
Philip Bailey

Q8
John Du Prez

Q9
'The Road to Hell (Part 2)'

Q10
Chess

QUIZ 063

Q1
'I Knew You Were Waiting (For Me)'

Q2
Scritti Politti

Q3
'Being with You'

Q4
'Holiday'

Q5
'Always On My Mind'

Q6
'Don't You Want Me'

Q7
'The Wind Beneath My Wings'

Q8
'The Tide Is High'

Q9
'One Day In Your Life'

Q10
'The Living Daylights'

QUIZ 065 POPMASTER

HITS OF THE FIFTIES (2)

QUESTION 1
What was the last No 1 hit of the Fifties that was also the first of the Sixties?

QUESTION 2
In 1959, Elvis Presley had his first official double A-sided No 1 hit with 'One Night' and what other song?

QUESTION 3
Can you provide the title of Shirley Bassey's only No 1 hit of the Fifties?

QUESTION 4
What was the title of the song that was a hit for both Andy Williams and Charlie Gracie in 1957?

QUESTION 5
In 1959, Cliff Richard achieved the first of two No 1 hits in that year. The first was 'Living Doll'. What was the second?

QUESTION 6
Can you name the American crooner who had No 1 hits with 'Don't Let the Stars Get in Your Eyes' and 'Magic Moments'?

QUESTION 7
The 1959 plane crash in which Buddy Holly and The Big Bopper were killed also took the life of another rock and roll star best remembered for his hits 'La Bamba' and 'Donna'. Can you name him?

QUESTION 8
Two versions of 'Blue Suede Shoes' made the Top 10 in 1956 – one by Elvis Presley, and the other original recording was by whom?

QUESTION 9
Which Fifties rock and roller was born Richard Wayne Penniman?

QUESTION 10
Can you name the British crooner who had No 1 hits with 'Finger of Suspicion' and 'Christmas Alphabet'?

POPMASTER 

HITS OF THE NOUGHTIES (1)

QUESTION 1
First released in 1979, which Elton John record topped the chart in 2003 after being remixed?

QUESTION 2
Hear-Say, the winners of the 2001 TV talent show "Pop Stars" achieved two No 1 hits in that year. The first was 'Pure and Simple,' but can you name the other?

QUESTION 3
Can you name the legendary guitarist who was featured on Dappy's 2012 Top 5 hit, 'Rockstar'?

QUESTION 4
Which American singer was featured on the 2002 Top 10 hit by Romeo titled, 'It's All Gravy'?

QUESTION 5
Can you name the George Harrison hit that topped the chart for the second time after being issued as a posthumous re-release in 2002?

QUESTION 6
What Top 3 hit from 2013 by Wil.I.am shares its title with a 1979 No 2 by B.A. Robertson?

QUESTION 7
Which 2008 chart-topping single by Kid Rock samples Warren Zevon's 'Werewolves of London' and Lynyrd Skynyrd's 'Sweet Home Alabama'?

QUESTION 8
Can you provide the title of the chart topping debut hit from 2009 by Pixie Lott?

QUESTION 9
In 2003, Simply Red made the chart with the revival of which 1974 Top 10 hit by The Stylistics?

QUESTION 10
In 2011, British singer-songwriter Rebecca Ferguson released her first hit single, 'Nothing's Real But Love', that was taken from her debut album. Can you give me its title?

A answers

QUIZ 064

Q1 *'Smoke Gets in Your Eyes'*

Q2 *Stan Freberg*

Q3 *'I'm Walking Behind You'*

Q4 *'The Little Shoemaker'*

Q5 *'I Go Ape'*

Q6 *The Coasters*

Q7 *"Guys and Dolls"*

Q8 *'Whole Lotta Shakin' Goin' On'*

Q9 *'Cry Me a River'*

Q10 *Eddie Calvert*

QUIZ 065

Q1 *'What Do You Want to Make those Eyes at Me For?' by Emile Ford & The Checkmates*

Q2 *'I Got Stung'*

Q3 *'As I Love You'*

Q4 *'Butterfly'*

Q5 *'Travellin' Light'*

Q6 *Perry Como*

Q7 *Ritchie Valens*

Q8 *Carl Perkins*

Q9 *Little Richard*

Q10 *Dickie Valentine*

QUIZ 067 POPMASTER

HITS OF THE NOUGHTIES (2)

QUESTION 1
Who sang with Pitbull on the first new No 1 of 2014 that was titled 'Timber'?

QUESTION 2
Can you name the singer who topped the chart in 2005 with the revival of the Phil Collins hit, 'Against All Odds' after winning the first series of "The X Factor?"

QUESTION 3
Which successful boy band were formed from individual entrants in the 2010 "X Factor" and who topped the chart with their first single, 'What Makes You Beautiful'?

QUESTION 4
By what name is Marshall Mathers III, one of the most successful rappers in the history of the UK chart, better known?

QUESTION 5
Bob the Builder achieved two No 1 hits in 2001. The first was called 'Can We Fix It'?, but what was the title of the other?

QUESTION 6
In 2005, the band Athlete made it into the Top 10 for the first time in their career. What was the title of the song?

QUESTION 7
Which group achieved a Top 10 hit in 2014 with 'Superheroes'?

QUESTION 8
Can you name the female performer who joined Robbie Williams on the 2001 No 1 hit single 'Somethin' Stupid', the revival of the No 1 from 1967 by Frank and Nancy Sinatra?

QUESTION 9
In the year 2000, All Saints topped the chart with a song that was featured in the Leonardo DiCaprio movie, "The Beach". What was the title of the song?

QUESTION 10
Who was the American singer and songwriter who topped the chart in 2010 with 'Forget You', having once been one half of Gnarls Barkley, who had a No 1 in 2006 with 'Crazy'?

POPMASTER QUIZ 068

HITS OF THE NINETIES (1)

QUESTION 1
What two songs by Westlife, released as a double A side, make up the last No 1 of the Nineties and the first of the Noughties?

QUESTION 2
In 1992, Right Said Fred achieved their only No 1. Can you give me the title?

QUESTION 3
Can you name the female singer who had Top 10 hits with 'Ain't that Just The Way,' 'Stranded' and 'Someone Loves You Honey'?

QUESTION 4
Who played the famous guitar solo on Michael Jackson's 1991 No 1 hit, 'Black or White'?

QUESTION 5
Jamaican singer Orville Richard Burrell achieved two No 1 hits in the Nineties with 'Oh Carolina' and the revival of Mungo Jerry's 'In the Summertime' but by what name is he better known?

QUESTION 6
What was the title of the Righteous Brothers hit from 1965 that topped the chart in 1990 when it was re-released?

QUESTION 7
Who wrote Whitney Houston's chart-topping 1993 hit single – 'I Will Always Love You'?

QUESTION 8
Swedish act Rednex achieved two Top 20 hits in the Nineties, the first was their chart topping 'Cotton Eye Joe'. What was the title of the other?

QUESTION 9
What song title does a 1991 Top 20 hit by Dannii Minogue share with a Sixties No 1 by The Supremes?

QUESTION 10
What No 1 hit by The Police is sampled on the Puff Daddy and Faith Evans 1997 chart topping single, 'I'll Be Missing You'?

QUIZ 66

Q1 *'Are you Ready for Love?'*

Q2 *'The Way to Your Love'*

Q3 *Brian May*

Q4 *Christina Milian*

Q5 *'My Sweet Lord'*

Q6 *'Bang Bang'*

Q7 *'All Summer Long'*

Q8 *'Mama Do'*

Q9 *'You Make Me Feel Brand New'*

Q10 *Heaven*

QUIZ 067

Q1
Ke$ha

Q2
Steve Brookstein

Q3
One Direction

Q4
Eminem

Q5
'Mambo No 5'

Q6
'Wires'

Q7
The Script

Q8
Nicole Kidman

Q9
'Pure Shores'

Q10
CeeLo Green

QUIZ 069 POPMASTER

HITS OF THE NINETIES (2)

QUESTION 1
In 1993, which legendary singer made the Top 5 performing a duet with Bono on the Cole Porter song, 'I've Got You Under My Skin'?

QUESTION 2
What was the title of Jason Donovan's 1991 No 1 hit that came from the musical "Joseph and the Amazing Technicolour Dreamcoat"?

QUESTION 3
Which Seventies Doobie Brothers release found its way into the Top 10 in 1993 after being reissued?

QUESTION 4
What was the title of the 1994 Top 5 hit by actor and singer Jimmy Nail that was also the theme song to one of his TV series?

QUESTION 5
The German act Snap! achieved two No 1 hits in the Nineties, the first was called 'The Power' what was the second?

QUESTION 6
Which male and female vocal trio achieved their only hit in 1991 when they made the Top 10 with 'Hippy Chick'?

QUESTION 7
What was the title of the only Top 10 hit achieved by David Bowie in the Nineties?

QUESTION 8
In 1995, Oasis achieved their first No 1 hit. What was the title?

QUESTION 9
Can you give the title of the only hit single by the Spice Girls not to have reached No 1 in the Nineties?

QUESTION 10
Which male singer made the Top 3 in 1994 with the revival of The Searchers' 1963 No 1 'Sweets for My Sweet'?

POPMASTER QUIZ 070

HITS OF THE SEVENTIES (1)

QUESTION 1
What was the last No 1 of the Seventies that was also the first of the Eighties?

QUESTION 2
Bachman-Turner Overdrive achieved two Top 40 hits in the Seventies, the first was 'You Ain't Seen Nothin' Yet' what was the other?

QUESTION 3
Who made his chart debut dressed as a clown for his hit single, 'The Show Must Go On'?

QUESTION 4
What was the title of the Top 10 hit by Laurel and Hardy that was featured in their 1937 movie, "Way Out West" and found its way into our chart in 1976?

QUESTION 5
Can you name the singer who had Top 20 hits in the Seventies with 'Lamplight,' 'Rollin' Stone' and 'If I Could'?

QUESTION 6
In 1979 Israel's Eurovision Song Contest winner 'Hallelujah' made the Top 5, but can you name the group that sang it?

QUESTION 7
Can you name the duo who achieved their only UK hit in 1976 with 'We Do It'?

QUESTION 8
The Hollies only managed to achieve two Top 10 hits in the Seventies, the second was 'The Air that I Breathe,' what was the first?

QUESTION 9
In 1971 Rod Stewart achieved his first solo hit that was also a No 1. It was a double A side with one of the songs being 'Reason To Believe', what was the other?

QUESTION 10
Which Sixties hit by The Small Faces found its way back into the Top 10 in 1975 when it was re-released?

A answers

QUIZ 068

Q1 *'I Have A Dream' and 'Seasons In The Sun'*

Q2 *'Deeply Dippy'*

Q3 *Lutricia McNeal*

Q4 *Slash From Guns 'N' Roses*

Q5 *Shaggy*

Q6 *'Unchained Melody'*

Q7 *Dolly Parton*

Q8 *'Old Pop in an Oak'*

Q9 *'Baby Love'*

Q10 *'Every Breath You Take'*

QUIZ 069

Q1
Frank Sinatra

Q2
'Any Dream Will Do'

Q3
'Long Train Running'

Q4
'Crocodile Shoes'

Q5
'Rhythm is aDancer'

Q6
Soho

Q7
'Jump They Say'

Q8
'Some Might Say'

Q9
'Stop'

Q10
C.J. Lewis

QUIZ 071 POPMASTER

HITS OF THE SEVENTIES (2)

QUESTION 1
Mud's last Top 10 hit of the Seventies was a revival of a well-known Bill Withers composition. What was the title?

QUESTION 2
In 1978, Queen made the Top 20 with a double A-sided hit. One of the songs was 'Bicycle Race', but what was the title of the other non-PC track?

QUESTION 3
Can you name the American group who achieved a Stateside No 1 with a cover of Paper Lace's UK chart-topper 'Billy Don't Be A Hero'?

QUESTION 4
What was the title of Elton John's 1974 Top 10 hit written by John Lennon and Paul McCartney?

QUESTION 5
Can you name the group who made their Top 10 chart debut in 1975 with 'If You Think You Know How to Love Me'?

QUESTION 6
Which female duo achieved their only Top 10 hit in 1974, 'Guilty', co-produced by the co-author of this book?

QUESTION 7
Although the Bay City Rollers achieved ten Top 10 hits in the Seventies, only two reached No 1. One was 'Bye Bye Baby' what was the other?

QUESTION 8
With whom did Neil Diamond sing 'You Don't Bring Me Flowers' on the 1978 Top 5 hit?

QUESTION 9
In 1971, Slade made the Top 20 for the first time. Can you name their debut hit?

QUESTION 10
Barry Manilow's first UK hit, 'Mandy', was a cover of the only hit achieved by Scott English. Under what title did Scott originally record the song?

POPMASTER QUIZ 072

HITS OF THE SIXTIES (1)

QUESTION 1
In 1967, which father and daughter act topped the chart with 'Somethin' Stupid'?

QUESTION 2
What was the only Top 10 hit by The Beatles *not* to have been written by John Lennon and Paul McCartney?

QUESTION 3
By what name was Cherilyn Sarkisian LaPierre better known?

QUESTION 4
What was the title of the only No 1 hit achieved by Dave Dee, Dozy, Beaky, Mick and Tich?

QUESTION 5
Can you provide the title of the only Top 10 hit achieved by The Ronettes?

QUESTION 6
What was the first No 1 hit by The Rolling Stones to be written by Mick Jagger and Keith Richards?

QUESTION 7
Which two composers wrote Sandie Shaw's first No 1, '(There's) Always Something There to Remind Me'?

QUESTION 8
Lonnie Donegan achieved a No 1 hit in 1960 with a song about a refuse collector. Name it?

QUESTION 9
What was the title of the theme song to Cilla Black's 1968 BBC TV show, "Cilla" that was also a Top 10 hit for her that same year?

QUESTION 10
Can you name the song from 1969 when Diana Ross & The Supremes joined forces with The Temptations for a Top 10 hit?

A answers

QUIZ 070

Q1 *'Another Brick In The Wall' by Pink Floyd*

Q2 *'Roll On Down The Highway'*

Q3 *Leo Sayer*

Q4 *'The Trail of the Lonesome Pine'*

Q5 *David Essex*

Q6 *'Milk and Honey'*

Q7 *R & J Stone*

Q8 *'I Can't Tell the Bottom From the Top'*

Q9 *'Maggie May'*

Q10 *'Itchycoo Park'*

QUIZ 071

Q1 'Lean on Me'

Q2 'Fat Bottomed Girls'

Q3 Bo Donaldson & The Heywoods

Q4 'Lucy in the Sky With Diamonds'

Q5 Smokie

Q6 The Pearls

Q7 'Give A Little Love'

Q8 Barbra Streisand

Q9 'Get Down and Get with It'

Q10 'Brandy'

QUIZ 073 POPMASTER

HITS OF THE SIXTIES (2)

QUESTION 1
Although not related in any way, can you give the real names of the two Righteous Brothers?

QUESTION 2
What was the title of the only No 1 hit for Sandie Shaw written by Chris Andrews?

QUESTION 3
In the Sixties The Tornados achieved two Top 10 hits, the first being their No 1, 'Telstar'. What was the title of the other?

QUESTION 4
In 1966, Tom Jones made the Top 20 with a double A-sided hit. On one side of the record was 'Once There Was A Time', but can you name the other song?

QUESTION 5
Can you name the female singer who sang a duet with Marvin Gaye on the 1967 Top 20 hit, 'It Takes Two'?

QUESTION 6
What was the title of the only No 1 hit achieved by The Move?

QUESTION 7
Can you name the song that Cole Porter wrote in 1936 that The Four Seasons took into the Top 20 in 1966?

QUESTION 8
Which American drummer had hits in the Sixties with 'Teen Beat', 'Let There Be Drums' and 'Drums Are My Beat'?

QUESTION 9
The Kinks achieved three No 1 hits in the Sixties, two of which were 'You Really Got Me' and 'Sunny Afternoon.' What was the title of the other?

QUESTION 10
Can you recall the title of Dusty Springfield's 1964 American Top 10 hit, written by Burt Bacharach and Hal David, that was never released as a single in the UK?

POPMASTER QUIZ 074

HOUSE MUSIC

QUESTION 1
Madness had two hit singles in the early Eighties that featured the word House in the title. 'Our House' was one – what was the other?

QUESTION 2
'Shout', 'Everybody Wants To Rule The World' and 'Mother's Talk' were singles from the album "Songs From The Big Chair" recorded by a group formed in Bath. Name the group.

QUESTION 3
Which song, originally by The Doors, did Will Young take to No 1 in 2002?

QUESTION 4
'Mirror In The Bathroom' was a Top 5 single in 1980 for which group?

QUESTION 5
What was 'In My Kitchen' according to the title of a hit single by UB40?

QUESTION 6
Who had her debut solo hit in 2001 with the Top 3 song 'Take Me Home (A Girl Like Me)'?

QUESTION 7
The song 'Fixing A Hole' appears on which of The Beatles' albums?

QUESTION 8
Under what name did the duo consisting of Neil Arthur and Stephen Luscombe record their 1982 Top 10 hit 'Living On The Ceiling'?

QUESTION 9
According to the title of their 1970 Top 10 hit, The Supremes went 'Up The Ladder To',… where?

QUESTION 10
'This Old House' was a No 1 for Shakin' Stevens, but it had been a No 1 in 1954 for an American singer. Who is she?

QUIZ 072

Q1
Frank and Nancy Sinatra

Q2
'Something' (written by George Harrison)

Q3
Cher

Q4
'The Legend Of Xanadu'

Q5
'Be My Baby'

Q6
'The Last Time'

Q7
Burt Bacharach and Hal David

Q8
'My Old Man's a Dustman'

Q9
'Step Inside Love'

Q10
'I'm Gonna Make You Love Me'

QUIZ 073

Q1
Bill Medley and Bobby Hatfield

Q2
Long Live Love

Q3
Globetrotter

Q4
Not Responsible

Q5
Kim Weston

Q6
'Blackberry Way'

Q7
'I've Got You Under My Skin'

Q8
Sandy Nelson

Q9
'Tired Of Waiting For You'

Q10
'Wishing And Hoping'

QUIZ 075 POPMASTER

HOW DOES YOUR GARDEN GROW?

QUESTION 1
What is the name of the Australian duo that had hits in the late Nineties with 'Truly Madly Deeply', 'To The Moon And Back' and 'I Knew I Loved You'?

QUESTION 2
George Michael's No 1 'Fastlove' features parts of a 1982 Top 10 song originally recorded by Patrice Rushen – what is the title of that song?

QUESTION 3
Which group sang about 'Flowers In The Rain' in 1967?

QUESTION 4
The song 'In Bloom' was a hit single from which album by Nirvana?

QUESTION 5
With whom did Kylie Minogue duet on the song 'Where The Wild Roses Grow'?

QUESTION 6
What four herbs feature in the title of Simon & Garfunkel's 1966 album?

QUESTION 7
Jarivs Cocker is the lead singer of the group that had a hit double 'A' side single in 2001 called 'Sunrise' and 'The Trees'. Name the band?

QUESTION 8
Released in 1968, The Foundations reached the Top 3 with the song 'Build Me Up...' what?

QUESTION 9
Released in 1981 and prior to them becoming one of the most successful acts of the Eighties – which duo's first album was called "In The Garden"?

QUESTION 10
Lynn Anderson's 1971 hit 'Rose Garden' was her only chart hit and, it was sampled in the chorus of the 1989 Top 5 single by Kon Kan. What was the title of this only chart hit by the Canadian duo?

POPMASTER QUIZ 076

I SPY

QUESTION 1
Who sang 'You Know My Name' – the theme song from the first Daniel Craig James Bond film "Casino Royale"?

QUESTION 2
Released in 1982 and reaching No 2, what was the title of the first single from Dire Straits' album "Love Over Gold"?

QUESTION 3
Which two members of U2 provided the title theme to the 1996 film version of "Mission: Impossible"?

QUESTION 4
What was the title of the 1986 collaboration between Art of Noise and guitarist Duane Eddy?

QUESTION 5
"Spies Like Us" was a 1985 film starring Chevy Chase and Dan Aykroyd. Which superstar wrote and performed the title song for the film?

QUESTION 6
What was the title of Carly Simon's hit song from the 1977 Bond film "The Spy Who Loved Me"?

QUESTION 7
'We Are Detective' was a Top 10 song for which trio?

QUESTION 8
What type of 'Eyes' did Daryl Hall and John Oates sing about on their hit single?

QUESTION 9
Which group sang 'Spy In The House Of Love' in 1987?

QUESTION 10
Shirley Bassey recorded the title songs to three James Bond films – "Diamonds Are Forever", "Goldfinger" and which other?

QUIZ 074

Q1 *House Of Fun*

Q2 *Tears For Fears*

Q3 *Light My Fire*

Q4 *The Beat*

Q5 *Rat*

Q6 *Sophie Ellis-Bextor*

Q7 *Sgt. Pepper's Lonely Hearts Club Band*

Q8 *Blancmange*

Q9 *The Roof*

Q10 *Rosemary Clooney (the aunt of George Clooney)*

QUIZ 075

Q1
Savage Garden

Q2
'Forget Me Nots'

Q3
The Move

Q4
Nevermind

Q5
Nick Cave & The Bad Seeds

Q6
Parsley, Sage, Rosemary and Thyme

Q7
Pulp

Q8
Buttercup

Q9
Eurythmics

Q10
'I Beg Your Pardon'

QUIZ 077 POPMASTER

I WHO HAVE NOTHING

QUESTION 1
Who reached No 2 in 1988 with the song 'Nothing's Gonna Change My Love For You'?

QUESTION 2
What was the title of Destiny Child's 1998 debut UK hit?

QUESTION 3
Who wrote Sinead O'Connor's biggest hit, 'Nothing Compares 2 U'?

QUESTION 4
What was the title of the only No 1 for The Stylistics during their UK chart career?

QUESTION 5
In 1998, Echobeatz reached the Top 10 and Tamba Trio the Top 40 with a song that was originally written and recorded in the Sixties by Jorge Ben and was the signature song of Sergio Mendes. What is it called?

QUESTION 6
The lead singer with Ultravox prior to Midge Ure joining the group had a solo hit in 1980 called 'No-One Driving' – what is he called?

QUESTION 7
What was the title of Blondie's Top 40 follow-up to their 1999 comeback No 1 'Maria'?

QUESTION 8
Although it failed to chart, the 1977 single 'Less Than Zero' was the first release by Elvis Costello on which record label?

QUESTION 9
Mike Edwards is the lead singer with the group whose final Top 40 hit was the 1993 song 'Zeroes & Ones' – what are they called?

QUESTION 10
Shirley Bassey in 1963 and Tom Jones in 1970 both had hits with the same song – what is the song?

POPMASTER QUIZ 078

IF I ONLY HAD TIME

QUIZ 076

QUESTION 1
Who made his 1968 chart debut with 'If I Only Had Time'?

Q1 *Chris Cornell*

QUESTION 2
Can you name the group whose second Top 10 hit was in 1982 with 'Time (Clock Of The Heart)'?

Q2 *'Private Investigations'*

QUESTION 3
Which group successfully revived Maria Muldaur's 1974 Top 40 hit, 'Midnight At The Oasis' in 1994?

Q3 *Adam Clayton & Larry Mullen (Mullen dropped his 'Jr' for this release)*

QUESTION 4
What was the name of the country singer whose only UK hit was in 1972 with 'It's Four In The Morning'?

Q4 *'Peter Gunn'*

QUESTION 5
Which close harmony group scored an American Top 20 hit in 1967 with 'Twelve Thirty (Young Girls Are Coming To The Canyon)'?

Q5 *Paul McCartney (a Top 20 hit for him in 1985)*

QUESTION 6
Can you name the Scottish singer who achieved an American No 1 and a UK Top 5 hit in 1980 with '9 to 5'?

Q6 *'Nobody Does li Better'*

QUESTION 7
In which year did Cliff Richard top the chart with 'The Minute You're Gone'?

Q7 *The Thompson Twins*

QUESTION 8
In 1963, who according to his hit was only 'Twenty-Four Hours From Tulsa'?

Q8 *'Private Eyes'*

QUESTION 9
Which Philadelphia-based group made the UK Top 40 in 1975 with 'Sixty Minute Man'?

Q9 *Was Not Was*

QUESTION 10
After leaving Island records, which act achieved their only UK Top 10 hit for the Virgin label with 'Beat The Clock'?

Q10 *'Moonraker'*

QUIZ 077

Q1
Glenn Medeiros

Q2
"No, No, No"

Q3
Prince

Q4
'Can't Give You Anything (But My Love)'

Q5
'Mas Que Nada'

Q6
John Foxx

Q7
'Nothing Is Real But The Girl'

Q8
Stiff

Q9
Jesus Jones

Q10
'I (Who Have Nothing)'

QUIZ 079 POPMASTER

IFS AND BUTS

QUESTION 1
In 1993, which American singer made the Top 20 with 'Said I Loved You But I Lied'?

QUESTION 2
UK rapper, Mike Skinner achieved a Top 5 hit in 2004 titled 'Fit But You Know It' but under what name did he release the record?

QUESTION 3
Can you name the singer who made the Top 10 in 1970 with his single, 'I Don't Believe In 'If' Anymore'?

QUESTION 4
What was the title of the 1968 Top 20 hit for The Showstoppers that returned to the Top 40 in 1971?

QUESTION 5
'It's Not Right But It's OK' became a 1999 Top 5 hit for which successful female singer?

QUESTION 6
In 1959, Ricky Nelson's number three hit 'It's Late' included another song that also made the Top 20 Can you name that song?

QUESTION 7
Can you name the male singer who reached No 2 position in 1999 in the UK with 'If I Could Turn Back The Hands Of Time'?

QUESTION 8
Name the female singer who reached the Top 10 in 1989 in the UK with 'If I Could Turn Back Time'?

QUESTION 9
After three consecutive No 1 hits in 1962, Frank Ifield's next release peaked at No 4. What was the song?

QUESTION 10
What was the title of the song performed by Yvonne Elliman in the movie, "Saturday Night Fever" that also became a Top 5 hit in 1978?

POPMASTER QUIZ 080

IN COMMON

What do the following have in common?

QUESTION 1
'Pyjamarama' by Roxy Music, 'Smells Like Teen Spirit' by Nirvana, 'Stockholm Syndrome' by Muse and 'Viva La Vida' by Coldplay

QUESTION 2
Enrique Iglesias, Aretha Franklin, George Michael and Mariah Carey

QUESTION 3
The groups Talk Talk, Living In A Box, Visage and Doop

QUESTION 4
'Another Brick In The Wall (Part 2)' by Pink Floyd, 'Do They Know Its Christmas' by Band Aid II, 'I Have A Dream/Seasons In The Sun' by Westlife

QUESTION 5
Guitarists Midge Ure, Snowy White and Gary Moore

QUESTION 6
'I Feel For You' by Chaka Khan, 'There Must Be An Angel (Playing With My Heart)' by Eurythmics, 'I Guess That's Why They Call it the Blues' by Elton John

QUESTION 7
The groups Ace, Squeeze and Mike and the Mechanics

QUESTION 8
'More Than Words' by Extreme, 'I'm Too Sexy' by Right Said Fred, 'Let's Talk About Sex' by Salt 'n Pepa, 'Wind Of Change' by The Scorpions

QUESTION 9
Sheryl Crow, Sting, Roberta Flack and Gene Simmons of Kiss

QUESTION 10
'Imagine' by John Lennon, 'Reet Petite (The Sweetest Girl In Town)' by Jackie Wilson, 'Ghetto Gospel' by 2Pac, 'More Than A Woman' by Aaliyah

QUIZ 078

Q1
John Rowles

Q2
Culture Club

Q3
The Brand New Heavies

Q4
Faron Young

Q5
The Mamas and the Papas

Q6
Sheena Easton

Q7
1965

Q8
Gene Pitney

Q9
The Trammps

Q10
Sparks

QUIZ 079

Q1
Michael Bolton

Q2
The Streets

Q3
Roger Whittaker

Q4
'Ain't Nothing But A Houseparty'

Q5
Whitney Houston

Q6
'Never Be Anyone Else But You'

Q7
R. Kelly

Q8
Cher

Q9
'Nobody's Darlin' But Mine'

Q10
'If I Can't Have You'

QUIZ 081 POPMASTER

INITIAL HITS

These ten questions relate to groups whose names can be abbreviated or are made up of letters, numbers or a combination of both

QUESTION 1
In 1995, this group achieved three consecutive Top 10 hits with 'I've Got A Little Something For You', 'If You Only Let Me In' and 'Happy'.

QUESTION 2
Can you name the rock band who had hits in the Eighties with 'Rock 'n Roll Ain't Noise Pollution', 'Who Made You' and 'Let's Get It Up'?

QUESTION 3
Any one of the three Top 20 hits achieved by EYC in the Nineties?

QUESTION 4
By what name were Nineties band with members James Atkin, Derry Brownson, Mark Decloedt, Ian Dench and Zac Foley best known?

QUESTION 5
In 2002, rapper Richard Breen, once a member of the group Five, released his first solo Top 10 hit, 'What You Got'. Under what three letter name?

QUESTION 6
In the Seventies, 10CC achieved three No 1s with 'Rubber Bullets', 'I'm Not In Love' and which other song?

QUESTION 7
In 1970, the group C.C.S. achieved their first Top 20 hit with a cover of Led Zeppelin's 'Whole Lotta Love'. What do the initials C.C.S. stand for?

QUESTION 8
In the year 2000 a Norwegian female duo called M2M achieved their only UK chart entry. Can you name this hit which also featured in the film "Pokemon-The First Movie"?

QUESTION 9
From 1981, can you name the only UK Top 10 hit for REO Speedwagon?

QUESTION 10
Can you name the female singer whose first hit from 1993, 'Show Me Love' made the chart again in 2009 when she was featured on the recording by Steve Angello and Laidback Luke?

POPMASTER QUIZ 082

INSTRUMENTAL HITS (1)

QUESTION 1
Which trumpet player had a Top 20 hit and American No 1 in 1979 with the track 'Rise'?

QUESTION 2
What type of 'Kiss' featured in the title of Lil' Louis' 1989 Top 3 hit?

QUESTION 3
'Animals' was No 1 in 2013 for the Dutch DJ Martin... who?

QUESTION 4
Who was the saxophonist who recorded the early Nineties hit 'Lily Was Here' with David A. Stewart?

QUESTION 5
B Bumble & The Stingers, 'Nut Rocker', which was a hit in both 1962 and 1972 was based on music from the ballet "Nutcracker" by which classical composer?

QUESTION 6
'Rockit' was a Top 10 instrumental in 1983 for which American keyboard player?

QUESTION 7
Mr Oizo reached No 1 in 1999 with which instrumental track?

QUESTION 8
Which band had No 1 instrumentals in the 1960s called 'Apache', 'Wonderful Land' and 'Kon-Tiki'?

QUESTION 9
Jan Hammer had a hit in the mid-80s with his theme tune to which American TV detective series?

QUESTION 10
What was the title of the 1977 Top 3 instrumental hit by the French group Space?

A answers

QUIZ 080

Q1
The title of the song doesn't appear in the lyrics

Q2
All had hit duets with Whitney Houston

Q3
They've all recorded Top 40 singles with the same name as the group

Q4 *All No 1 singles over the turn of a decade (70s/80s, 80s/90s, 70s/00s, 90s/00s)*

Q5
Have all at some time been members of Thin Lizzy

Q6
All feature harmonica solos by Stevie Wonder

Q7
Paul Carrack has been a member of each of them

Q8 *All held off No 1 by '(Everything I do) I do it for you' by Bryan Adams*

Q9
Have all spent time working as teachers

Q10
All posthumous No 1 hits

QUIZ 081

QUIZ 083 POPMASTER

INSTRUMENTAL HITS (2)

Q1
MN8

QUESTION 1
What was the title of Fleetwood Mac's 1969 instrumental No 1 that reached the Top 3 again when it was re-issued in 1973?

Q2
AC/DC

QUESTION 2
Who is the American saxophonist best known for his 1987 hit 'Songbird'?

Q3
'Feelin' Alright,' 'The Way You Work It' or 'Black Book.'

QUESTION 3
'Children' by Robert Miles reached No 2 and spent 18 weeks on the chart in 1996 – but what nationality was Robert Miles?

Q4
EMF

QUESTION 4
What was the title of the only UK hit for the American guitarist Mason Williams, which reached the Top 10 in 1968?

Q5
Abs

QUESTION 5
Orbital had a Top 10 single in 1997 with an updated version of the theme tune to a 1960s TV series starring Roger Moore. What is the name of the track and the TV series?

Q6
'Dreadlock Holiday'

QUESTION 6
'Clog Dance' was the title of 1979 hit for a band formed by Mik Kaminski of Electric Light Orchestra. What were they called?

Q7
Collective Consciousness Society

QUESTION 7
What was the title of Harold Faltermeyer's 1985 Top 3 single from the film 'Beverly Hills Cop'?

Q8
'Don't Say You Love Me'

QUESTION 8
… And what was the title of the 'artist' that took a cover of 'Axel F' to No 1 in 2005?

Q9
'Keep On Loving You'

QUESTION 9
Composer David Arnold had a Top 10 hit in 1997 with 'On Her Majesty's Secret Service', recorded with production duo Alex Gifford and Will White. But under what name do Alex and Will record?

Q10
Robin S

QUESTION 10
What was the title of Lieutenant Pigeon's Top 20 follow-up to their 1972 No 1, 'Moudly Old Dough'?

POPMASTER QUIZ 084

INSTRUMENTAL HITS (3)

QUESTION 1
Which group is credited alongside Booker T. on the hit 'Green Onions'?

QUESTION 2
What nationality was the group Space, who reached No 2 in 1977 with 'Magic Fly'?

QUESTION 3
Duane Eddy joined Art of Noise on a 1986 remake of his Top 10 hit from 1959. What was it called?

QUESTION 4
Under what name did the production duo of Paul Oakenfold and Andy Gray record their Top 5 single of the 'Big Brother UK TV Theme' in 2000?

QUESTION 5
'Life In Technicolor' is the instrumental opening track to which of Coldplay No 1 album, released in 2008?

QUESTION 6
Which female pianist had a No 1 hits in the Fifties with 'Let's Have Another Party' and 'Poor People Of Paris'?

QUESTION 7
Name one of Jan Hammer's two instrumental Top 10 hits of the 1980s.

QUESTION 8
Spiro & Wix recorded their Top 3 single 'Tara's Theme' as the theme tune for the BBC's coverage of the 1996 Olympic Games held in which city?

QUESTION 9
'Popcorn' was the title of a Top 5 instrumental in 1972, but was it recorded by The Peppers, Hot Butter or The Rah Band?

QUESTION 10
Robert Miles reached No 2 in the mid-Nineties with a debut hit that was No 1 all across Europe. What was its one word title?

QUIZ 082

Q1
Herb Alpert

Q2
'French Kiss' (instrumental apart from a little bit of moaning!)

Q3
Garrix

Q4
Candy Dulfer

Q5
Tchaikovsky

Q6
Herbie Hancock

Q7
'Flat Beat'

Q8
The Shadows

Q9
'Miami Vice'

Q10
'Magic Fly'

QUIZ 083

Q1
'Albatross'

Q2
Kenny G

Q3
Italian (born Roberto Concina)

Q4
'Classical Gas'

Q5
'The Saint' (recorded for the soundtrack of the film released that year)

Q6
Violinski

Q7
'Axel F'

Q8
Crazy Frog

Q9
Propellerheads

Q10
'Desperate Dan'

QUIZ 085 POPMASTER

JEALOUSY

QUESTION 1
Who wrote Roxy Music's 1981 No 1 'Jealous Guy'?

QUESTION 2
Released in 2004, the first Top 10 single by The Killers was a song about a man who thinks his girlfriend/wife/partner is cheating on him. What is it called?

QUESTION 3
Who made his chart debut in 1979 with the song 'Is She Really Going Out With Him?'?

QUESTION 4
What song was an American hit for The Go-Gos and a UK hit for Fun Boy Three?

QUESTION 5
Which duo had a hit in 1983 with the song 'Who's That Girl?'?

QUESTION 6
Released in 1974, what is the title of Alvin Stardust's only UK No 1?

QUESTION 7
The song 'Who's David' was No 1 in 2004 for which pop rock trio?

QUESTION 8
Which duo had a hit in 1979 with the song 'Who Were You With In The Moonlight?'?

QUESTION 9
Which Elvis Presley hit became a Top 10 cover version for Fine Young Cannibals in 1986?

QUESTION 10
Which duo had a hit in 1991 with their song 'Jealousy'?

POPMASTER QUIZ 086

JESSIE J

QUIZ 084

QUESTION 1
What is Jessie J's full real name?

QUESTION 2
What was the title of Jessie's first UK hit single?

QUESTION 3
As an 11-year-old, in which Andrew Lloyd-Webber musical did she appear?

QUESTION 4
For which American singer was Jessie J the support act in 2008 for her "Bring Ya To The Brink" tour?

QUESTION 5
Jessie co-wrote the song, 'Party In The U.S.A' which became a Top 20 hit for which successful American female performer?

QUESTION 6
What is the title of Jessie J's 2013 album?

QUESTION 7
With whom did Jessie J perform a duet in 2010 on the Top 40 hit, 'Up'?

QUESTION 8
Can you name the two rappers who appeared on the original version of Jessie's 2013 Top 10 hit single, 'Wild'?

QUESTION 9
What does she call her fans, a name inspired by her 2011-12 tour?

QUESTION 10
What was the title of Jessie's 2011 debut album?

Q1 *The MG's*

Q2 *French*

Q3 *'Peter Gunn'*

Q4 *Elementfour*

Q5 *Viva La Vida or Death and All His Friends*

Q6 *Winifred Atwell*

Q7 *'Miami Vice Theme' (1985), 'Crockett's Theme' (1987)*

Q8 *'Atlanta' ('Tara's Theme' originally written for "Gone With the Wind", set in Georgia)*

Q9 *'Hot Butter' (the Peppers instrumental was 'Pepper Box' and the Rah Band's was 'The Crunch')*

Q10 *'Children'*

QUIZ 085

Q1
John Lennon

Q2
'Mr Brightside'

Q3
Joe Jackson

Q4
'Our Lips Are Sealed'

Q5
Eurythmics

Q6
'Jealous Mind'

Q7
Busted

Q8
Dollar

Q9
'Suspicious Minds'

Q10
Pet Shop Boys

QUIZ 087 POPMASTER

JOURNEY INTO SPACE

QUESTION 1
In 1959, two versions of the song 'Venus' reached number twenty in the chart. One was the original by Frankie Avalon. Can you name the other?

QUESTION 2
Can you name the act that topped the chart in 1998 with 'Gym And Tonic'?

QUESTION 3
What was the title of Freddie Mercury's only solo No 1 hit that topped the chart in 1993?

QUESTION 4
In 1969, the American group, The Fifth Dimension achieved a Top 20 hit with a medley of two songs from the musical, "Hair". One was 'Let The Sunshine In', what was the other?

QUESTION 5
Which female singer had a Top 20 hit in 1991 with the revival of Elton John's 'Rocket Man (I Think It's Going To Be A Long, Long Time)'?

QUESTION 6
In 2001, what was the title of the Top 40 hit achieved by the group, Train?

QUESTION 7
What was the name of the instrumental group that topped the chart for five weeks in 1962 with 'Telstar'?

QUESTION 8
Which indie group achieved a Top 20 hit in 1994 with 'Saturn 5'?

QUESTION 9
In 1961, Shirley Bassey topped the chart with a double A-sided single. One of the songs was 'Climb Ev'ry Mountain', what was the other?

QUESTION 10
Which rock band, who had their first hit in1980, achieved a Top 5 hit in 2007 with 'Different World'?

POPMASTER QUIZ 088

JUNGLE ROCK

QUESTION 1
In 1988, which group had a hit with a re-issue of their single 'Welcome To The Jungle'?

QUESTION 2
Which song was No 1 in both 1996 and 1998 for Baddiel and Skinner with The Lightning Seeds?

QUESTION 3
Which Scottish singer-songwriter had a Top 5 album in 2010 called 'Tiger Suit'?

QUESTION 4
What colour 'Savannah' did Erasure sing about on their Top 3 song from 1990?

QUESTION 5
Born Jimmy McShane, under what name did this singer record his 1985 Top 3 hit 'Tarzan Boy'?

QUESTION 6
With which song did The Monkees make their chart debut in 1967?

QUESTION 7
'Elephant' was the title of a 2003 No 1 album by which American duo?

QUESTION 8
The group Latin Quarter reached the Top 20 in 1986 singing about 'Radio...what?

QUESTION 9
The American singer who had a Top 3 hit in 1976 with 'Jungle Rock' was called Hank...who?

QUESTION 10
Released in 1997, was the final Top 40 single by Genesis called 'Amazon', 'Congo', 'Corcovado' or 'Kakadu'?

QUIZ 086

Q1 *Jessica Ellen Cornish*

Q2 *'Do It Like A Dude'*

Q3 *'Whistle Down The Wind'*

Q4 *Cyndi Lauper*

Q5 *Miley Cyrus*

Q6 *Alive*

Q7 *James Morrison*

Q8 *Big Sean and Dizzee Rascal*

Q9 *Heartbeats*

Q10 *Who You Are*

QUIZ 087

Q1
Dickie Valentine

Q2
Spacedust

Q3
'Living on My Own'

Q4
'Aquarius'

Q5
Kate Bush

Q6
'Drops of Jupiter (Tell Me)'

Q7
The Tornados

Q8
Inspiral Carpets

Q9
'Reach For The Stars'

Q10
Iron Maiden

QUIZ 089 POPMASTER

KINGS AND QUEENS

QUESTION 1
Which famous singer and songwriter had a No 1 album in 1971 called "Tapestry"?

QUESTION 2
De La Soul were guest vocalists on a 1990 hit, 'Mama Gave Birth To The Soul Children', by which rapper and actress?

QUESTION 3
Can you name the female singer who had a Top 40 hit in 1963 with 'Queen For Tonight'?

QUESTION 4
What was the title of the first No 1 hit achieved by Queen?

QUESTION 5
The group King achieved two Top 10 hits in 1985, the second was 'Alone Without You', what was the first?

QUESTION 6
Which soul singer had a 1968 Top 40 hit with his 'Tribute To A King' dedicated to the late Otis Redding?

QUESTION 7
Who was the female singer whose only Top 10 hit was her 1982 recording of 'Love Come Down'?

QUESTION 8
Can you name the group which had hits in the Noughties with 'No One Knows' and '3's And 7's'?

QUESTION 9
Roger Miller's 1965 No 1 hit, 'King Of The Road', returned to the Top 10 in 1990 as part of an EP by which duo?

QUESTION 10
Out of the nine No 1 hits by ABBA, which one spent the most number of weeks at the top of the chart?

POPMASTER QUIZ 090

LADIES FIRST

Each of these ladies had their first (and in most cases only) Top 40 hit reach No 1. In each case, name the No 1 song

QUESTION 1
Freda Payne

QUESTION 2
Robin Beck

QUESTION 3
Charlene

QUESTION 4
Althea & Donna

QUESTION 5
Phyllis Nelson

QUESTION 6
Anita Ward

QUESTION 7
Jennifer Rush

QUESTION 8
Kelly Marie

QUESTION 9
Lena Martell

QUESTION 10
Maria McKee

A answers

QUIZ 088

Q1
Guns N' Roses

Q2
'Three Lions' (the 1998 version was called 'Three Lions '98')

Q3
KT Tunstall

Q4
'Blue Savannah'

Q5
Baltimora

Q6
'I'm A Believer' (the group's only No 1)

Q7
White Stripes

Q8
Africa

Q9
Mizell

Q10
'Congo'

QUIZ 089

Q1
Carole King

Q2
Queen Latifah

Q3
Helen Shapiro

Q4
'Bohemian Rhapsody'

Q5
'Love And Pride'

Q6
William Bell

Q7
Evelyn King

Q8
Queens of the Stone Age

Q9
The Proclaimers

Q10
'Dancing Queen' (6 weeks)

QUIZ 091 POPMASTER

LAST NAME, FIRST NAME

These are two-part questions in which the last name of one act is also the first name the second.

QUESTION 1
The first achieved his biggest hit in 1973 with 'Me And Mrs Jones' and the second was the lead singer on early Manfred Mann hits.

QUESTION 2
The first composed the theme music to the TV series, "Juke Box Jury" and wrote many of the title songs to the James Bond movies and the second had a Top 20 hit in 1974 with 'School Love.'

QUESTION 3
The first had a hit in 1983 with 'True Love Ways' that also featured the London Philharmonic Orchestra and the second made the Top 20 in 1962 with 'Three Stars Will Shine Tonight', a vocal version of the theme from TV's "Doctor Kildare".

QUESTION 4
The first achieved his only Top 40 hit in 1962 with 'Walk With Me My Angel' and the second topped the UK chart in 1974 with the song 'She' from the theme to the TV series, "Seven Faces Of Women."

QUESTION 5
The first topped the chart in 2013 with her single, 'Roar,' and the second did likewise in 1958 with 'Magic Moments'.

QUESTION 6
The first performed a hit duet with LeAnn Rimes in 1999 with 'Written in the Stars' and the second topped the chart in 1961 with 'Johnny Remember Me'.

QUESTION 7
The first made the chart both in 1962 and 1972 with 'The Loco-Motion' and the second, who died in 1996, sang with Katie Mellua on the 2007 chart topping single, 'What A Wonderful World'.

QUESTION 8
The first enjoyed his only major UK hit in 1967 with 'Knock On Wood' and the second topped the chart in 1961 with his instrumental hit, 'On The Rebound'.

QUESTION 9
The first achieved her first solo No 1 in 2009 with 'Fight For This Love' and the second was the composer of the classic song, 'I Get a Kick Out of You.'

QUESTION 10
The first achieved her only UK hit back in 1954 with 'Tennessee Wig Walk' and the second appeared as himself in the 1988 movie, "Permanent Record".

POPMASTER QUIZ 092

LEAD SINGERS (1)

In each case, simply name the lead singers of each of these groups

QUESTION 1
Red Hot Chilli Peppers

QUESTION 2
The Script

QUESTION 3
Muse

QUESTION 4
The Sweet

QUESTION 5
Mumford & Sons

QUESTION 6
Stereophonics

QUESTION 7
The Verve

QUESTION 8
Simply Red

QUESTION 9
Wet Wet Wet

QUESTION 10
Arctic Monkeys

QUIZ 090

Q1 *'Band Of Gold' (follow-up 'Deeper and Deeper' reached No. 33)*

Q2 *'The First Time'*

Q3 *'I've Never Been To Me'*

Q4 *'Uptown Top Ranking'*

Q5 *'Move Closer' (song charted again at No. 34 when it was re-issued)*

Q6 *'Ring My Bell'*

Q7 *'The Power Of Love' (follow-up and only other solo hit 'Ring Of Ice' reached No. 14)*

Q8 *'Feels Like I'm in Love' (two other minor Top 40 hits: Loving Just For Fun & Hot Love')*

Q9 *'One Day At A Time'*

Q10 *'Show Me Heaven' (one other minor Top 40 hit, I'm Gonna Soothe You', reached No. 35)*

QUIZ 091

Q1
Billy Paul – Paul Jones

Q2
John Barry – Barry Blue

Q3
Cliff Richard – Richard Chamberlain

Q4
Don Charles – Charles Aznavour

Q5
Katy Perry – Perry Como

Q6
Elton John – John Leyton

Q7
Little Eva – Eva Cassidy

Q8
Eddie Floyd – Floyd Cramer

Q9
Cheryl Cole – Cole Porter

Q10
Bonnie Lou – Lou Reed

QUIZ 093 POPMASTER

LEAD SINGERS (2)

In each case, simply name the lead singers of each of these groups

QUESTION 1
Destiny's Child

QUESTION 2
Suede

QUESTION 3
KC & The Sunshine Band

QUESTION 4
The Killers

QUESTION 5
ABC

QUESTION 6
Elastica

QUESTION 7
The Darkness

QUESTION 8
Joy Division

QUESTION 9
Jamiroquai

QUESTION 10
The Charlatans

POPMASTER QUIZ 094

LEAD SINGERS (3)

In each case, simply name the lead singers of each of these groups

QUESTION 1
Coldplay

QUESTION 2
The Tourists

QUESTION 3
Maroon 5

QUESTION 4
The Sugarcubes (female)

QUESTION 5
Bush

QUESTION 6
Beady Eye

QUESTION 7
Public Image Ltd

QUESTION 8
Sleeper

QUESTION 9
Travis

QUESTION 10
Electronic

QUIZ 092

Q1
Anthony Kiedis

Q2
Danny O'Donoghue

Q3
Matthew Bellamy

Q4
Brian Connolly

Q5
Marcus Mumford

Q6
Kelly Jones

Q7
Richard Ashcroft

Q8
Mick Hucknall

Q9
Marti Pellow

Q10
Alex Turner

QUIZ 093

Q1 *Beyoncé Knowles*

Q2 *Brett Anderson*

Q3 *Harry Wayne 'KC' Casey*

Q4 *Brandon Flowers*

Q5 *Martin Fry*

Q6 *Justine Frischmann*

Q7 *Justin Hawkins*

Q8 *Ian Curtis*

Q9 *Jay Kay*

Q10 *Tim Burgess*

QUIZ 095 POPMASTER

LET'S GO CRAZY

QUESTION 1
Which group is affectionately known as 'The Nutty Boys'?

QUESTION 2
Peter Andre made a chart comeback in 2004 with a No 1 re-issue of 'Mysterious Girl' and a Top 3 hit with which song?

QUESTION 3
Which duo had a Top 10 single in 2006 called 'I'm With Stupid'?

QUESTION 4
What was the title of Seal's 1990 Top 3 debut solo hit?

QUESTION 5
Name the Australian-born singer who had an American No 1 and UK Top 5 hit in the mid-Seventies called 'Angie Baby'?

QUESTION 6
What was the title of the 2009 No 1 by Dizzee Rascal featuring Armand Van Helden?

QUESTION 7
The song 'Can I Play With Madness' was a Top 3 song in 1988 for which group?

QUESTION 8
The Band Of The Black Watch reached the Top 40 in 1975 with an instrumental known as 'The "Laurel & Hardy" Theme'. What is it called?

QUESTION 9
Led by singer and guitarist Huey Morgan, which group went 'Loco' according to the title of their 2001 Top 5 hit?

QUESTION 10
Prince's song 'Let's Go Crazy' was a 1985 Top 10 double 'A' side with which other song from his album 'Purple Rain'?

POPMASTER QUIZ 096

LIKE CLOCKWORK

QUESTION 1
Which group had its first Top 10 hit in 1992 with a cover of the song 'It Only Takes A Minute'?

QUESTION 2
In 1963, Gene Pitney sang that he was 'Twenty Four Hours From… where?

QUESTION 3
Released in 2001, what was the title of the debut hit and only No 1 by So Solid Crew?

QUESTION 4
…and who duetted with Neneh Cherry on the 1994 Top 3 hit '7 Seconds'?

QUESTION 5
What time of day is mentioned in all three of these songs – 'E-Bow The Letter' by R.E.M., 'You Get What You Give' by New Radicals and 'Someone Saved My Life Tonight' by Elton John?

QUESTION 6
Which band released a Top 3 single in 1982 called 'Time (Clock Of The Heart)'?

QUESTION 7
At what time of day did Agnetha arrive at her office desk in the ABBA song 'The Day Before You Came'?

QUESTION 8
Which group released an album in 2013 called 'Midnight Memories'?

QUESTION 9
'3:A.M. Eternal' was the title of a 1991 chart-topper for which act?

QUESTION 10
Released in 1978, what was the title of the first Top 10 single by The Boomtown Rats?

QUIZ 094

Q1 *Chris Martin*

Q2 *Annie Lennox*

Q3 *Adam Levine*

Q4 *Björk*

Q5 *Gavin Rossdale*

Q6 *Liam Gallagher*

Q7 *John Lydon*

Q8 *Louise Wener*

Q9 *Fran Healy*

Q10 *Bernard Sumner*

QUIZ 095

Q1
Madness

Q2
'Insania'

Q3
Pet Shop Boys

Q4
'Crazy'

Q5
Helen Reddy

Q6
'Bonkers'

Q7
Iron Maiden

Q8
'Dance Of The Cuckoos'

Q9
Fun Lovin' Criminals

Q10
'Take Me With U'

QUIZ 097 POPMASTER

LIVERPOOL

QUESTION 1
Ian McCulloch is the lead singer of which Liverpool group?

QUESTION 2
Which Beatles' song was a No 1 double 'A' side in 1965 with 'Day Tripper'?

QUESTION 3
'Sinful' is the title of a 1986 solo single by the lead singer and founder of the group Wah! Who is he?

QUESTION 4
What was the title of Sonia's 1993 UK Eurovision Song Contest entry?

QUESTION 5
Which group had Top 10 singles in the Noughties called 'Don't Think You're The First', 'Pass It On' and 'In The Morning'?

QUESTION 6
'Reward' was the first of three Top 40 singles by The Teardrop Explodes – name one of the other two.

QUESTION 7
After the split-up of The La's, bassist John Power went on to form a new band and have a string of hits with songs such as 'Finetime', 'Walkaway', 'Sandstorm' and 'Free Me'. What is the name of the band?

QUESTION 8
Which 2006 Top 10 single by The Zutons became a Top 3 cover by Mark Ronson and Amy Winehouse the following year?

QUESTION 9
Featuring Paul McCartney's brother Mike McGear, which group tasted success in 1974 with the Top 10 song 'Liverpool Lou'?

QUESTION 10
"Welcome To The Pleasuredome" was the title of the first album by Frankie Goes To Hollywood, but what was the title of the second and only other studio album by the group?

POPMASTER QUIZ 098

LONDON CALLING

QUESTION 1
Which band was 'Down in the Tube Station At Midnight' according to the title of their 1978 single?

QUESTION 2
What was the title of Lily Allen's Top 10 follow-up to her 2006 No 1 'Smile'?

QUESTION 3
Which boy band reached the chart in 1993 with their version of Pet Shop Boys' 'West End Girls'?

QUESTION 4
Released in 1968, Dave Dee, Dozy, Beaky, Mick & Tich had their final Top 10 single with 'Last Night In…where?

QUESTION 5
'The Only Living Boy In New Cross' is the title of the only Top 10 single for which act?

QUESTION 6
The songs 'Plaistow Patricia' and 'Billericay Dickie' both featured on the 1977 album by Ian Dury. What was it called?

QUESTION 7
Which highly successful songwriter who had her own recording career during the Nineties had her final Top 40 hit in 1997 with a cover version of 'Waterloo Sunset'?

QUESTION 8
'Watching The Detectives' was the title of the debut hit by Elvis Costello and The Attractions, but what was the title of their next hit?

QUESTION 9
The late Eighties Top 5 hits 'Requiem' and 'London Nights' were recorded by which duo?

QUESTION 10
What was the title of Eddy Grant's Top 10 follow-up to his No 1 'I Don't Wanna Dance'?

QUIZ 096

Q1 *Take That*

Q2 *Tulsa*

Q3 *'21 Seconds'*

Q4 *Youssou N'Dour*

Q5 *4 am (in both R.E.M. and New Radicals) and 4 o'clock in the morning (in Elton's song)*

Q6 *Culture Club*

Q7 *'A Quarter After Nine'*

Q8 *One Direction*

Q9 *The KLF (full billing is The KLF featuring the Children of the Revolution)*

Q10 *Like Clockwork*

QUIZ 097

Q1
Echo & The Bunnymen

Q2
'We Can Work it Out'

Q3
Pete Wylie

Q4
'Better the Devil You Know' (her final Top 40 hit – No. 15)

Q5
The Coral

Q6
'Treason (It's Just A Story)', 'Passionate Friend'

Q7
Cast

Q8
'Valerie'

Q9
The Scaffold

Q10
Liverpool

QUIZ 099 POPMASTER

LUCK OF THE IRISH

QUESTION 1
What was the title of Enya's 1988 No 1 single?

QUESTION 2
Who is the lead singer of The Script?

QUESTION 3
Which traditional Irish song was recorded by Thin Lizzy for their debut hit in 1973?

QUESTION 4
Which two members of U2 had a Top 10 single in 1996 with 'Theme From "Mission:Impossible"'?

QUESTION 5
Johnny Logan won the Eurovision Song Contest for Ireland in both 1980 and 1987. Name both of those winning songs.

QUESTION 6
What is the surname of twins John and Edward – better known as Jedward?

QUESTION 7
The Boomtown Rats had two No 1 singles – 'I Don't Like Mondays' was one, what was the other?

QUESTION 8
Which member of Westlife had his debut solo hit in 2013 with the song 'Everything To Me'?

QUESTION 9
The Pogues had their only two Top 10 singles in 1987 – both were duets, one with The Dubliners, the other with Kirsty MacColl. Name either of these songs?

QUESTION 10
Andrea, Caroline and Sharon were the three sisters in The Corrs, who was the brother?

POPMASTER QUIZ 100

LUCKY NUMBERS (1)

QUIZ 098

QUESTION 1
Who are Harry, Zayn, Niall, Liam and Louis?

QUESTION 2
What was the group Bran Van 3000 doing '...In L.A.', according to the title of their 1999 Top 3 song?

QUESTION 3
What is the name of the American rock band formed by Trent Reznor whose hit albums include "The Downward Spiral", "With Teeth", "Year Zero" and "Hesitation Marks"?

QUESTION 4
What was the phone number featured in the title of City Boy's 1978 Top 10 single?

QUESTION 5
What are the first names of any three of the members that made up S Club 7?

QUESTION 6
Patsy Kensit and her band Eighth Wonder had its biggest hit in 1988 with a song written by Pet Shop Boys. What is it called?

QUESTION 7
How many colours were 'In Her Hair' according to the title of McFly's 2004 debut hit?

QUESTION 8
Name the Italian group that reached No 1 in 1999 with 'Blue (Da Ba Dee)'.

QUESTION 9
How many 'Hearts' did Kylie Minogue sing about on her 2007 Top 5 single?

QUESTION 10
Which American singer had her first and biggest hit in 1979 with the song 'Lucky Number'?

Q1 *The Jam*

Q2 *LDN*

Q3 *East 17*

Q4 *Soho*

Q5 *Carter – The Unstoppable Sex Machine*

Q6 *"New Boots and Panties" (not originally credited as Ian Dury & The Blockheads)*

Q7 *Cathy Dennis*

Q8 *'(I Don't Want To Go To) Chelsea'*

Q9 *London Boys*

Q10 *'Electric Avenue' (a street in Brixton, south London)*

QUIZ 099

Q1
'Orinoco Flow'

Q2
Danny O'Donoghue

Q3
'Whiskey in the Jar'

Q4
Adam Clayton & Larry Mullen (Jr was missing from his credited name)

Q5
'What's Another Year' (1980), 'Hold Me Now' (1987)

Q6
Grimes

Q7
'Rat Trap'

Q8
Shane Filan

Q9
'The Irish Rover', 'Fairytale of New York'

Q10
Jim

QUIZ 101 POPMASTER

QUESTION 1
Add together the members in the original charting line-ups of Eternal, Destiny's Child and Spice Girls – how many ladies are there?

QUESTION 2
Which group recorded '(Meet) The Flintstones' for the 1994 live action film starring John Goodman?

QUESTION 3
How many 'Hours From Tulsa' was Gene Pitney in 1963?

QUESTION 4
Featuring singer Jess Glynne, who reached No 1 in 2014 with his single 'My Love'?

QUESTION 5
Having had hits in both the 1970s and 1980, which group's first hit of the 1990s was called '96 Tears'?

QUESTION 6
What was the title of the 2008 No 1 by Madonna featuring Justin Timberlake and Timbaland?

QUESTION 7
'Swords Of A Thousand Men' was a Top 10 single in 1981 for which group?

QUESTION 8
How many members were there in Blazin' Squad?

QUESTION 9
'1979' was a 1996 single from the 1995 album 'Mellon Collie and the Infinite Sadness' by which American group?

QUESTION 10
The Stray Cats had their final Top 40 hit in 1983 with the song '(She's) Sexy And…what?

POPMASTER QUIZ 102

MADONNA

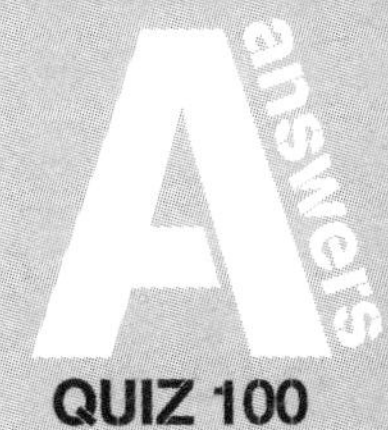

QUIZ 100

QUESTION 1
What is Madonna's surname?

Q1
One Direction

QUESTION 2
What was the title of her first UK No 1?

Q2
Drinking

QUESTION 3
Her 1984 debut hit, 'Holiday' returned to the Top 10 in the Nineties. Can you name the precise year?

Q3
Nine Inch Nails

QUESTION 4
Madonna's 1992 single 'This Used To Be My Playground' was the theme to which baseball-themed film?

Q4
'5.7.0.5.'

QUESTION 5
In which movie did Madonna perform her hits 'Don't Cry For Me Argentina' and 'Another Suitcase in Another Hall'?

Q5
Jo, Rachel, Hannah, Tina, Jon, Bradley, Paul

QUESTION 6
What was the title of her 1990 album that featured music 'from and inspired by' the film "Dick Tracy"?

Q6
'I'm Not Scared'

QUESTION 7
In which year did she make her chart debut with the song 'Holiday'?

Q7
Five ('5 Colours in Her Hair' was the debut single, the first of seven No 1s)

QUESTION 8
Which ABBA song is incorporated into her 2005 No 1 'Hung Up'?

Q8
Eiffel 65

QUESTION 9
What was the title of the record label she co-founded in the early Nineties?

Q9
2

QUESTION 10
Madonna was a guest vocalist on a 2003 single by Britney Spears. What was it called?

Q10
Lene Lovich

QUIZ 101

Q1 *13 (Eternal and Destiny's Child were both quartets on their earliest hits, Spice Girls were a five-piece)*

Q2 *The BC-52s (The B-52's adapted their name for this hit)*

Q3 *Twenty Four*

Q4 *Route 94*

Q5 *The Stranglers*

Q6 *'4 Minutes'*

Q7 *Tenpole Tudor*

Q8 *Ten*

Q9 *The Smashing Pumpkins*

Q10 *17*

QUIZ 103 POPMASTER

MALE DUOS

QUESTION 1
Which two superstars teamed up for the 1985 No 1 'Dancing In The Street'?

QUESTION 2
What was the title of the 1992 No 1 by American duo Charles and Eddie?

QUESTION 3
Who had the original 1967 hit with 'Something's Gotten Hold of My Heart' and went on to duet with Marc Almond under the billing 'special guest star' on his 1989 No 1 version of the song?

QUESTION 4
What was the title of the 2010 Top 3 duet by Robbie Williams and Gary Barlow that featured on Robbie's greatest hits compilation "In And Out Of Consciousness"?

QUESTION 5
Who recorded the 1987 hit version of 'Soul Man' with Sam Moore of Sam and Dave fame?

QUESTION 6
Paul McCartney and Michael Jackson had two hit duets – name both of them.

QUESTION 7
Which country star featured alongside Nelly on his 2004 No 1 'Over And Over'?

QUESTION 8
Frank Sinatra had his final Top 40 hit in 1993 with a Top 5 duet with Bono. What was the song?

QUESTION 9
Who were the two 'Phils' on the 1985 No 1 'Easy Lover'?

QUESTION 10
What was the title of the 1997 hit by Babyface featuring Stevie Wonder?

POPMASTER QUIZ 104

MAMAS AND PAPAS

Parents and their children in pop

QUESTION 1
Who is the rock and roll dad of singer Kim Wilde?

QUESTION 2
What was the title of the 2003 No 1 by Kelly and Ozzy Osbourne?

QUESTION 3
The two daughters of Brian Poole from The Tremeloes had a run of hits in the late Nineties, recording as which duo?

QUESTION 4
The son of another member of The Tremeloes reached No 1 in 1991 with a song written by Eighties star Nik Kershaw. Name both the singer and the song.

QUESTION 5
Will Smith's daughter Willow Smith had a Top 3 hit in 2010, released just before her tenth birthday, called 'Whip My… what?

QUESTION 6
Albert Hammond. Jr, son of singe-songwriter Albert Hammond is a member of which American indie-rock band?

QUESTION 7
Released in 1992, what is the title of the first and biggest UK hit for the father of Miley Cyrus, Billy Ray?

QUESTION 8
Neneh Cherry's step-dad Don Cherry is also father to someone who had Top 10 hits in 1998 with the songs 'Save Tonight' and 'Falling In Love Again'. Who is he?

QUESTION 9
Sam Brown, the daughter of early British rock and roll singer Joe Brown had her biggest hit in 1988 with a Top 5 song with a one-word title. What is it?

QUESTION 10
Redfoo, the son of the founder of Motown Records, Berry Gordy, is a member of which group?

QUIZ 102

Q1
Ciccone

Q2
'Into The Groove' (August 1985)

Q3
1991

Q4
"A League of Their Own"

Q5
Evita

Q6
I'm Breathless

Q7
1984

Q8
'Gimme, Gimme, Gimme (a Man After Midnight)'

Q9
Maverick

Q10
'Me Against the Music'

QUIZ 103

Q1
David Bowie and Mick Jagger

Q2
'Would I Lie to You'

Q3
Gene Pitney

Q4
'Shame'

Q5
Lou Reed (featured in the comedy film of the same name)

Q6 *'The Girl is Mine' (as Michael Jackson and Paul McCartney); 'Say Say Say' (the other way around)*

Q7
Tim McGraw

Q8
'I Got You Under My Skin'

Q9
Philip Bailey and Phil Collins

Q10
'How Come, How Long'

QUIZ 105 POPMASTER

A MAN'S BEST FRIEND

QUESTION 1
Which singer had a Top 10 hit in 1971 with 'Me and You and a Dog Named Boo'?

QUESTION 2
From the year 2000, what was the title of the only Top 10 hit achieved by The Baha Men?

QUESTION 3
In 1953, two versions of '(How Much Is) that Doggie in the Window' made the Top 10, the original American version by Patti Page and the UK cover that went to No 1. Can you name that singer?

QUESTION 4
Which successful Sixties band released an album titled 'A Salty Dog" in 1969'?

QUESTION 5
Can you name the rapper who appeared on the 2014 Top 10 hit by Enrique Iglesias titled 'I'm A Freak'?

QUESTION 6
Who was the singer-songwriter who made his chart debut in 1966 with his composition 'I Love My Dog'?

QUESTION 7
In 1986 who had a successful single and No 1 album titled 'Hounds Of Love'?

QUESTION 8
Who appeared with Dr Dre on the 2001 Top 10 hit, 'The Next Episode'?

QUESTION 9
From 1969, can you name the group whose only hit was 'A Way Of Life'?

QUESTION 10
Which female singer had a Top 10 hit in 2006 with a song called 'Beware Of The Dog'?

POPMASTER QUIZ 106

MEET THE ANGELS

QUESTION 1
Name the female singer who made her 1994 solo Top 40 chart debut with 'Patience Of Angels'

QUESTION 2
In 1973, Wizzard achieved two No 1 hit singles. The first was 'See My Baby Jive', what was the other?

QUESTION 3
What is the hit song title shared by Sham 69 and Sugababes?

QUESTION 4
Can you name the group who had a Top 10 hit in the late Eighties with 'Angel Of Harlem'?

QUESTION 5
Which group made their chart debut in 1976 with 'Heaven Must Be Missing An Angel', which returned to the Top 20 in 1986 in a re-mixed version?

QUESTION 6
What was the name of the rock band whose only Top 20 hit was in 1993 with 'Womankind'?

QUESTION 7
In 1979, ABBA achieved a Top 3 hit with a double A-sided single, one song was 'Voulez-Vous,' what was the other?

QUESTION 8
Which group had a Top 20 hit in 1991 with 'Monsters And Angels'?

QUESTION 9
What was the name of the group who made their 1973 chart debut with 'Broken Down Angel'?

QUESTION 10
Can you name the Dutch duo who had Top 20 hits in 2004 with 'Touch Me' and 'Do You Know (I Go Crazy)'?

QUIZ 104

Q1 *Marty Wilde*

Q2 *'Changes'*

Q3 *Alisha's Attic*

Q4 *Chesney Hawkes/'The One And Only' (son of Chip Hawkes of The Tremeloes)*

Q5 *Hair*

Q6 *The Strokes*

Q7 *'Achy Breaky Heart'*

Q8 *Eagle-Eye Cherry*

Q9 *'Stop'*

Q10 *LMFAO*

QUIZ 105

Q1
Lobo

Q2
'Who Let the Dogs Out'

Q3
Lita Roza

Q4
Procol Harum

Q5
Pitbull

Q6
Cat Stevens

Q7
Kate Bush

Q8
Snoop Dogg

Q9
Family Dogg

Q10
Jamelia

QUIZ 107 POPMASTER

MIXED DOUBLES

QUESTION 1
The title song to the movie, "Endless Love" was a 1981 Top 10 hit for which two Motown recording artists?

QUESTION 2
Which 1986 hit did Peter Gabriel record with Kate Bush?

QUESTION 3
Besides her father, Nancy Sinatra had hit duets with another male singer in the late Sixties and early Seventies – who is he?

QUESTION 4
…and was what the title of the 2005 Top 3 single by Audio Bullys featuring Nancy Sinatra that spent four months on the chart?

QUESTION 5
Marvin Gaye had hit duets with Tammi Terrell, Diana Ross and Kim Weston – but with which of these singers did he record 'It Takes Two'?

QUESTION 6
Both of Jennifer Warnes Top 10 hits in the 1980s were duets with two different make singers – name both singers and both songs?

QUESTION 7
Which duo recorded the 1977 Top 10 song and American No 1 'You Don't Have To Be a Star (To Be In My Show)'?

QUESTION 8
What was the title of Blu Cantrell's 2003 No 1 that also featured Jamaican artist Sean Paul?

QUESTION 9
Who is the uncredited vocalist on Prince's 1987 single 'U Got The Look'?

QUESTION 10
Name the 1995 duet by Nick Cave and The Bad Seeds + Kylie Minogue?

POPMASTER QUIZ 108

MOTOWN

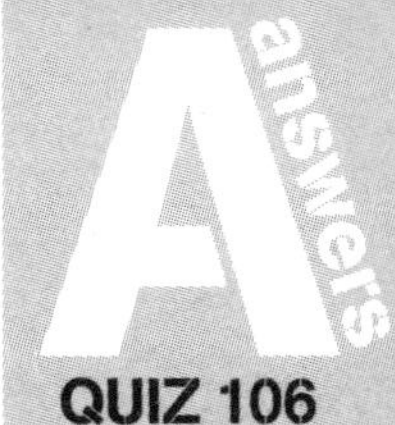

QUIZ 106

QUESTION 1
In which city was the Motown label founded?

QUESTION 2
What is the title of the only UK No 1 for The Commodores?

QUESTION 3
Name one of the two members alongside Diana Ross in the classic line-up of The Supremes from 1962 to 1967.

QUESTION 4
Ne-Yo's 2012 album "R.E.D" contained the singer's fourth UK No 1 single. What was it called?

QUESTION 5
Which vocal group had a UK No 1 in 1966 and a Top 20 hit on its 1988 remix with the song 'Reach Out I'll Be There'?

QUESTION 6
What is the name of the backing band of session musicians that played on the majority of the label's hits in the 1960s?

QUESTION 7
The singer Shanice had her biggest hit in the early Nineties with a song that was Top 3 in both the UK and America. What was it called?

QUESTION 8
Who had an American No 1 and a UK Top 10 hit in 1977 with the song 'Got To Give It Up (Part 1)'?

QUESTION 9
Written by Diane Warren and featured in the film "The Last Dragon", what was the title of the 1985 Top 5 single by DeBarge?

QUESTION 10
Which one-time member of The Temptations had solo hits in the 1970s with the songs 'Keep On Truckin" and 'Boogie Down'?

Q1 *Eddi Reader*

Q2 *'Angel Fingers'*

Q3 *'Angels With Dirty Faces'*

Q4 *U2*

Q5 *Tavareis*

Q6 *Little Angels*

Q7 *'Angeleyes'*

Q8 *Voice Of The Beehive*

Q9 *Nazareth*

Q10 *Angel City*

QUIZ 107

Q1
Diana Ross and Lionel Richie

Q2
'Don't Give Up'

Q3
Lee Hazlewood

Q4
'Shot You Down'

Q5
Kim Weston

Q6
Joe Cocker, 'Up Where We Belong', Bill Medley, '(I've Had) The Time Of My Life'

Q7
Marilyn McCoo and Billy Davis. Jr

Q8
'Breathe'

Q9
Sheena Easton

Q10
'Where the Wild Roses Grow'

QUIZ 109 POPMASTER

THE MOVIE CONNECTION

These are questions about songs or bands that share the same title as a film, even though they might not be related in any way.

QUESTION 1
What was the title of Nick Heyward's first solo hit that shared its title with a 1961 movie starring Hayley Mills?

QUESTION 2
Can you name the group that made their 1978 chart debut with a song that had the same title as James Cagney's 1938 movie, "Angels With Dirty Faces".

QUESTION 3
Which Sixties hit-making group took their name from a 1956 movie starring John Wayne and Ward Bond?

QUESTION 4
U2 share a 1991 No 1 song title with a 1986 box office No 1 movie starring Jeff Goldblum and Geena Davis that in itself was a re-make of a 1958 science fiction film. What's the title?

QUESTION 5
Singers Pat and Greg Kane, achieved a Top 10 hit in 1987 with 'Labour Of Love' share their collective group name with a 1947 movie starring Alastair Sim, Harry Fowler and Joan Dowling. What is the name?

QUESTION 6
ABBA's first hit single shares its title with a 1970 Soviet-Italian film directed by Sergei Bondarchuk and produced by Dino De Laurentiis. What is the title?

QUESTION 7
Can you name the successful Welsh singer who shares his name with a 1963 four-times Academy Award-winning film starring Albert Finney?

QUESTION 8
In 1959, Marty Wilde achieved a Top 3 hit with a cover of a song by American singer Phil Phillips, which shares its title with a 1990 movie starring Al Pacino and Ellen Barkin. Can you come up with the name?

QUESTION 9
Can you name the group that achieved a Top 10 hit in 1978 with a song that had the same title as a 1970 disaster movie, called "Airport", starring Burt Lancaster and Dean Martin?

QUESTION 10
Middle of the Road achieved the last of their five Top 40 hits in 1972 with a song that shares its title with a 1949 movie starring Hedy Lamarr, Victor Mature and Angela Lansbury. What is the title?

POPMASTER QUIZ 110

MUSICAL INSTRUMENTS

QUESTION 1
Which singer and songwriter achieved her only Top 40 hit as a performer in 1988 with 'Piano In The Dark'?

QUESTION 2
Can you name the comedian who made his chart debut in 1960 with 'Love Is Like A Violin', that subsequently became his signature tune?

QUESTION 3
Who had a Top 10 hit in 1975, along with his backing group The Rebelettes, with 'Play Me Like You Play Your Guitar'?

QUESTION 4
Under what name did Australian producer Josh Abrahams release his 2002 Top 5 hit 'Addicted To Bass'?

QUESTION 5
From 1968 can you name the only Top 10 hit achieved by American group The Lemon Pipers?

QUESTION 6
Which female singer had a Top 10 hit in 1979 with 'Gonna Get Along Without You Now'?

QUESTION 7
Which trio of brothers achieved their final UK Top 20 hit in 1961 with '76 Trombones'?

QUESTION 8
Can you name the female singer who scored a Top 20 hit in 2010 with 'Drummer Boy'?

QUESTION 9
In 1958, Perry Como achieved a double A-sided hit with 'Love Makes the World Go Round' and which other song?

QUESTION 10
Which Danish duo had a Top 40 hit in 1960 with 'Banjo Boy'?

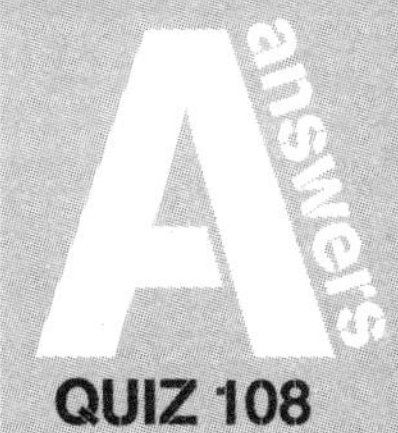

QUIZ 108

Q1 *Detroit*

Q2 *'Three Times a Lady'*

Q3 *Mary Wilson, Florence Ballard*

Q4 *'Let Me Love You (Until You Learn To Love Yourself)'*

Q5 *The Four Tops*

Q6 *The Funk Brothers*

Q7 *'I Love Your Smile'*

Q8 *Marvin Gaye*

Q9 *'Rhythm of the Night'*

Q10 *Eddie Kendricks*

QUIZ 109

Q1
'Whistle Down the Wind'

Q2
Sham 69

Q3
The Searchers

Q4
'The Fly'

Q5
Hue and Cry

Q6
'Waterloo'

Q7
Tom Jones

Q8
'Sea Of Love'

Q9
The Motors

Q10
'Sampson and Delilah'

QUIZ 111 POPMASTER

NAME THE ALBUM (1)

For each question, name both the artist and the album that contains these singles – a bonus point if you also know the year of the album's release!

QUESTION 1
'Rolling In The Deep', 'Someone Like You', 'Set Fire To The Rain'

QUESTION 2
'Ashes to Ashes', 'Fashion', 'Up The Hill Backwards'

QUESTION 3
'D'You Know What I Mean', 'Stand By Me', 'All Around The World'

QUESTION 4
'Run', 'Chocolate', 'Spitting Games'

QUESTION 5
'Tonight's the Night', 'The Killing of Georgie (Part I and II)', 'The First Cut is the Deepest'

QUESTION 6
'I Guess That's Why They Call it the Blues', 'I'm Still Standing', 'Kiss the Bride'

QUESTION 7
'Common People', 'Disco 2000', 'Mis-Shapes/Sorted For E's & Wizz'

QUESTION 8
'Let's Stay Together', 'Better be Good To Me', 'Private Dancer'

QUESTION 9
'She's So Lovely', 'Elvis Ain't Dead', 'Heartbeat'

QUESTION 10
'Go Your Own Way', 'Dreams', 'Don't Stop'

POPMASTER QUIZ 112

NAME THE ALBUM (2)

For each question, name both the artist and the album that contains these singles – a bonus point if you also know the year of the album's release!

QUESTION 1
'With or Without You', 'Where the Streets Have No Name', 'I Still haven't Found What I'm Looking For'

QUESTION 2
'Something Got Me Started', 'For Your Babies', 'Thrill Me'

QUESTION 3
'Picture This', 'Hanging on the Telephone', 'Heart of Glass'

QUESTION 4
'Somewhere Only We Know', 'Everybody's Changing', 'Bedshaped'

QUESTION 5
'Here With Me', 'Thank You', 'Hunter'

QUESTION 6
'All Night Long', 'Running With the Night', 'Hello'

QUESTION 7
'Patience', 'Shine', 'I'd Wait For Life'

QUESTION 8
'Running Up that Hill', 'Cloudbusting', 'The Big Sky'

QUESTION 9
'Dancing Queen', 'Knowing Me, Knowing You', 'Money, Money, Money'

QUESTION 10
'Bleeding Love', 'Better in Time', 'Footprints in the Sand'

A answers

QUIZ 110

Q1 *Brenda Russell*

Q2 *Ken Dodd*

Q3 *Duane Eddy*

Q4 *Puretone*

Q5 *'Green Tambourine'*

Q6 *Viola Wills*

Q7 *The King Brothers*

Q8 *Alesha Dixon*

Q9 *'Mandolins in the Moonlight'*

Q10 *Jan and Kjeld*

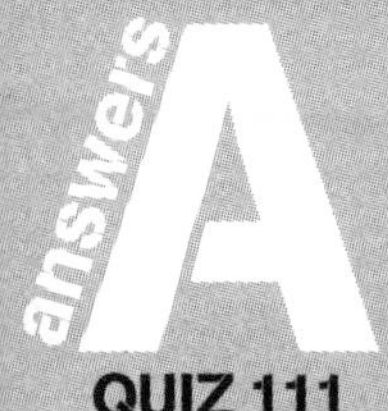

QUIZ 111

Q1
Adele – 19 (2011)

Q2
David Bowie – Scary Monsters (And Super Creeps) (1980)

Q3
Oasis – Be Here Now (1997)

Q4
Snow Patrol – Final Straw (originally 2003, re-released 2004!)

Q5
Rod Stewart – A Night On The Town (1976)

Q6
Elton John – Too Low For Zero (1983)

Q7
Pulp – Different Class (1995)

Q8
Tina Turner – Private Dancer (1984)

Q9
Scouting For Girls – Scouting For Girls (2007)

Q10
Fleetwood Mac – Rumours (1977)

QUIZ 113 POPMASTER

NAME THE ALBUM (3)

For each question, name both the artist and the album that contains these singles – a bonus point if you also know the year of the album's release!

QUESTION 1
'Sir Duke', 'I Wish', 'Another Star'

QUESTION 2
'Dance Little Sister', 'Wishing Well', 'Sign Your Name'

QUESTION 3
'Only Girl (In The World)', 'What's My Name?', 'California King Bed'

QUESTION 4
'Lucky Man', 'Bitter Sweet Symphony', 'The Drugs Don't Work'

QUESTION 5
'Nothing Can Divide Us', 'Too Many Broken Hearts', 'Sealed With A Kiss'

QUESTION 6
'Take Your Mama', 'Comfortably Numb', 'Mary'

QUESTION 7
'She's Out of My Life', 'Rock With You', 'Don't Stop Til You Get Enough'

QUESTION 8
'Smooth Operator', 'When Am I Going To Make a Living', 'Your Love is King'

QUESTION 9
'Speed of Sound', 'Fix You', 'Talk'

QUESTION 10
'Because You Loved Me', 'All By Myself', 'It's all Coming Back to Me Now'

POPMASTER QUIZ 114

NAME THE YEAR (1)

This quiz gives you the Top 3 records from a chart of a particular year in reverse order (3-2-1). All you need do is name the year.

QUESTION 1
'The Wild Boys by Duran Duran' (3), 'I Should Have Known Better' by Jim Diamond (2) and 'I Feel For You' by Chaka Khan (1).

QUESTION 2
'You Can Get It If You Really Want' by Desmond Dekker (3), 'Black Night' by Deep Purple (2) and 'Band of Gold' by Freda Payne (1)

QUESTION 3
'Take a Bow' by Rihanna (3), 'Closer by Ne-Yo' (2) and 'Viva La Vida' by Coldplay (1).

QUESTION 4
'Like I Do' by Maureen Evans (3), 'The Next Time/Bachelor Boy' by Cliff Richard & The Shadows (2) and 'Dance On' by The Shadows (1).

QUESTION 5
'Eve of the War' (Remix) by Jeff Wayne (3), 'Don't Know Much' by Linda Ronstadt featuring Aaron Neville (2) and 'You Got It (The Right Stuff)' by New Kids On The Block.

QUESTION 6
'Bend Me Shape Me' by Amen Corner (3), 'Everlasting Love' by The Love Affair (2) and 'Mighty Quinn' by Manfred Mann (1).

QUESTION 7
'Where Them Girls At' by David Guetta, Flo Rida and Nikki Minaj (3), 'Party Rock Anthem' by Lmfao, Lauren Bennett and Goonrock (2) and 'The Lazy Song' by Bruno Mars (1).

QUESTION 8
'I'll Be There For You' by The Rembrandts (3), 'Country House' by Blur (2) and 'You Are Not Alone' by Michael Jackson (1).

QUESTION 9
'All Shook Up' by Elvis Presley (3), 'Love Letters in the Sand' by Pat Boone (2) and 'Diana' by Paul Anka (1).

QUESTION 10
'If You Leave Me Now' by Chicago (3), 'When Forever Has Gone' by Demis Roussos (2) and 'Mississippi' by Pussycat (1).

QUIZ 112

Q1
U2 – The Joshua Tree (1987)

Q2
Simply Red – Stars (1991)

Q3
Blondie – Parallel Lines (1978)

Q4
Keane – Hopes And Fears (2004)

Q5
Dido – No Angel (1999)

Q6
Lionel Richie – Can't Slow Down (1983)

Q7
Take That – Beautiful World (2006)

Q8
Kate Bush – Hounds Of Love (1985)

Q9
ABBA – Arrival (1976)

Q10
Leona Lewis – Spirit (2007)

QUIZ 113

Q1 *Stevie Wonder – Songs In The Key Of Life (1976)*

Q2 *Terence Trent D'Arby – Introducing The Hardline According To Terence Trent D'Arby (1987)*

Q3 *Rihanna – Loud (2010)*

Q4 *The Verve – Urban Hymns (1997)*

Q5 *Jason Donovan – Ten Good Reasons (1989)*

Q6 *Scissor Sisters – Scissor Sisters (2004)*

Q7 *Michael Jackson – Off The Wall (1979)*

Q8 *Sade – Diamond Life (1984)*

Q9 *Coldplay – X&Y (2005)*

Q10 *Celine Dion – Falling Into You (1996)*

QUIZ 115 POPMASTER

NAME THE YEAR (2)

This quiz gives you the Top 3 records from a chart of a particular year in reverse order (3-2-1). All you need do is name the year.

QUESTION 1
'September' by Earth Wind & Fire (3), 'Y.M.C.A.' by Village People (2) and 'Hit Me With Your Rhythm Stick' by Ian (Dury) and the Blockheads (1).

QUESTION 2
'Case of the Ex' by Mya (3), 'Stuck in a Moment You Can't Get Out Of' by U2 (2) and 'Whole Again' by Atomic Kitten (1).

QUESTION 3
'Call Me' by Spagna (3), 'La Bamba' by Los Lobos (2) and 'I Just Can't Stop Loving You' by Michael Jackson and Siedah Garrett (3).

QUESTION 4
'Feel It' by Tamperer featuring Maya (3), 'Ray of Light' by Madonna (2) and 'Under The Bridge/Lady Marmalade' by All Saints (1).

QUESTION 5
'Man Of The World' by Fleetwood Mac (3), 'Get Back' by The Beatles with Billy Preston (2), 'Dizzy' by Tommy Roe (1).

QUESTION 6
'If There's Any Justice' by Lemar (3), 'Lose My Breath' by Destiny's Child (2) and 'I'll Stand By You' by Girls Aloud (1).

QUESTION 7
'Bad' by Michael Jackson (3), 'Full Metal Jacket (I Wanna Be Your Drill Instructor)' by Abigail Mead and Nigel Goulding (2) and 'Pump Up the Volume' by M/A/R/R/S (1).

QUESTION 8
'What is Love' by Haddaway (3), 'Dreams' by Gabrielle (2) and 'Pray' by Take That (1).

QUESTION 9
'Rockin' All Over The World' by Status Quo (3), 'We Are The Champions' by Queen (2) and 'The Name of the Game' by ABBA (1).

QUESTION 10
'Teenage Dream' by Katy Perry (3), 'Dynamite' by Taio Cruz (2) and 'Start Without You' by Alexandra Burke featuring Laza Morgan (1).

POPMASTER QUIZ 116

NAME THE YEAR (3)

This quiz gives you the Top 3 records from a chart of a particular year in reverse order (3-2-1). All you need do is name the year.

QUESTION 1
'You'll Never Walk Alone' by The Crowd (3), 'Crazy For You' by Madonna (2) and 'Frankie' by Sister Sledge (1).

QUESTION 2
'Chorus' by Erasure (3), 'I Wanna Sex You Up' by Color Me Badd (2) and 'Any Dream Will Do' by Jason Donovan (1).

QUESTION 3
'Warwick Avenue' by Duffy (3), 'That's Not My Name' by The Ting Tings (2) and 'Take a Bow' by Rihanna (1).

QUESTION 4
'There's a Ghost in My House' by R. Dean Taylor (3), 'Hey Rock And Roll' by Showaddywaddy (2) and 'The Streak' by Ray Stevens (1).

QUESTION 5
'Everybody's Free (To Wear Sunscreen)' by Baz Luhrmann (3), 'Beautiful Strange' by Madonna (2) and 'Bring It All Back' by S Club 7 (1).

QUESTION 6
'Get Over You / Move This Mountain' by Sophie Ellis Bextor (3), 'Love at First Sight' by Kylie Minogue (2) and 'A Little Less Conversation' by Elvis vs JXL (1).

QUESTION 7
'You Make Me Feel Like Dancing' by Leo Sayer (3), 'Mississippi' by Pussycat (2) and 'If You Leave Me Now' by Chicago (1).

QUESTION 8
'Union Of The Snake' by Duran Duran (3), 'All Night Long' (All Night) by Lionel Richie (2) and 'Uptown Girl' by Billy Joel (1).

QUESTION 9
'Black Night' by Deep Purple (3), 'Patches' by Clarence Carter (2) and 'Woodstock' by Matthews' Southern Comfort (1).

QUESTION 10
'Ain't Misbehavin'' by Tommy Bruce (3), 'Please Don't Tease' Cliff Richard & The Shadows (2) and 'Good Timin'' by Jimmy Jones (1)

A answers

QUIZ 114

Q1 *1984*

Q2 *1970*

Q3 *2008*

Q4 *1963*

Q5 *1989*

Q6 *1968*

Q7 *2011*

Q8 *1995*

Q9 *1957*

Q10 *1976*

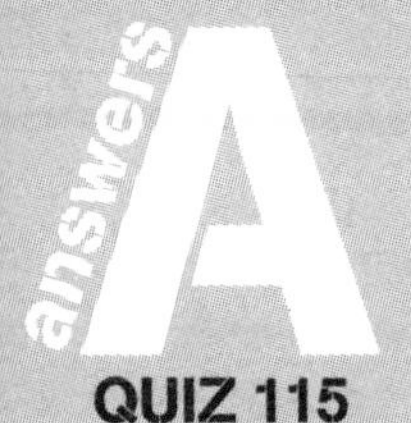

QUIZ 115

Q1
1979

Q2
2001

Q3
1987

Q4
1998

Q5
1969

Q6
2004

Q7
1987

Q8
1993

Q9
1977

Q10
2010

QUIZ 117 POPMASTER

NAME THE YEAR (4)

This quiz gives you the Top 3 records from a chart of a particular year in reverse order (3-2-1). All you need do is name the year.

QUESTION 1
'Freak Like Me' by Sugababes (3), 'One Step Closer' by S Club Juniors (2) and 'Kiss Kiss' by Holly Valance (1).

QUESTION 2
'Question' by The Moody Blues (3), 'Spirit in the Sky' by Norman Greenbaum (2) and 'Back Home' by The England World Cup Squad (1).

QUESTION 3
'Dedicated to the One I Love' by The Mamas and The Papas (3), 'Waterloo Sunset' by The Kinks (2) and 'Silence is Golden' by The Tremeloes (1).

QUESTION 4
'Master Blaster (Jammin')' by Stevie Wonder (3), 'One Day I'll Fly Away' by Randy Crawford (2) and 'Don't Stand So Close to Me' by The Police (1).

QUESTION 5
'Escaping' by Dina Carroll (3), 'Breakfast at Tiffany's' by Deep Blue Something (2) and 'Ready or Not' by The Fugees (1).

QUESTION 6
'Three Steps to Heaven' by Showaddywaddy (3), 'Whispering Grass' by Don Estelle and Windsor Davies (2) and 'I'm Not in Love' by 10cc (1).

QUESTION 7
'Love Plus One' by Haircut 100 (3), 'Mickey' by Toni Basil (2) and 'The Lion Sleeps Tonight' by Tight Fit (1).

QUESTION 8
'Don't Look Back in Anger' by Oasis (3), 'Children' by Robert Miles (2) and 'How Deep is Your Love' by Take That (1).

QUESTION 9
'In the Morning' by Razorlight (3), 'Hips Don't Lie' by Shakira featuring Wyclef Jean (2) and 'Smile' by Lily Allen (1).

QUESTION 10
'Under the Boardwalk' by Bruce Willis (3), 'Star Trekkin'' by The Firm (2) and 'It's a Sin' by Pet Shop Boys (1).

POPMASTER QUIZ 118

NAME THE YEAR (5)

This quiz gives you the Top 3 records from a chart of a particular year in reverse order (3-2-1). All you need do is name the year.

QUESTION 1
'Happy Hour' by The Housemartins (3), 'Papa Don't Preach' by Madonna (2) and 'The Edge of Heaven' by Wham! (1)?

QUESTION 2
'Life on Mars' by David Bowie (3), 'Welcome Home' by Peters And Lee (2) and 'Skweeze Me Pleeze Me' by Slade (1).

QUESTION 3
'Feel Good Time' by Pink (3), 'Hollywood' by Madonna (2) and 'Crazy In Love' by Beyoncé (1).

QUESTION 4
'Barbara Ann' by The Beach Boys (3), 'A Groovy Kind of Love' by The Mindbenders (2) and 'These Boots are Made for Walkin'' by Nancy Sinatra (1).

QUESTION 5
'Thank You For a Lifetime' by Cliff Richard (3), 'I Kissed a Girl' by Katy Perry (2) and 'Sex on Fire' by Kings Of Leon (1).

QUESTION 6
'No More Tears (Enough is Enough)' by Donna Summer and Barbra Streisand (3), 'Another Brick in the Wall (Part II)' by Pink Floyd (2) and 'Walking on the Moon' by The Police (1).

QUESTION 7
'Love Action (I Believe in Love)' by Human League (3), 'Japanese Boy' by Aneka (2) and 'Tainted Love' by Soft Cell (1).

QUESTION 8
'Would I Lie to You' by Charles & Eddie (3), 'Heal the World' by Michael Jackson (2) and 'I Will Always Love You' by Whitney Houston (1).

QUESTION 9
'Groovejet (If This Ain't Love)' by Spiller (3), 'Music' by Madonna (2) and 'Take On Me' by A1 (1).

QUESTION 10
'Ghostbusters' by Ray Parker. Jr (3), 'Careless Whisper' by George Michael (2) and 'I Just Called To Say I Love You' by Stevie Wonder (1).

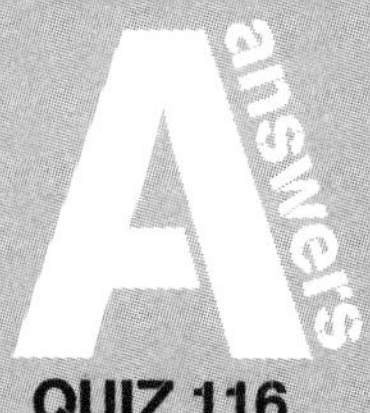

QUIZ 116

Q1 *1985*

Q2 *1991*

Q3 *2008*

Q4 *1974*

Q5 *1999*

Q6 *2002*

Q7 *1976*

Q8 *1983*

Q9 *1970*

Q10 *1960*

QUIZ 117

Q1
2002

Q2
1970

Q3
1967

Q4
1980

Q5
1996

Q6
1975

Q7
1982

Q8
1996

Q9
2006

Q10
1987

QUIZ 119 POPMASTER

NEW YORK

QUESTION 1
What is the title of the seasonal favourite recorded by The Pogues and Kirsty MacColl?

QUESTION 2
Released in 1983, which group's third and final Top 10 single was called 'Big Apple'?

QUESTION 3
What was the title of the U2 song written for Martin Scorcese's 2002 film "Gangs of New York" starring Leonardo DiCaprio and Daniel Day Lewis?

QUESTION 4
What is the name of the famous New York nightclub from the Seventies and early Eighties that both inspired and is mentioned in 'Le Freak' by Chic?

QUESTION 5
What was the title of Manhattan Transfer's 1977 No 1?

QUESTION 6
'Juicebox', 'Last Nite' and '12:51' are just three of the hit singles in the Noughties for which band formed in New York City?

QUESTION 7
Jay-Z's 1998 Top 3 hit 'Hard Knock Life (Ghetto Anthem)' samples a song from which Broadway musical?

QUESTION 8
'Central Park Arrest' was a Top 30 hit in 1974 for a British female vocal group – what were they called?

QUESTION 9
New York duo A Great Big World made their UK debut in 2014 with a Top 5 song that featured Christina Aguilera on vocals – what is the song?

QUESTION 10
The 2001 version of 'Lady Marmalade' was No 1 for Pink, Mya and two other female artists born in two of the boroughs of New York. Who are they?

POPMASTER QUIZ 120

ON THE STREET WHERE YOU LIVE

QUESTION 1
Can you name the group that successfully revived Gerry Rafferty's 1978 Top 5 hit 'Baker Street' in 1992?

QUESTION 2
In 1978, The Jam achieved a Top 40 hit with a double A-sided single. One track was 'David Watts' can you name the other?

QUESTION 3
What was the title of Paul Weller's 1995 album that contained the hit singles 'You Do Something To Me' and The 'Changingman'?

QUESTION 4
Des O'Connor scored a Top 20 hit in 1969, written by Jim Dale, called 'Dick-A-Dum-Dum' that was followed by what in brackets?

QUESTION 5
Who released the No 1 soundtrack album "Give My Regards To Broad Street" in 1984?

QUESTION 6
Can you name the group whose last UK Top 10 hit was their 1998 recording of 'Angel Street'?

QUESTION 7
Who wrote the 1967 Top 40 hit by Harpers Bizarre called '59th Street Bridge Song (Feelin' Groovy)'?

QUESTION 8
Can you name the 1988 Top 10 single recorded by Prince that was featured in his movie "Under The Cherry Moon"?

QUESTION 9
Which Irish trio recorded but failed to chart with their 1967 recording of the David McWilliams song '3 O'clock Flamingo Street'?

QUESTION 10
In 2001, who topped the chart with 'The Road To Mandalay'?

A answers

QUIZ 118

Q1 *1986*

Q2 *1973*

Q3 *2003*

Q4 *1966*

Q5 *2008*

Q6 *1979*

Q7 *1981*

Q8 *1992*

Q9 *2000*

Q10 *1984*

QUIZ 119

Q1 *'Fairytale Of New York'*

Q2 *Kajagoogoo*

Q3 *'The Hands That Built America'*

Q4 *Studio 54*

Q5 *Chanson D'amour*

Q6 *The Strokes*

Q7 *Annie*

Q8 *Thunderthighs (backing vocalists on 'Walk on The Wild Side' and 'Roll Away The Stone')*

Q9 *Say Something*

Q10 *Christina Aguilera (Staten Island), Lil' Kym (Brooklyn)*

QUIZ 121 POPMASTER

ONE FOR THE ALBUM

Name the artist or group that had the following No 1 albums (three listed for each act, although they may have had more than three No 1 albums)

QUESTION 1
Under The Iron Sea, Perfect Symmetry, Night Train

QUESTION 2
Pin-Ups, Tonight, The Next Day

QUESTION 3
Encore, Relapse, Recovery

QUESTION 4
Hard Candy, MDNA, Music

QUESTION 5
Parachutes, A Rush of Blood to the Head, Mylo Xyloto

QUESTION 6
Escapology, Intensive Care, Take the Crown

QUESTION 7
Be Here Now, Dig Out Your Soul, Don't Believe The Truth

QUESTION 8
Atom Heart Mother, The Division Bell, Wish You Were Here

QUESTION 9
The Rising, Devils & Dust, Wrecking Ball

QUESTION 10
The Game, The Miracle, Innuendo

POPMASTER QUIZ 122

ONE-HIT WONDERS

In this section you will be given clues to the artist and title of the act's one and only hit. You need to know both the artist and song title!

QUESTION 1
This German singer topped the chart in 1982 with the English version of her Eurovision Song Contest winner of that year.

QUESTION 2
This husband and wife team wrote and produced dozens of hits for a variety of stars including Diana Ross, Ray Charles and Chaka Khan. Released in 1985, this was their only Top 40 hit record as performers.

QUESTION 3
A record that was in the chart in 1977 and was the only hit for the band made up of musicians from the Yorkshire towns situated between Bradford and Huddersfield.

QUESTION 4
This group took their name from the initials of the surnames of the three group members, Tony Hymas, Jim Diamond and Simon Phillips. Their only hit reached number three in 1982.

QUESTION 5
This single topped the chart for just one week in 2002. The girls were a Spanish trio of three sisters, Pilar, Lola and Lucia, the daughters of flamenco dancer, Tomate.

QUESTION 6
Before his solo career, he worked as a backing vocalist for a variety of artists including Bette Midler and Ricky Lee Jones. He has worked as a producer with top acts No Doubt, Christina Aguilera and Miley Cyrus.

QUESTION 7
This record topped our chart for three weeks in 2003 and was featured in the movie "Donnie Darko". The song was previously recorded in 1982, when it became the first hit single for Tears for Fears.

QUESTION 8
Prior to becoming a solo singer, this lady was a member of the American girl group Poppies, also including Dorothy Moore. Her version of this No 1 hit topped our chart for one week in 1980.

QUESTION 9
A No 1 in 1981 for this American who formed his first group, Sugarcreek in 1966. He relocated to Australia in 1978 and created the character, Giuseppi, who gave him this huge, one-off novelty hit.

QUESTION 10
This instrumental topped the chart for four weeks in 1972. Despite the composer's credit going to Jack Trombey, it was in fact written by Jules Staffaro. It was used as the theme for the hit TV series "Van Der Valk".

QUIZ 120

Q1
Undercover

Q2
'A Bomb in Wardour Street'

Q3
Stanley Road

Q4
King's Road

Q5
Paul McCartney

Q6
M People

Q7
Paul Simon

Q8
'Alphabet Street'

Q9
The Bachelors

Q10
Robbie Williams

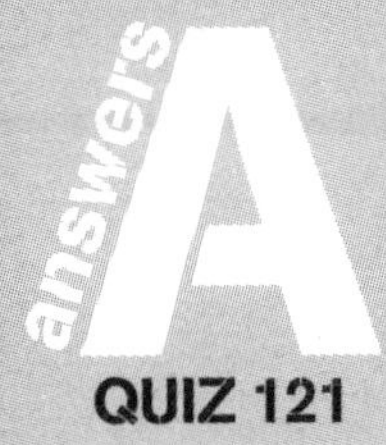

QUIZ 121

Q1
Keane

Q2
David Bowie

Q3
Eminem

Q4
Madonna

Q5
Coldplay

Q6
Robbie Williams

Q7
Oasis

Q8
Pink Floyd

Q9
Bruce Springsteen

Q10
Queen

QUIZ 123 POPMASTER

ONLY IN AMERICA

QUESTION 1
Which rock and roll singer only managed to achieve one UK Top 10 hit, in 1960, with 'Way Down Yonder In New Orleans'?

QUESTION 2
Which group successfully revived The Mamas and the Papas 1966 hit, 'California Dreamin'' taking it into the Top 20 in 1990?

QUESTION 3
From 1977, what was the title of Canadian singer Patsy Gallant's only UK hit single?

QUESTION 4
According to her 1981 Top 20 hit, who spent 'A Rainy Night In Georgia'?

QUESTION 5
Which successful Fifties crooner achieved his only Top 10 hit in the Sixties with 'Delaware'?

QUESTION 6
Who scored his biggest hit in 1971 with 'Indiana Wants Me'?

QUESTION 7
Can you name the group whose first No 1, titled 'Massachusetts', topped the chart for four weeks in 1967?

QUESTION 8
Which female singer scored her second Top 10 hit in 1971 with the song 'Banks Of The Ohio'?

QUESTION 9
What was the name of the group formed in Glasgow who made their chart debut in 1989 with 'I Don't Want A Lover'?

QUESTION 10
What was the full title of the only No 1 hit by Scott McKenzie that topped the chart in 1967 for four weeks?

POPMASTER QUIZ 124

ORDER! ORDER! (1)

For each of the following and beginning with the earliest, put the three songs by the given group or artist in the order they were originally hits

QUESTION 1
David Bowie – 'Let's Dance', 'Rebel Rebel', 'Thursdays Child'

QUESTION 2
Madness – 'Lovestruck', 'Michael Caine', 'One Step Beyond'

QUESTION 3
Michael Jackson – 'Rock With You', 'Stranger In Moscow', 'Leave Me Alone'

QUESTION 4
Prince – 'Alphabet Street', 'When Doves Cry', 'Diamonds And Pearls'

QUESTION 5
Cliff Richard – 'Devil Woman', 'Congratulations', 'My Pretty One'

QUESTION 6
Madonna – 'Material Girl', 'Die Another Day', 'Secret'

QUESTION 7
UB40 – 'One In Ten', 'Come Back Darling', 'Kingston Town'

QUESTION 8
Oasis – 'Let There Be Love', 'Who Feels Love?', 'Whatever'

QUESTION 9
Tina Turner – 'When The Heartache Is Over', 'The Best', 'Let's Stay Together'

QUESTION 10
The Beatles – 'Yellow Submarine', 'Please Please Me', 'Get Back'

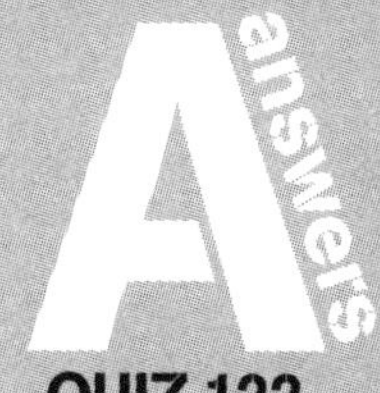

QUIZ 122

Q1
'A Little Peace' By Nicole

Q2
'Solid' by Ashford and Simpson

Q3
'The Floral Dance' by the Brighouse and Rastrick Band

Q4
'I Won't Let You Down' by PhD

Q5
'The Ketchup Song (Asereje)' by Las Ketchup

Q6
'Break My Stride' by Matthew Wilder

Q7
'Mad World' by Michael Andrews featuring Gary Jules

Q8
'Together we are Beautiful' by Fern Kinney

Q9
'Shaddap You Face' by Joe Dolce

Q10
'Eye Level' by The Simon Park Orchestra

QUIZ 123

Q1
Freddy Cannon

Q2
River City People

Q3
'From New York to L.A.'

Q4
Randy Crawford

Q5
Perry Como

Q6
R. Dean Taylor

Q7
Bee Gees

Q8
Olivia Newton-John

Q9
Texas

Q10
'San Francisco (Be Sure To Wear Some Flowers In Your Hair)'

QUIZ 125 POPMASTER

ORDER! ORDER! (2)

For each of the following and beginning with the earliest, put the three songs by the given group or artist in the order they were originally hits

QUESTION 1
Stevie Wonder – 'Uptight (Everything's Alright)', 'Part-Time Lover', 'I Wish'

QUESTION 2
The Stranglers 'No More Heroes', 'All Day And All Of The Night', 'Strange Little Girl'

QUESTION 3
The Rolling Stones – 'Tumbling Dice', 'Not Fade Away', 'Start Me Up'

QUESTION 4
Donna Summer – 'This Time I Know It's For Real', 'State Of Independence', 'Love's Unkind'

QUESTION 5
Queen – 'Now I'm Here', 'Let Me Live', 'I Want To Break Free'

QUESTION 6
Robbie Williams – 'Radio', 'Let Me Entertain You', 'You Know Me'

QUESTION 7
Fleetwood Mac – 'Dreams', 'Little Lies', 'Oh Well'?

QUESTION 8
Duran Duran – 'Notorious', 'Ordinary World', 'Rio'

QUESTION 9
'Discotheque', 'Vertigo', 'Desire'

QUESTION 10
R.E.M. – 'Orange Crush', 'Leaving New York', 'Daysleeper'

POPMASTER QUIZ 126

ORDER! ORDER! (3)

For each of the following and beginning with the earliest, put the three songs by the given group or artist in the order they were originally hits

QUESTION 1
Status Quo – 'Caroline', 'The Anniversary Waltz, Part One', 'Marguerita Time'

QUESTION 2
George Michael – 'A Different Corner', 'Flawless (Go To The City)', 'Spinning The Wheel'

QUESTION 3
Diana Ross – 'Touch Me In The Morning', 'Not Over You Yet', 'Work That Body'

QUESTION 4
The Pretenders – 'I'll Stand By You', 'Don't Get Me Wrong', 'Talk Of The Town'

QUESTION 5
Eric Clapton – 'Change The World', 'Behind The Mask', 'I Shot The Sheriff'

QUESTION 6
Kylie Minogue – 'Confide In Me', 'Slow' 'Wouldn't Change A Thing'

QUESTION 7
Simple Minds – 'She's A River', 'Belfast Child', 'Glittering Prize'

QUESTION 8
Rod Stewart – 'Baby Jane', 'Sailing', 'Tom Traubert's Blues'?

QUESTION 9
Dusty Springfield – 'In Private', 'Son Of A Preacher Man', 'I Only Want To Be With You'

QUESTION 10
Depeche Mode – 'Enjoy The Silence', 'Leave In Silence', 'Precious'

QUIZ 124

Q1
'Rebel Rebel' (74), 'Let's Dance' (83), 'Thursday's Child' (99)

Q2
'One Step Beyond '(79), 'Michael Caine' (84), 'Lovestruck' (99)

Q3
'Rock With You' (80), 'Leave Me Alone' (89) 'Stranger In Moscow' (96)

Q4
'When Doves Cry' (84), 'Alphabet Street' (88), 'Diamonds And Pearls' (91)

Q5
'Congratulations' (68), 'Devil Woman' (76) 'My Pretty One' (87)

Q6
'Material Girl' (85), 'Secret (94), Die Another Day (02)

Q7
One In Ten (81), Kingston Town' (90), 'Come Back Darling' (98)

Q8
'Whatever' (94), 'Who Feels Love?' (00), 'Let There Be Love' (05)

Q9
'Let's Stay Together' (83), 'The Best' (89), 'When the Heartache is Over' (99)

Q10
'Please Please Me' (63), 'Yellow Submarine' (66) 'Get Back' (69)

QUIZ 125

Q1
'Uptight (Everything's Alright)' (66), 'I Wish' (76), 'Part-Time Lover' (85)

Q2 *'No More Heroes' (77), 'Strange Little Girl '(82), 'All Day And All Of The Night '(88)*

Q3
'Not Fade Away' (64), 'Tumbling Dice' (72), 'Start Me Up' (81)

Q4 *'Love's Unkind' (77), 'State of Independence' (82), 'This Time I Know it's for Real' (89)*

Q5
'Now I'm Here' (75), I' Want To Break Free' (84), 'Let Me Live' (96)

Q6
'Let Me Entertain You' (98), 'Radio' (04), 'You Know Me' (09)

Q7
'Oh Well' (69), 'Dreams' (77), 'Little Lies' (87)

Q8
'Rio' (82) , 'Notorious' (86), 'Ordinary World' (93)

Q9
'Desire' (88), 'Discotheque' (97), 'Vertigo' (04)

Q10
'Orange Crush' (89), 'Daysleeper' (98), 'Leaving New York' (04)

QUIZ 127 POPMASTER

PICTURE THIS (1)

Can you name both the famous album and the group that recorded it from the description of the sleeve, the year of release and the title of the opening track?

QUESTION 1
1976 – The four group members sat in a glass-domed helicopter – 'When I Kissed The Teacher'

QUESTION 2
1985 – A silver guitar pictured against clouds – 'So Far Away'

QUESTION 3
2000 – An orange globe on a dark background – 'Don't Panic'

QUESTION 4
1997 – The singer surrounded by a multitude of photographers – 'Lazy Days'

QUESTION 5
1966 – Members of the band feeding goats – 'Wouldn't It Be Nice'

QUESTION 6
2008 – The four group members tightrope walking – 'The Garden'

QUESTION 7
1984 – The artist sat on a motorbike and a woman stood by an open door – 'Let's Go Crazy'

QUESTION 8
1971 – A closeup of a pair of jeans and a zip –'Brown Sugar'

QUESTION 9
1994 – Two greyhounds running – 'Girls And Boys'

QUESTION 10
1983 – The singer looking like a boxer, complete with boxing gloves – 'Modern Love'

POPMASTER QUIZ 128

PICTURE THIS (2)

QUESTION 1
Which band had its only Top 10 hit in 1982 with the song 'Wishing (If I Had A Photograph Of You)'?

QUESTION 2
Which artist was the subject of Brian & Michael's 1978 No 1 'Matchstalk Men And Matchstalk Cats And Dogs'?

QUESTION 3
Which Duran Duran hit begins with the sound of a repeated camera shutter?

QUESTION 4
The 2001 Top 5 single 'Bohemian Like You' was a hit for an American band whose name is a play on the name of a leading figure in the pop-art movement. Name the band.

QUESTION 5
In 1971 the progressive rock trio Emerson Lake & Palmer released a live album based around a piece of classical music by the composer Mussorgsky. What was it called?

QUESTION 6
The song 'Black Man Ray' was a 1985 Top 20 single for which group?

QUESTION 7
The Polaroid picture is mentioned in the lyrics of which hit by Outkast?

QUESTION 8
Which band recorded the 1996 Top 10 song 'Kevin Carter'?

QUESTION 9
'Making Your Mind Up' and 'The Land Of Make Believe' were two of the three No 1s for Bucks Fizz. What was the third?

QUESTION 10
Who had a Top 5 single in 2009 called 'Paparazzi'?

QUIZ 126

Q1 *'Caroline' (73), 'Marguerita Time' (83), 'The Anniversary Waltz Part One' (90)*

Q2 *'A Different Corner' (86), 'Spinning the Wheel' (96), 'Flawless (Go to the City)' (04)*

Q3 *'Touch Me in the Morning' (73), 'Work That Body' (82), 'Not Over You Yet' (99)*

Q4 *'Talk of the Town' (80), 'Don't Get Me Wrong' (86), 'I'll Stand By You' (94)*

Q5 *'I Shot The Sheriff' (74), 'Behind The Mask' (87), 'Change The World' (96)*

Q6 *'Wouldn't Change A Thing' (89), 'Confide In Me' (94), 'Slow' (03)*

Q7 *'Glittering Prize' (82), 'Belfast Child' (89), 'She's a River '(95)*

Q8 *'Sailing' (75), 'Baby Jane' (83), 'Tom Traubert's Blues (Waltzing Matilda)' (92)*

Q9 *'I Only Want To Be With You' (63), 'Son Of A Preacher Man' (68), I'n Private' (89)*

Q10 *'Leave in Silence' (82), 'Enjoy the Silence' (90), 'Precious' (05)*

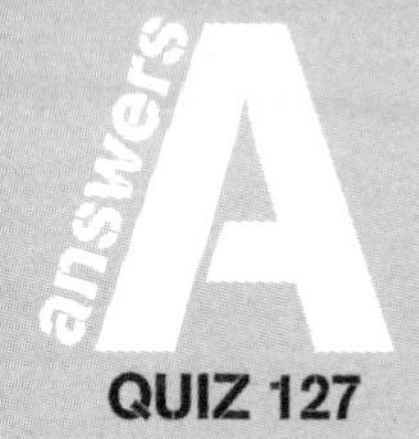

QUIZ 127

Q1
ABBA – Arrival

Q2
Dire Straits – Brothers In Arms

Q3
Coldplay – Parachutes

Q4
Robbie Williams – Life Thru A Lens

Q5
The Beach Boys – Pet Sounds

Q6
Take That – The Circus

Q7
Prince (and The Revolution) – Purple Rain

Q8
The Rolling Stones – Sticky Fingers

Q9
Blur – Parklife

Q10
David Bowie – Let's Dance

QUIZ 129 POPMASTER

PLAY YOUR CARDS RIGHT

QUESTION 1
Who had a hit with and sang the title song to the 1972 James Bond movie, "Diamonds Are Forever"?

QUESTION 2
Can you name the singer, guitarist, producer and songwriter whose last solo Top 20 hit was with his 1979 recording of 'Queen Of Hearts'?

QUESTION 3
Which Fifties skiffle star had a Top 20 hit in 1957 with 'Jack o' Diamonds'?

QUESTION 4
First released in 1973, which group topped the chart in 1990 with 'The Joker'?

QUESTION 5
Can you name the group that made their chart debut in 1974 with 'Queen Of Clubs'?

QUESTION 6
Which two ex-members of The Shadows achieved a No 1 hit in 1963 with the instrumental, 'Diamonds'?

QUESTION 7
Name the female group that had hits in 1965, 1972 and again in 1976 with 'Leader Of The Pack'.

QUESTION 8
Which heavy metal group had a Top 5 hit EP titled 'St Valentine's Day Massacre'?

QUESTION 9
First released in 1959 when it became a Top 20 hit, the single, 'Deck Of Cards' was re-issued in 1963 and made the Top 5. Can you name the performer?

QUESTION 10
Which American singer's only Top 40 UK hit was his 1963 release, 'From A Jack To A King'?

POPMASTER QUIZ 130

POP CORN

Know your comedy and novelty songs

QUESTION 1
Characters from which TV show reached No 1 in 1986 with 'The Chicken Song'?

QUESTION 2
What mode of transport did Jasper Carrott consider to be 'Funky' in 1975?

QUESTION 3
Can you name the act that made the Top 10 in 1976 with 'Disco Duck'?

QUESTION 4
Which legendary R&B and soul singer had a No 1 hit as Chef from "South Park" in 1998?

QUESTION 5
'Agadoo' was one of three Top 10 novelty records by Black Lace in the early 1980s – name one of the other two?

QUESTION 6
Which group spent three weeks at No 1 at the beginning of 1995 with 'Cotton Eye Joe'?

QUESTION 7
J.J. Barrie reached No 1 in 1976 with a song about a little boy and his 'mom' who listed all the jobs they'd done for each other. What was it called?

QUESTION 8
Which comedian is credited alongside Tony Christie on the 2005 No 1 '(Is This The Way To) Amarillo'?

QUESTION 9
Which group wanted 'Two Pints Of Lager And A Packet Of Crisps Please' in 1980?

QUESTION 10
Which character from Saturday evening television knocked Take That off the top of the chart to be the Christmas No 1 in 1993?

QUIZ 128

Q1
A Flock of Seagulls

Q2
L.S. Lowry

Q3
'Girls On Film'

Q4
The Dandy Warhols

Q5
Pictures at an Exhibition

Q6
China Crisis

Q7
'Hey Ya'

Q8
Manic Street Preachers (Carter was a Pulitzer-Prize -winning photographer)

Q9
'My Camera Never Lies'

Q10
Lady Gaga

QUIZ 129

Q1
Shirley Bassey

Q2
Dave Edmunds

Q3
Lonnie Donegan

Q4
The Steve Miller Band

Q5
KC & The Sunshine Band

Q6
Jet Harris and Tony Meehan

Q7
The Shangri-Las

Q8
Motörhead

Q9
Wink Martindale

Q10
Ned Miller

QUIZ 131 POPMASTER

READ ALL ABOUT IT

QUESTION 1
What is the title of Kate Bush's 1978 chart debut and only No 1?

QUESTION 2
The song 'White Rabbit' was recorded for the 1967 album "Surrealistic Pillow" and became an American Top 10 hit for which Californian band?

QUESTION 3
Which Dire Straits single shares its title with a play by William Shakespeare?

QUESTION 4
The song 'Books' was a Top 20 hit in 2004 for a Glaswegian group that took its name from a French book and TV series of the 1960s. What is the group called?

QUESTION 5
The Russian novelist Vladimir Nabokov is mentioned in the lyrics of which No 1 song by The Police?

QUESTION 6
Which rock star released the 1995 album "The Ghost Of Tom Joad"?

QUESTION 7
Which 1973 single by Elton John has a title influenced by a 1900 novel by L. Frank Baum and a film from 1939?

QUESTION 8
Which duo released the single 'Sexcrime', from the film version of George Orwell's "1984"?

QUESTION 9
What type of 'Writer' did The Beatles sing about on their 1966 No 1?

QUESTION 10
Featuring vocals by Emeli Sandé, who recorded the 2011 No 1 'Read All About It'?

POPMASTER QUIZ 132

REAL NAMES (1)

Here are the real names of ten successful pop stars. Who are they better known as?

QUESTION 1
Marshall Mathers III

QUESTION 2
Declan MacManus

QUESTION 3
Rosemary Brown

QUESTION 4
Neville Keighley

QUESTION 5
Alecia Moore

QUESTION 6
James Newell Osterberg

QUESTION 7
Michael Barrett

QUESTION 8
Marie McDonald McLaughlin Lawrie

QUESTION 9
Arnold George Dorsey

QUESTION 10
Niomi McLean-Daley

QUIZ 130

Q1
Spitting Image

Q2
Moped ('Funky Moped' was a double A side with 'Magic Roundabout')

Q3
Rick Dees and His Cast of Idiots

Q4
Isaac Hayes

Q5
'Superman (Gioca Jouer)', 'Do The Conga'

Q6
Rednex

Q7
'No Charge'

Q8
Peter Kay

Q9
Splogenessabounds

Q10
Mr Blobby

QUIZ 131

Q1 *'Wuthering Heights'*

Q2 *Jefferson Airplane*

Q3 *'Romeo And Juliet'*

Q4 *Belle & Sebastian*

Q5 *'Don't Stand So Close To Me'(the song refers to Nabakov's novel "Lolita")*

Q6 *Bruce Springsteen (Tom Joad is a character in John Steinbeck's "The Grapes Of Wrath')*

Q7 *'Goodbye Yellow Brick Road'*

Q8 *Eurythmics (full title is 'Sexcrime (Nineteen Eighty Four)')*

Q9 *'Paperback Writer'*

Q10 *Professor Green*

QUIZ 133 POPMASTER

REAL NAMES (2)

Another chance for you to reveal the better known identity of ten successful pop stars from their real names.

QUESTION 1
Cornell Haynes Jr

QUESTION 2
Diane Earle

QUESTION 3
Robert Allen Zimmerman

QUESTION 4
Alison Moira Clarkson

QUESTION 5
Barry Alan Pincus

QUESTION 6
Pauline Matthews

QUESTION 7
Roberto Concina

QUESTION 8
Curtis Jackson

QUESTION 9
Charles Westover

QUESTION 10
Gordon Sumner

POPMASTER QUIZ 134

THE REAL THING

QUESTION 1
American female rapper, Joanne Martinez scored her only major UK hit in 1986 with 'Bang Zoom (Let's Go Go)'.Under what name did she release the record?

QUESTION 2
Which American singer made his solo chart debut in 1985 with 'Feel So Real'?

QUESTION 3
Can you name the American rapper who achieved his first No 1 in the year 2000 with 'The Real Slim Shady'?

QUESTION 4
Which female singer scored a Top 3 hit in 1989 with 'This Time I Know It's For Real'?

QUESTION 5
In 1994 MC Sar achieved a Top 3 hit with 'Another Night'. Can you name the band who were also credited with the success?

QUESTION 6
Can you name the male and female duo who achieved a Top 40 hit in 1968 with 'Ain't Nothing Like The Real Thing'?

QUESTION 7
Can you name the group whose only Top 40 hit was their 1992 release called 'Believer'?

QUESTION 8
Who achieved his first solo hit in 1986 with 'Real Wild Child (Wild One)'?

QUESTION 9
Which legendary group enjoyed a Top 10 hit in 1992 with a re-mixed version of their hit 'Even Better Than The Real Thing'?

QUESTION 10
What was the title of the only No 1 hit achieved by The Real Thing?

QUIZ 132

Q1 *Eminem*

Q2 *Elvis Costello*

Q3 *Dana*

Q4 *Belouis Some*

Q5 *P!nk*

Q6 *Iggy Pop*

Q7 *Shakin' Stevens*

Q8 *Lulu*

Q9 *Engelbert Humperdinck*

Q10 *Ms Dynamite*

QUIZ 133

Q1 *Nelly*

Q2 *Diana Ross*

Q3 *Bob Dylan*

Q4 *Betty Boo*

Q5 *Barry Manilow*

Q6 *Kiki Dee*

Q7 *Robert Miles*

Q8 *50 Cent*

Q9 *Del Shannon*

Q10 *Sting*

QUIZ 135 POPMASTER

RECORD PRODUCERS

This round celebrates the unsung heroes of pop, the record producers. Three hit records by each producer – but can you name them?

QUESTION 1
'Rolling In The Deep', by Adele, 'Like Eating Glass' by Bloc Party and 'Dominos' by The Big Pink.

QUESTION 2
'My Best Friend's Girl,' by The Cars, 'Heart And Soul' by T'Pau and 'Bohemian Rhapsody' by Queen.

QUESTION 3
'The Look Of Love' by ABC, 'Two Tribes' by Frankie Goes to Hollywood and 'Kiss From A Rose' by Seal.

QUESTION 4
'You've Lost That Lovin' Feelin'', by The Righteous Brothers, River Deep-Mountain High' by Ike & Tina Turner and 'Baby, I Love You' by the Ramones.

QUESTION 5
'Total Eclipse Of The Heart,' by Bonnie Tyler, 'I'd Do Anything For Love (But I Won't Do That)' by Meat Loaf and 'This Corrosion' by The Sisters of Mercy.

QUESTION 6
'You Got It', by Roy Orbison, 'Livin' Thing' by the Electric Light Orchestra and 'Got My Mind Set On You' by George Harrison.

QUESTION 7
Let's Dance' by David Bowie, 'Moonlighting Theme' by Al Jarreau and 'Workin' Overtime' by Diana Ross.

QUESTION 8
'Change The World' by Eric Clapton, 'Exhale (Shoop Shoop)' by Whitney Houston and 'Missing You' by Mary J Blige.

QUESTION 9
'Kung Fu Fighting' by Carl Douglas, 'I Love To Love (But My Baby Loves To Dance)' by Tina Charles and 'Now Is The Time' by Jimmy James.

QUESTION 10
'You're My World' by Cilla Black, 'Hymn' by Ultravox and 'Ebony And Ivory' by Paul McCartney and Stevie Wonder.

POPMASTER QUIZ 136

ROCK, PAPER, SCISSORS

QUESTION 1
What type of 'Roses' did Marie Osmond sing about on her 1973 hit single?

QUESTION 2
Which Pink Floyd song was the covered by Scissor Sisters for the group's first Top 10 hit?

QUESTION 3
Born Perri McKissack, under what name did this American singer record her 1988 Top 10 hit 'Girlfriend'?

QUESTION 4
Which song has been a hit for Ketty Lester, Elvis Presley and Alison Moyoet?

QUESTION 5
Which group had hits in 1974 called 'The Night Chicago Died' and 'The Black Eyed Boys'?

QUESTION 6
What band did John Squire, guitarist with The Stone Roses form after he left the group in 1996?

QUESTION 7
Rod Stewart's 1977 No 1 was a double 'A' side of 'I Don't Want To Talk About It' and which other song?

QUESTION 8
The songs 'Fell In Love With A Boy' and 'You Had Me' were hits in 2004 for which singer?

QUESTION 9
Released in 1986, what was the title of the first and biggest hit by Cutting Crew?

QUESTION 10
Who is the drummer with The Rolling Stones?

QUIZ 134

Q1
The Real Roxanne

Q2
Steve Arrington

Q3
Eminem

Q4
Donna Summer

Q5
The Real McCoy

Q6
Marvin Gaye and Tammi Terrell

Q7
The Real People

Q8
Iggy Pop

Q9
U2

Q10
'You To Me Are Everything'

QUIZ 135

Q1
Paul Epworth

Q2
Roy Thomas Baker

Q3
Trevor Horn

Q4
Phil Spector

Q5
Jim Steinman

Q6
Jeff Lynne

Q7
Nile Rodgers

Q8
Babyface

Q9
Biddu

Q10
George Martin

QUIZ 137 POPMASTER

SCHOOL'S OUT

QUESTION 1
'What I Go To School For' was the 2002 debut hit for which group?

QUESTION 2
What song was the UK's No 1 over the Christmas/New Year period of 1979/1980?

QUESTION 3
Released in 1958 and 1979, which easy listening singer's Top 40 career began with 'Teacher, Teacher' and ended with 'Gone, Gone, Gone'?

QUESTION 4
What is the title of the Sam Cooke hit in which the singer confesses to not knowing much about trigonometry, history, geography and biology?

QUESTION 5
Who was kept from having a posthumous Christmas No 1 in 1980 by 'There's No One Quite Like Grandma' by St Winifred's School Choir?

QUESTION 6
Name the song that spent four weeks at No 1 in 1972 that has the subtitle '(In Perfect Harmony)'.

QUESTION 7
Which band had its biggest hit in 1980 with the Top 10 song 'Everybody's Got To Learn Sometime'?

QUESTION 8
The American female duo Daphne & Celeste had all three of their chart hits in 2000 – the third was a cover of Alice Cooper's 'School's Out'. Name one of the other two.

QUESTION 9
Who had a Top 20 hit in 1974 with the song 'School Love'?

QUESTION 10
Which of the early Eighties hits for Madness is a song reminiscing about their school days?

POPMASTER QUIZ 138

SCOTLAND THE BRAVE

QUESTION 1
Who is the lead singer with the group Garbage?

QUESTION 2
Name the 1999 multi-million selling album by Travis that includes the singles 'Writing To Reach You', 'Driftwood', 'Why Does It Always Rain On Me' and 'Turn'

QUESTION 3
Whose 2005 debut hit was called 'Black Horse and the Cherry Tree'?

QUESTION 4
The 1979 single 'Into The Valley' was the first of five Top 40 hits for The Skids. Name one of the other four.

QUESTION 5
What is the surname of Proclaimers brothers Craig and Charlie?

QUESTION 6
What was the Scottish-flavoured title of 1958 No 1 by Lord Rockingham's XI?

QUESTION 7
Who is the lead guitarist with Simple Minds?

QUESTION 8
What is the original title of Biffy Clyro's song that was renamed 'When We Collide' for Matt Cardle's No 1 in 2010?

QUESTION 9
Who is the former backing vocalist for Eurythmics who became lead singer with Fairground Attraction and went on to have solo hits in the 1990s with 'Patience Of Angels' and 'Town Without Pity'?

QUESTION 10
Name the single by Rod Stewart featuring the Scottish World Cup Squad '78.

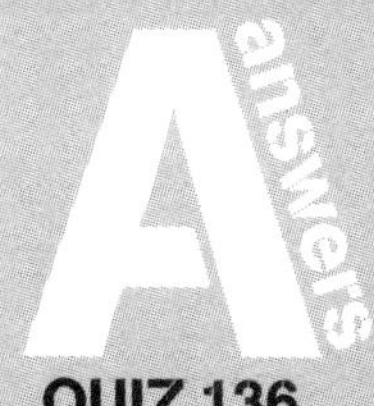

QUIZ 136

Q1
'Paper Roses'

Q2
'Comfortably Numb'

Q3
Pebbles

Q4
'Love Letters'

Q5
Paper Lace

Q6
The Seahorses

Q7
'First Cut Is The Deepest'

Q8
Joss Stone

Q9
('I Just) Died In Your Arms'

Q10
Charlie Watts

QUIZ 137

Q1
Busted

Q2
'Another Brick In The Wall (Pt 1)' by Pink Floyd

Q3
Johnny Mathis

Q4
'Wonderful World'

Q5
John Lennon (with '(Just Like) Starting Over)

Q6
'I'd Like To Teach The World To Sing' by The New Seekers

Q7
The Korgis

Q8
'Ooh Stick You, Ugly'

Q9
Barry Blue

Q10
'Baggy Trousers'

QUIZ 139 POPMASTER

QUESTION 1
Who spent six weeks at No 1 in 1967 and over a year on the chart with the song 'Release Me'?

QUESTION 2
'Wake Me Up Before You Go Go' was the title of Wham!'s first No 1, but what was the title of the duo's second?

QUESTION 3
Who sang the duet 'The Best Things In Life Are Free' with Janet Jackson?

QUESTION 4
Which band had both a hit single and album in 1976 called 'Jailbreak'?

QUESTION 5
The group Let Loose had three Top 10 hits in the Nineties. Name one of them.

QUESTION 6
What was 'My Brother…'called according to the title of the hit single by the rock group Free?

QUESTION 7
"The Element Of Freedom" was a No 1 album in 2010 for which American singer-songwriter and pianist?

QUESTION 8
Roger Daltrey's 1973 hit 'I'm Free' was a song taken from which rock opera by Pete Townshend?

QUESTION 9
Name the Italian singer who reached No 2 in 1997 with her single 'Freed From Desire'.

QUESTION 10
Which album by Paul McCartney and Wings features boxer John Conteh, actor Christopher Lee and journalist and chat-show host Michael Parkinson amongst its cover stars?

POPMASTER QUIZ 140

SEXY SONGS

QUIZ 138

QUESTION 1
Which group made their chart debut in 1991 with Top 3 hit 'I'm Too Sexy'?

QUESTION 2
From 1998, what was the title of the only Top 10 hit by Dutch group T-Spoon?

QUESTION 3
Which duo achieved their only Top 10 hit in 1992 with 'The Only Living Boy In New Cross'?

QUESTION 4
Can you name the act with whom Rod Stewart was featured on a new version of his 1978 No 1 hit 'Da Ya Think I'm Sexy', taking it back into the Top 10 in 1997?

QUESTION 5
Which group, featuring Dennis Locorriere and Ray Sawyer, had a Top 10 hit in 1980 with 'Sexy Eyes'?

QUESTION 6
What was the title of the first Top 10 hit by the Sex Pistols?

QUESTION 7
What was the title of the Hot Chocolate hit that made the Top 10 on three separate occasions in 1975, 1987 and 1997?

QUESTION 8
In 1987, which singer caused controversy over his Top 3 hit 'I Want Your Sex'?

QUESTION 9
Which legendary soul singer recorded the song 'Get Up I Feel Like Being A Sex Machine'?

QUESTION 10
Can you name the group whose only No 1 was the 2005 hit 'Sex On Fire'?

Q1 *Shirley Manson*

Q2 *The Man Who*

Q3 *KT Tunstall*

Q4 *'Masquerade', 'Charde', 'Working For The Yankee Dollar', 'Circus Games'*

Q5 *Reid*

Q6 *'Hoots Mon'*

Q7 *Charlie Burchill*

Q8 *'Many Of Horror'*

Q9 *Eddi Reader*

Q10 *'Ole Ola (Mulher Brasileira)'*

QUIZ 139

Q1
Engelbert Humperdinck

Q2
'Freedom'

Q3
Luther Vandross

Q4
Thin Lizzy

Q5
'Crazy For You '(No 2 and 24 weeks on chart), 'Best In Me', 'Make It With You'

Q6
Jake

Q7
Alicia Keys (album released late 2009, but was No 1 in UK in February 2010)

Q8
'Tommy'

Q9
Gala

Q10
Band On The Run

QUIZ 141 POPMASTER

SHALL WE ROCK OR SHALL WE ROLL?

QUESTION 1
Which successful American songwriter achieved his only solo hit as a performer in 1974 with 'Rock Me Gently'?

QUESTION 2
Can you name the British singer and actor who made his chart debut in 1956 with 'Rock With The Caveman'?

QUESTION 3
Which legendary rock band made the Top 10 in 1981 with a song called 'Rock 'n' Roll'?

QUESTION 4
In 2005, who insisted that he wanted to 'Destroy Rock And Roll'?

QUESTION 5
Can you name the title of either of the first two Top 20 hits achieved by Showaddywaddy in the Seventies?

QUESTION 6
What was the title of the song from 1974 that took George McCrae to the top of both the UK and American charts?

QUESTION 7
In 2002, the female group Mis-Teeq achieved a Top 10 hit with a double 'A'- sided hit 'This Is How We Do It' and what other title?

QUESTION 8
Can you name the group that included the song 'Blame It On The Love Of Rock And Roll' on their 1992 album "Keep The Faith"?

QUESTION 9
Which comedy act made the Top 10 in 1956 with 'Bloodnok's Rock 'n' Roll Call'?

QUESTION 10
In the Seventies, Argent achieved two Top 10 hit singles. The first was 'Hold Your Head Up,' what was the title of the other?

POPMASTER QUIZ 142

SING A RAINBOW

QUESTION 1
Which song by Deep Purple was written about a fire at a casino in Montreux?

QUESTION 2
What are the first names of the four members of the vocal group Blue?

QUESTION 3
The 1980 single 'Computer Game (Theme From "The Invaders") was the only UK hit for which Japanese group?

QUESTION 4
What 2004 single by P!nk has the same title as a 1998 single by Faithless?

QUESTION 5
Billie Joe Armstrong is the lead singer with which Californian punk-influenced band?

QUESTION 6
Stone Roses lead singer Ian Brown had a Top 5 single in 2000 called 'Dolphins Are…' what?

QUESTION 7
Which group had Top 10 singles in the mid-Eighties called 'Lean On Me (Ah-Li-Ayo)' and 'For America'?

QUESTION 8
Who was the guitarist in Sixties supergroup Cream?

QUESTION 9
"Back To Black" was the title of the second album by Amy Winehouse, but what was the first?

QUESTION 10
The duo Scarlet Fantastic had their only hit in 1987 with 'No Memory', but the duo had previously charted in 1984 as members of a three piece group whose only hit was called 'Soul Train'. Name that group.

QUIZ 140

Q1
Right Said Fred

Q2
'Sex On The Beach'

Q3
Carter - The Unstoppable Sex Machine

Q4
N-Trance

Q5
Dr Hook

Q6
'God Save The Queen'

Q7
'You Sexy Thing'

Q8
George Michael

Q9
James Brown

Q10
Kings of Leon

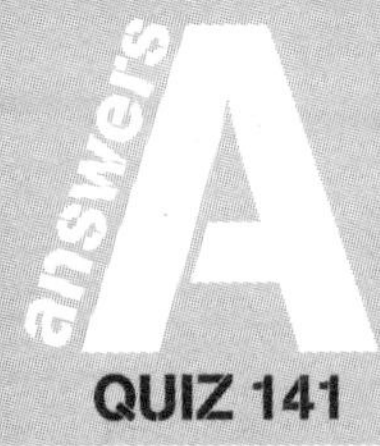

QUIZ 141

Q1 *Andy Kim*

Q2 *Tommy Steele*

Q3 *Status Quo*

Q4 *Mylo*

Q5 *'Hey Rock And Roll 'or 'Rock 'N' Roll Lady'*

Q6 *'Rock Your Baby'*

Q7 *'Roll On'*

Q8 *Bon Jovi*

Q9 *The Goons*

Q10 *'God Gave Rock And Roll To You'*

QUIZ 143 POPMASTER

SING SOMETHING SIMPLE

QUESTION 1
Can you name the successful American female group who had a Top 10 hit in 1979 with 'My Simple Heart'?

QUESTION 2
In 2008, the group Simple Plan made the Top 40 for the first time. Can you name the song that gave them their debut hit?

QUESTION 3
Who released a single titled 'Simple Life' from his album "The One" in 1993?

QUESTION 4
Written by Mike Pinder of The Moody Blues, what was the title of the 1971 Top 5 hit by The Four Tops?

QUESTION 5
What was the title of the only No 1 hit achieved by Simply Red in the Nineties?

QUESTION 6
Can you name the group who were created in the TV talent show, "Popstars"and topped the chart with their first release in 2001, 'Pure And Simple'?

QUESTION 7
Although it failed to make the Top 40 in the UK, which British male singer made No 2 in America in 1988 with 'Simply Irresistible'?

QUESTION 8
Can you name the song that Paul McCartney contributed to the 1986 'Anti-Heroin Project' that was later included as a bonus track on the 1993 re-mastered edition of his album, "Pipes Of Peace?"

QUESTION 9
Which legendary singer achieved his last Top 20 hit of the Nineties in 1994 with 'The Simple Things'?

QUESTION 10
What was the title of the first single to make the UK Top 10 by Simple Minds?

POPMASTER QUIZ 144

THE SINGING DETECTIVES

QUESTION 1
Released towards the end of 1976, who was the "Starsky & Hutch" actor who reached No 1 in 1977 with the song 'Don't Give Up On Us'?

QUESTION 2
...and what was the title of his other UK No 1?

QUESTION 3
'Caught By The Fuzz' was the first single released from the 1995 album "I Should Coco". Name the group.

QUESTION 4
The actor Nick Berry had a Top 3 hit in 1992 with song that had previously reached the chart for both Buddy Holly and Showaddywaddy. What was it called?

QUESTION 5
The three members of The Police were Sting on bass and lead vocals, Stewart Copeland on drums, who plays guitar?

QUESTION 6
Which 1973 No 1 by The Sweet begins with the sound of a police siren?

QUESTION 7
The song 'Karma Police' was a 1997 Top 10 single for which group?

QUESTION 8
In 1985, the American group Eddy and The Soul Band had its only hit with a updated version of the theme from an early Seventies detective film. What was it called?

QUESTION 9
Who was the Jamaican singer who had a hit in 1980 with his version of the song 'Police And Thieves'?

QUESTION 10
Telly Savalas reached No 1 in 1975 with his version of the David Gates song 'If', following his success playing which TV detective?

Answers

QUIZ 142

Q1 *'Smoke On The Water'*

Q2 *Simon (Webbe), Lee (Ryan), Duncan (James), Antony (Costa)*

Q3 *Yellow Magic Orchestra*

Q4 *'God Is A DJ'*

Q5 *Green Day*

Q6 *Monkeys*

Q7 *Red Box*

Q8 *Eric Clapton*

Q9 *Frank*

Q10 *Swans Way*

QUIZ 143

Q1
The Three Degrees

Q2
'When I'm Gone'

Q3
Elton John

Q4
'Simple Game'

Q5
'Fairground'

Q6
Hear'Say

Q7
Robert Palmer

Q8
'Simple As That'

Q9
Joe Cocker

Q10
'Don't You (Forget About Me)'

QUIZ 145 POPMASTER

A SMALL SAMPLE

These are questions about one hit record sampling another. Can you name the record sampled on each of these hits?

QUESTION 1
'All Night All Right' by Peter Andre

QUESTION 2
'Set Adrift On Memory Bliss' by PM Dawn

QUESTION 3
'Made It Back' by Beverley Knight featuring Redman

QUESTION 4
'1,2,3,4 (Sumpin' New)' by Coolio

QUESTION 5
'Eye Know' by De La Soul

QUESTION 6
'I Beg Your Pardon' by Kon Kan

QUESTION 7
'Let's Talk About Sex' by Salt-n-Pepa

QUESTION 8
'Let Me Take You There' by Betty Boo

QUESTION 9
'Something Good' by Utah Saints

QUESTION 10
'If You Buy This Record, Your Life Will Be Better' by The Tamperer featuring Maya

POPMASTER QUIZ 146

SMITH, BROWN OR JONES

QUESTION 1
Who, according to the Alan Price Set's 1967 Top 10 hit, had an 'Amazing Dancing Bear'?

QUESTION 2
In 1995, the group Smokie successfully revived their Seventies Top 10 hit 'Living Next Door To Alice' with a little help from which comedian?

QUESTION 3
What was the title of the only hit by Tom Jones to have made the Top 20 on two separate occasions, first in 1965 and again in 1987?

QUESTION 4
In 1981, which funk band achieved a Top 20 hit telling the story of 'Jones Vs Jones'?

QUESTION 5
In 1953, which American female scored her only UK hit with 'Hold Me, Thrill Me Kiss Me'?

QUESTION 6
Which UK act topped the American chart in 1965 with 'Mrs Brown You've Got A Lovely Daughter'?

QUESTION 7
Which successful group ended their long run of Top 40 hits in 1992 with 'There's A Light That Never Goes Out'?

QUESTION 8
As a child performer and now an established TV and radio presenter, who had a Top 10 hit in 1985 with 'Walking In The Air'?

QUESTION 9
Can you name the actress who made the Top 40 in 1994 performing a duet with David Essex with the song 'True Love Ways'?

QUESTION 10
What was the title of the Bee Gees' 1967 debut hit that is occasionally sub-titled 'Have You Seen My Wife Mr Jones'?

Answers

QUIZ 144

Q1
David Soul

Q2
'Silver Lady '(also 1977)

Q3
Supergrass ('Caught By The Fuzz' just missed the Top 40 in 1994)

Q4
"Heartbeat "(the title song of his TV police series set in the Sixties)

Q5
Andy Summers

Q6
'Blockbuster!'

Q7
Radiohead

Q8
The Theme From "Shaft"

Q9
Junior Murvin

Q10
Kojak

QUIZ 145

Q1
'Boogie Oogie Oogie' by A Taste of Honey

Q2
'True' by Spandau Ballet

Q3
'Good Times' by Chic

Q4
'Wikka Wrap' by The Evasions

Q5
'(Sittin' On) The Dock Of The Bay' by Otis Redding

Q6
'Rose Garden' by Lynn Anderson

Q7
'I'll Take You There' by The Staple Singers

Q8
'It's All In The Game' by The Four Tops

Q9
'Cloudbusting' by Kate Bush

Q10
'Material Girl' by Madonna

QUIZ 147 POPMASTER

SOMETHING STARTING WITH SEE

QUESTION 1
Roy Wood's group Wizzard had both of their No 1s in 1973 – one was called 'Angel Fingers', what was the title of the other?

QUESTION 2
'See Those Eyes' was the title of a 1982 hit for which group?

QUESTION 3
Which 1991 R.E.M. Top 10 song includes a guest vocal by Kate Pierson of The B-52's?

QUESTION 4
Mark Hoppus, Tom DeLonge and Travis Barker had Top 40 hits in the Noughties including 'All The Small Things', 'I Miss You', 'The Rock Show' and 'Feeling This'. What is the name of their American band?

QUESTION 5
Which hit single from De La Soul's acclaimed 1989 album "3 Feet High And Rising" includes a sample of the Steely Dan song 'Peg'?

QUESTION 6
Who is the American producer who had a Top 10 hit in 1995 and again in 1996 with his track 'Higher State Of Consciousness'?

QUESTION 7
What type of 'Eyes' did The Charlatans sing about on their 2006 hit single?

QUESTION 8
Which model, actress and singer provided a guest vocal on Thompson Twins' 1983 song 'Watching'?

QUESTION 9
Released in 1990, what was the title of Mariah Carey's debut UK hit?

QUESTION 10
Annabella Lwin was the lead singer with the group whose chart debut was the 1980 song 'C'30, C'60, C'90 Go'. What were they called?

POPMASTER QUIZ 148

SOMETHING STARTING WITH WHY

QUESTION 1
Which female singer had a UK Top 5 hit in 1981 with the revival of Frankie Lymon & The Teenagers' 1956 No 1,'Why Do Fools Fall In Love'?

QUESTION 2
Can you name the group that reached No 2 in the UK in 1993 with 'Why Can't I Wake Up With You'?

QUESTION 3
In 1957, top teen idol Pat Boone achieved a Top 20 hit with a song that had a three-word title beginning with 'Why'. Can you name it?

QUESTION 4
Can you name the group who achieved their one and only Top 20 hit in 1975 with 'Why Did You Do It'?

QUESTION 5
Which member of Queen had a minor solo hit in 1998 with 'Why Don't We Try Again'?

QUESTION 6
Under what name did producer and musician Richard Hall achieve a Top 20 hit in 1999 and again a year later with 'Why Does My Heart Feel So Bad'?

QUESTION 7
In 1973, who made the Top 10 with a song called 'Why, Oh Why, Oh Why'?

QUESTION 8
Although they are different songs, what is the hit title shared by Anthony Newley, Carly Simon Bronski Beat and Annie Lennox?

QUESTION 9
In 1973, which American performer achieved his only major hit with 'Why Can't We Live Together'?

QUESTION 10
Having made hits since 1997, Travis achieved their first Top 10 entry in 1999. Name the song.

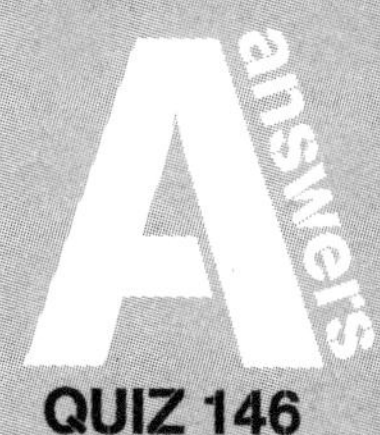

QUIZ 146

Q1 *Simon Smith*

Q2 *Roy 'Chubby' Brown*

Q3 *'It's Not Unusual'*

Q4 *Kool & The Gang*

Q5 *Muriel Smith*

Q6 *Herman's Hermits*

Q7 *The Smiths*

Q8 *Aled Jones*

Q9 *Catherine Zeta Jones*

Q10 *'New York Mining Disaster'*

QUIZ 147

Q1
'See My Baby Jive'

Q2
Altered Images

Q3
'Shiny Happy People'

Q4
Blink-182

Q5
'Eye Know'

Q6
Josh Wink (the 1996 Top 10 was a re-mix credited to Wink)

Q7
'Blackened Blue Eyes'

Q8
Grace Jones

Q9
'Vision Of Love'

Q10
Bow Wow Wow

QUIZ 149 POPMASTER

SOMETHING STARTING WITH YOU (1)

QUESTION 1
What was the title of the 1976 No 1 and debut hit for The Real Thing?

QUESTION 2
Michael Jackson reached No 1 in 1995 with the song 'You Are Not Alone', but which group spent two weeks at No 1 in 1997 with a song called 'You're Not Alone'?

QUESTION 3
Which song was a hit for James Taylor in 1971, Brand New Heavies in 1997 and No 1 for McFly in 2005?

QUESTION 4
What are the names of the fictitious DJs played by Harry Enfield and Paul Whitehouse who rock along to Bachman Turner Overdrive's song 'You Ain't Seen Nothin' Yet'?

QUESTION 5
The song 'You'll Never Walk Alone' has been No 1 on three occasions in 1963, 1985 and 1996. Name all three acts to reach No 1 with the song.

QUESTION 6
'(The Right Stuff)' is the subtitle of a 1989 No 1 by New Kids on the Block. What is its actual title?

QUESTION 7
Who is the house music DJ and producer who reached No 1 in 1999, along with vocalist Duane Harden with 'You Don't Know Me'?

QUESTION 8
What is the title of James Blunt's 2005 No 1 song from his album "Back To Bedlam"?

QUESTION 9
Which song was a hit for The Supremes in 1966, Vanilla Fudge in 1967 and Kim Wilde in 1986?

QUESTION 10
Released in 1974, whose final Top 10 single of that decade was called 'You You You'?

POPMASTER QUIZ 150

SOMETHING STARTING WITH YOU (2)

QUESTION 1
Which song became a No 1 hit for Dusty Springfield in 1966 and a Top 10 hit for both Elvis Presley in 1971 and Guys 'n' Dolls in 1976?

QUESTION 2
What nationality was the duo Ten Sharp, who had their only Top 10 hit in 1992 with the song 'You' – Dutch, Swiss, Norwegian or Belgian?

QUESTION 3
...and which British pop group had a No 2 single in 2002 with a different song simply called 'You'?

QUESTION 4
What Motown group features on backing vocals on Stevie Wonder's 1974 hit 'You Haven't Done Nothin''?

QUESTION 5
What was the title of Sonia's 1989 chart debut and only No 1?

QUESTION 6
The song 'You're My Angel' was a Top 20 single in 2000 for which member of Boyzone?

QUESTION 7
In 1974, which performer achieved his fourth consecutive Top 10 hit with the song,'You, You, You'?

QUESTION 8
Which band had a hit in 1996 with the song 'You Don't Fool Me'?

QUESTION 9
Anne-Marie David's 1973 Eurovision-winning song was originally called 'Tu Te Reconnaîtres', translated as 'You'll Recognize Yourself' – but what was its English-language title when it became a UK Top 20 hit that year?

QUESTION 10
The 1981 single 'Fire' kick-started the Top 40 career of which Irish band?

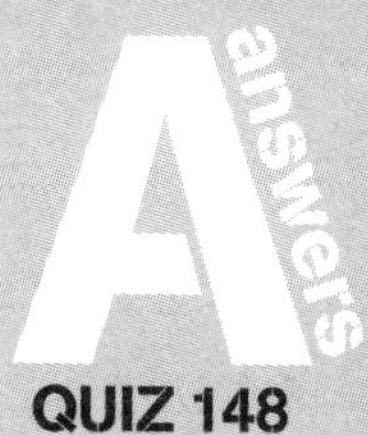

QUIZ 148

Q1 *Diana Ross*

Q2 *Take That*

Q3 *'Why Baby Why'*

Q4 *Stretch*

Q5 *Brian May*

Q6 *Moby*

Q7 *Gilbert O'Sullivan*

Q8 *'Why'*

Q9 *Timmy Thomas*

Q10 *'Why Does It Always Rain On Me?'*

QUIZ 151 POPMASTER

SPORTS DAY

QUESTION 1
In which year did the England World Cup Squad reach No 1 with the song 'Back Home'?

QUESTION 2
What was the title of Kraftwerk's 1983 single about cycling?

QUESTION 3
Which member of the Spice Girls was known as "Sporty Spice"?

QUESTION 4
Richard Hartley had a Top 10 EP titled 'The Music Of Torvill And Dean' and the lead track was the music that accompanied their gold medal winning routine in Sarajevo. What was it called?

QUESTION 5
Which footballer was 'Head Over Heels In Love' according to the title of his 1979 Top 40 single?

QUESTION 6
Released in 1999, The Flaming Lips had their first Top 40 hit with the song 'Race For…' what?

QUESTION 7
One of the most successful songwriters ever released a No 1 album in 1982 called 'Tug Of War'. Who is he?

QUESTION 8
Formed in 2009, what is the name of the Irish band formed by Neil Hannon of The Divine Comedy named after a cricketing term for calculating a team's target score?

QUESTION 9
Which duo had a Top 10 single in 1969 called 'The Boxer'?

QUESTION 10
What was the title of the England World Cup Squad's Top 3 song released to accompany their appearance at the 1982 Finals in Spain?

QUIZ 149

Q1
'You To Me Are Everything'

Q2
Olive

Q3
'You've Got A Friend'

Q4
Smashie and Nicey

Q5
Gerry And The Pacemakers (1963), The Crowd (1985) Robson & Jerome (1996)

Q6
You Got It (The Right Stuff)

Q7
Armand Van Helden

Q8
'You're Beautiful'

Q9
'You Keep Me Hangin' On'

Q10
Alvin Stardust (he had Top 40 hits in the 1970s and Top 10s in the 1980s)

POPMASTER QUIZ 152

STONE ME WHAT A LIFE

QUIZ 150

QUESTION 1
Which legendary crooner had a Top 10 hit in 1975 with the revival of The Stylistics' 1972 chart success, 'I'm Stone In Love With You'?

QUESTION 2
Can you name the group whose first Top 10 hit was the 1989 double 'A' sided single 'What The World Is Waiting For,'/'Fool's Gold'?

QUESTION 3
Which American female vocal group had a Top 3 hit in 1971 with 'Stoned Love'?

QUESTION 4
On which of Bob Dylan's original albums was his hit 'Like A Rolling Stone' the opening track?

QUESTION 5
Which female singer made her solo chart debut in 2009 with 'Stone Cold Sober'?

QUESTION 6
They had their first hit in 1963, then continued to make regular chart appearances throughout the next four decades.Their first Top 20 hit in the Nineties was 'You've Got Me Rocking.' Who are they?

QUESTION 7
Which Irish singer made his chart debut in 1973 when his single,'Heart Of Stone' reached the Top 20?

QUESTION 8
What was the name of the group whose 1967 single,'Different Drum,' written by Michael Nesmith, who made the American Top 20?

QUESTION 9
In 2006, Chicane made the Top 10 with 'Stoned In Love'. The single featured which legendary male vocalist?

QUESTION 10
Which American rock act made the Top 20 in 1990 with the revival of The Temptations' classic,'Papa Was A Rolling Stone'?

Q1 *'You Don't Have To Say You Love Me'*

Q2 *Dutch*

Q3 *S Club 7*

Q4 *'Jackson Five'*

Q5 *'You'll Never Stop Me Loving You'*

Q6 *Mikey Graham*

Q7 *Alvin Stardust*

Q8 *Queen*

Q9 *'Wonderful Dream'*

Q10 *U2*

QUIZ 151

Q1
1970

Q2
Tour-De-France

Q3
Melanie C (Melanie Chisholm)

Q4
'Bolero'

Q5
Kevin Keegan

Q6
The Prize

Q7
Paul McCartney

Q8
The Duckworth-Lewis Method

Q9
Simon & Garfunkel

Q10 *'This Time (We'll Get It Right)' (a double 'A' side with 'England we'll Fly the Flag'*

QUIZ 153 POPMASTER

TAKE A WALK

QUESTION 1
Robert Smith is the lead singer of the group that had a hit in 1983 with 'The Walk'. Name the band?

QUESTION 2
Released in 1977, what is the only British hit for the American act Mink DeVille?

QUESTION 3
Who sang the title song to the Kevin Bacon film "Footloose"?

QUESTION 4
The Danish duo Junior Senior had their debut hit in 2003 with a Top 3 song that spent over four months on the chart. What was it called?

QUESTION 5
Which group made their chart debut in 1997 with the line-dancing song '5,6,7,8'?

QUESTION 6
What was the title of the 1975 northern soul hit by Wigan's Chosen Few?

QUESTION 7
Who recorded her version of 'These Boots Are Made For Walkin' for the 2005 film version of "The Dukes Of Hazzard" in which she starred as Daisy Duke?

QUESTION 8
Which hit single for Cher was originally recorded by and a hit for the song's writer Marc Cohn?

QUESTION 9
The songs 'If You Could Read My Mind', 'Sundown' and 'The Wreck Of The Edmund Fitzgerald' were hits in the Seventies for which Canadian singer-songwriter?

QUESTION 10
What song was a hit for Dionne Warwick in the Sixties, The Stranglers in the Seventies and both Sybil and Gabrielle in the Nineties?

POPMASTER QUIZ 154

TALK OF THE DEVIL

QUESTION 1
Can you name the group whose only Top 20 hit was their 1979 release 'The Devil Went Down To Georgia'?

QUESTION 2
On which album by The Beatles did the song 'Devil In Her Heart' first appear?

QUESTION 3
From 1993, which group's second and final single to make the Top 10 was 'The Devil You Know'?

QUESTION 4
What hit song title is shared by Kylie Minogue, Sonia and Steps?

QUESTION 5
Which yodelling singer achieved his first UK Top 40 hit in 1960 with 'Lucky Devil'?

QUESTION 6
Atomic Rooster enjoyed two Top 20 hits in 197. The first was 'Tomorrow Night'. What was the other?

QUESTION 7
In 1974, which female singer's second and final No 1 was titled 'Devil Gate Drive'?

QUESTION 8
Can you name the group who achieved their biggest hit in 1987 when they reached number 11 with 'Lil' Devil'?

QUESTION 9
Which drummer made his solo chart debut in 1973 with his instrumental hit, 'Dance With The Devil'?

QUESTION 10
Name the world-famous rock and roll singer who topped the charts in 1963 with '(You're The) Devil In Disguise)'?

QUIZ 152

Q1 *Johnny Mathis*

Q2 *The Stone Roses*

Q3 *The Supremes*

Q4 *Highway 61 Revisited*

Q5 *Paloma Faith*

Q6 *The Rolling Stones*

Q7 *Kenny*

Q8 *The Stone Poneys*

Q9 *Tom Jones*

Q10 *Was (Not Was)*

QUIZ 153

Q1
The Cure

Q2
'Spanish Stroll'

Q3
Kenny Loggins

Q4
'Move Your Feet'

Q5
Steps

Q6
'Footsee'

Q7
Jessica Simpson

Q8
'Walking In Memphis'

Q9
Gordon Lightfoot

Q10
'Walk On By'

QUIZ 155 POPMASTER

TEN TIMES A LADY

All of the following questions are about Lady Gaga

QUESTION 1
In which American city was Lady Gaga born?

QUESTION 2
What is her real first name and surname?

QUESTION 3
What was the title of her first album, released in 2008?

QUESTION 4
What was unusual about the dress she wore to the 2010 MTV awards?

QUESTION 5
In which of these TV series did she have a cameo appearance as herself in the episode "The Last Days Of Disco Stick" – was it "Ugly Betty", "Gossip Girl" or "Desperate Housewives"?

QUESTION 6
Which other American singer featured alongside her on the 2010 single 'Telephone'?

QUESTION 7
What was the title of her first UK No 1 single?

QUESTION 8
She sang the duet 'Hello Hello' in the 2011 film "Gnomeo & Juliet" with which male superstar?

QUESTION 9
What was the title of the first single from her third studio album "Artpop" which was a Top 5 hit in the summer of 2013?

QUESTION 10
What is the name of her younger sister, who was born in 1992?

POPMASTER QUIZ 156

THERE'S NO PLACE LIKE HOME

QUESTION 1
Who topped the chart for three weeks in 1983 with 'Wherever I Lay My Hat (That's My Home)'?

QUESTION 2
The 1998 Top 20 hit,'Home Alone', featuring Keith Murray was performed by which successful singer?

QUESTION 3
Who was featured on the 2008 Top 10 hit 'Homecoming' by Kanye West?

QUESTION 4
In 1983, singer Tracie achieved her only solo Top 10 hit with a song that shared its title with a 1967 hit by Alan Price. What was the title?

QUESTION 5
Which group of brothers had a Top 40 hit in 1958 with 'Put A Light In The Window'?

QUESTION 6
What was the title of the first hit single achieved in the UK by Simon & Garfunkel?

QUESTION 7
Can you name the Top 10 hit by UB40 in 1989 that was a cover of a 1974 hit for The Chi-Lites?

QUESTION 8
Which singer, whose Second World War radio show was popular with servicemen around the world, had a Top 10 hit in 1952 with 'The Homing Waltz'?

QUESTION 9
Which boy band released their eighth studio album in 2008 under the title "Back Home"?

QUESTION 10
'Home Lovin' Man' was a Top 10 hit in 1970 for which legendary crooner?

A answers

QUIZ 154

Q1 *The Charlie Daniels Band*

Q2 *With The Beatles*

Q3 *Jesus Jones*

Q4 *'Better The Devil You Know'*

Q5 *Frank Ifield*

Q6 *'The Devil's Answer'*

Q7 *Suzi Quatro*

Q8 *The Cult*

Q9 *Cozy Powell*

Q10 *Elvis Presley*

QUIZ 155

Q1
New York

Q2
Stefani Germanotta

Q3
The Fame

Q4
It was made out of meat

Q5
'Gossip Girl'

Q6
Beyoncé

Q7
'Just Dance'

Q8
Elton John

Q9
'Applause'

Q10
Natali

QUIZ 157 POPMASTER

THEY ARE ONLY CHILDREN

QUESTION 1
Which group had a Top 3 hit in 1972 with 'Children Of The Revolution'?

QUESTION 2
Can you name the group made their 1983 chart debut with their Top 5 hit, 'Speak Like A Child'?

QUESTION 3
What was the name of the Italian DJ who recorded his first hit single, 'Children', in his own studio in Venice in 1986 and saw it go on to sell over 13 million copies worldwide?

QUESTION 4
During their career, Billy J Kramer and The Dakotas achieved two No 1 hits in the Sixties, the first was 'Bad To Me', what was the other?

QUESTION 5
In 1975 which successful group had a Top 10 hit with 'A Child's Prayer'?

QUESTION 6
Which sister and brother duo sang the title song to the 1971 movie, "Bless The Beasts And Children"?

QUESTION 7
Can you name the legendary crooner who had a Christmas No 1 in 1976 with 'When A Child Is Born'?

QUESTION 8
From 1981, which female singer made her chart debut when she reached the Top 5 with 'Kids In America'?

QUESTION 9
Which instrumental outfit had a Top 5 hit in 1962 with 'March Of The Siamese Children' from the musical, 'The King And I'?

QUESTION 10
In 1970, which female singer made her final appearance in the Top 20 with 'Think About Your Children'?

POPMASTER QUIZ 158

THIS IS YOUR LIFE

QUESTION 1
Which Dutch painter was the subject of a 1972 No 1 by Don McLean?

QUESTION 2
Which Tina Turner hit was used as the title of the 1993 film of her life starring Angela Bassett?

QUESTION 3
George Harrison's 'Something', Eric Clapton's 'Wonderful Tonight' and Derek and the Dominoes' 'Layla' are all believed to be inspired by the same woman. Who is she?

QUESTION 4
Which song by Sting is about about the writer and raconteur Quentin Crisp?

QUESTION 5
Who was the subject of Elton John's original recording of 'Candle In The Wind'?

QUESTION 6
Stevie Wonder's 'Happy Birthday' and U2's 'Pride (In The Name Of Love)' are both about which civil rights leader?

QUESTION 7
... and who are Abraham and John in the Marvin Gaye hit 'Abraham Martin and John'?

QUESTION 8
What epic nine-part song on Pink Floyd's album "Wish You Were Here" is a tribute to former band member Syd Barrett?

QUESTION 9
Who is the 'Geno' in the title of Dexy's Midnight Runners' No 1 from 1980?

QUESTION 10
Sally Herbert and Caroline Buckley were the female duo had their only Top 40 hit in 1991 with a song called 'This Is Your Life'. Under what name did they record?

QUIZ 156

Q1
Paul Young

Q2
R. Kelly

Q3
Chris Martin

Q4
'The House That Jack Built'

Q5
The King Brothers

Q6
'Homeward Bound'

Q7
'Homely Girl'

Q8
Vera Lynn

Q9
Westlife

Q10
Andy Williams

QUIZ 157

Q1 *T. Rex*

Q2 *The Style Council*

Q3 *Robert Miles*

Q4 *'Little Children'*

Q5 *Hot Chocolate*

Q6 *Carpenters*

Q7 *Johnny Mathis*

Q8 *Kim Wilde*

Q9 *Kenny Ball & His Jazzmen*

Q10 *Mary Hopkin*

QUIZ 159 POPMASTER

THIS MEANS NOTHING TO ME

QUESTION 1
Which group went 'Do Wah Diddy Diddy' on their 1964 No 1?

QUESTION 2
Which album is missing from this list of the five studio albums released by The Police – "Outlandos D'Amour", "Regatta De Blanc", "Ghost In The Machine", "Synchronicity"?

QUESTION 3
Name the Canadian band that went 'Mmm Mmm Mmm Mmm' on their Top 3 single in 1994?

QUESTION 4
Which song, featured in a popular Muppet Show TV sketch in the Seventies, was also a Top 10 song in 1977 for Piero Umiliani?

QUESTION 5
… and the answer to question 4 also featured in the chorus of a 1997 Top 20 song called 'No Way No Way' by a short-lived girl group of the time – but were they called Vanilla, Shampoo or Precious?

QUESTION 6
Who was the singer credited alongside The Mindbenders on the group's first Top 10 single 'Um Um Um Um Um'?

QUESTION 7
The songs 'Scatman (Ski-Ba-Bop-Ba-Dop-Bop)' and 'Scatman's World' were both Top 10 singles in 1995 for which artists?

QUESTION 8
It's alleged that the cartoon character Scooby Doo got its name from a Frank Sinatra vocal passage in which of his hit songs?

QUESTION 9
Name the 1994 largely instrumental No 1 where the title of the act is also the title of the track.

QUESTION 10
Which song spent four weeks at No 2 in 1981 thanks to 'Woman' by John Lennon and 'Shaddap You Face' by Joe Dolce Music Theatre both reaching No 1?

POPMASTER QUIZ 160

TRAINS AND BOATS AND PLANES

QUESTION 1
The song 'Sailing On The Seven Seas' was a Top 10 hit in 1991 for which group?

QUESTION 2
In which early hit for Elton John did the singer witness the "red tail lights of a plane" heading in the direction of Spain?

QUESTION 3
'Ship Of Fools' was the title of a Top 10 single in 1988 for which duo?

QUESTION 4
According to the title of their 1991 Top 3 single, The KLF took the 'Last Train To…' where?

QUESTION 5
A UK rockabilly group had hits in the Eighties with 'Yes Tonight Josephine' and 'Love Makes The World Go Round'. They shared a name with a US group that hit the Top 10 in 1987 with 'Crush On You'. What was it?

QUESTION 6
"Trans Europe Express" was a 1977 electronic album that reportedly influenced artists as diverse as Afrika Bambaata and New Order – which group recorded it?

QUESTION 7
What type of Train did Liverpool band The Farm sing about on their debut Top 10 hit?

QUESTION 8
Which band reached the Top 10 in 1978 with the song 'Airport'?

QUESTION 9
Released in 1980, the lead track on Madness' Top 10 EP 'Work Rest And Play' was called 'Night Boat To...'where?

QUESTION 10
Which legendary songwriting team wrote the 1965 Billy J Kramer and the Dakotas hit 'Trains And Boats And Planes'?

QUIZ 158

Q1
Vincent Van Gogh ('Vincent' had two weeks at No 1 in 1972)

Q2
'What's Love Got To Do With It'

Q3
Pattie Boyd (married to both George Harrison and then Eric Clapton)

Q4
'An Englishman In New York'

Q5
Marilyn Monroe

Q6
Martin Luther King

Q7
Abraham Lincoln, John F. Kennedy

Q8
'Shine On You Crazy Diamond'

Q9
Geno Washington

Q10
Banderas

QUIZ 159

Q1
Manfred Mann

Q2
"Zenyatt Mondatta", in between "Regatta De Blanc" and "Ghost In The Machine"

Q3
Crash Test Dummies

Q4
'Mah-Na, Mah-Na'

Q5
Vanilla

Q6
Wayne Fontana

Q7
Scatman John

Q8
'Strangers In The Night'

Q9
'Doop', By Doop

Q10
'Vienna' by Ultravox

QUIZ 161 POPMASTER

THE UK AT EUROVISION

Simply name the UK's song from the year and artist

QUESTION 1
1975 – The Shadows

QUESTION 2
1996 – Gina G

QUESTION 3
2011 – Blue

QUESTION 4
1982 – Bardo

QUESTION 5
2002 – Jessica Garlick

QUESTION 6
1968 – Cliff Richard

QUESTION 7
1998 – Imaani

QUESTION 8
1983 – Sweet Dreams

QUESTION 9
1970 – Mary Hopkin

QUESTION 10
2006 – Daz Sampson

POPMASTER QUIZ 162

USUAL SUSPECTS

Who is the group member missing from the most successful line-ups of each of these bands?

QUESTION 1
Melanie B, Melanic C, Victoria Beckham, Geri Halliwell and…?

QUESTION 2
Freddie Mercury, John Deacon, Brian May and…?

QUESTION 3
Liam Payne, Louis Tomlinson, Zayn Malik, Harry Styles and…?

QUESTION 4
Claire, Faye, H, Lisa and…?

QUESTION 5
Roger Daltrey, Keith Moon, Pete Townshend and…?

QUESTION 6
Gary Barlow, Robbie Williams, Mark Owen, Jason Orange and…?

QUESTION 7
Siobhan Fahey, Sara Dallin and…?

QUESTION 8
Brian Connolly, Mick Tucker, Andy Scott and…?

QUESTION 9
Peter Hook, Gillian Gilbert, Stephen Morris and…?

QUESTION 10
Topper Headon, Joe Strummer, Paul Simonon and…?

A answers

QUIZ 160

Q1 *Orchestral Manoeuvres In The Dark*

Q2 *'Daniel'*

Q3 *Erasure*

Q4 *Trancentral*

Q5 *The Jets*

Q6 *Kraftwerk*

Q7 *'Groovy Train'*

Q8 *The Motors*

Q9 *Cairo*

Q10 *Burt Bacharach and Hal David*

QUIZ 161

Q1
'Let Me Be The One'

Q2
'Ooh Aah...Just A Little Bit'

Q3
'I Can'

Q4
'One Step Further'

Q5
'Come Back'

Q6
'Congratulations'

Q7
'Where Are You?'

Q8
'I'm Never Giving Up'

Q9
'Knock Knock Who's There?'

Q10
'Teenage Life'

QUIZ 163 POPMASTER

WAKE ME UP BEFORE YOU GO-GO

QUESTION 1
Which group made its chart debut in 1984 with 'Get Out Of Your Lazy Bed'?

QUESTION 2
Gabrielle's 1993 chart debut was also her first No 1 – what was it called?

QUESTION 3
The song 'Daydream In Blue' was a Top 20 hit in 2001 for which act?

QUESTION 4
Kylie Minogue in 1990 and Johnny Nash in 1975 had different No 1s with songs that have the same four-word title. Name it.

QUESTION 5
'The Bed's Too Big Without You' was the lead single in a six single set called "Six Pack" that reached the Top 20 in 1980. Which band released it?

QUESTION 6
'Insomnia' was the title of a hit song in both 1995 and 1996 for which club and pop-house group?

QUESTION 7
Ray Davies of The Kinks wrote two of the hit singles for The Pretenders – 'I Go To Sleep' was one, what was the other?

QUESTION 8
Name the boy band that achieved a Top 3 hit in 2003 with 'Sleeping With The Light On'?

QUESTION 9
Released in 1991, Metallica's first Top 10 single in the UK was called 'Enter...what?

QUESTION 10
Which Beatles song gave Suggs of Madness his first Top 10 hit as a solo artist?

POPMASTER QUIZ 164

SOMETHING I SAID?

Spoken word songs and songs with spoken sections

QUESTION 1
Although credited as a 'rap', which actor narrates the closing section of Michael Jackson's song 'Thriller'?

QUESTION 2
What was the title of Paul Hardcastle's No 1 from 1985 about the average age of soldiers in the Vietnam War?

QUESTION 3
Name the American artist who reached the Top 10 in 1972 with 'Desiderata'?

QUESTION 4
On which of ABC's Top 10 hits does Martin Fry muse about whether he will find true love?

QUESTION 5
Which Australian film producer and director had a No 1 single in 1999 with 'Everybody's Free (To Wear Sunscreen) – The Sunscreen Song (Class of '99)'?

QUESTION 6
Wink Martindale and Max Bygraves both had a hit in 1973 with the same song. What was it?

QUESTION 7
Who can hardly speak for laughing in the spoken section of the live recording of his hit 'Are You Lonesome Tonight'?

QUESTION 8
What was the title of the 1981 Top 3 single by the multi-instrumentalist and performance artist Laurie Anderson?

QUESTION 9
A parody version of Telly Savalas' No 1 'If' was recorded by the duo Chris Sanford and Bill Mitchell in 1975. Under what name did they release their version?

QUESTION 10
On which of Britney Spears' No 1s does she talk about the engagement present dropped into the ocean at the end of the film 'Titanic'?

QUIZ 162

Q1 *Emma Bunton (Spice Girls)*

Q2 *Roger Taylor (Queen)*

Q3 *Niall Horan (One Direction)*

Q4 *Lee (Steps)*

Q5 *John Entwistle (The Who)*

Q6 *Howard Donald (Take That)*

Q7 *Keren Woodward (Bananarama)*

Q8 *Steve Priest (The Sweet)*

Q9 *Bernard Sumner (New Order)*

Q10 *Mick Jones (The Clash)*

QUIZ 165 POPMASTER

WE ARE FAMILY

QUESTION 1
What type of 'Horses' did The Osmonds sing about on their 1972 Top 3 single?

QUESTION 2
Caleb, Nathan, Jared and Matthew Followell are all members of which group?

QUESTION 3
Which 1979 hit for The Pointer Sisters was written by Bruce Springsteen?

QUESTION 4
What is the surname of the brothers and sisters who were the members of Five Star?

QUESTION 5
Haim had a No 1 album in 2013 called '"Days Are…" what?

QUESTION 6
What are the first names of the two twin Goss brothers who formed Bros?

QUESTION 7
The Staple Singers had two UK hits in the Seventies. Name either of them?

QUESTION 8
Cleo, Yonah and Zainam Higgins had a Top 5 single in 1998 with a cover of the Jackson Five hit 'I Want You Back'. Under what name did these sisters record this hit?

QUESTION 9
Released in 2000, what is the title of the only UK No 1 for The Corrs?

QUESTION 10
In 1973, The Handley Family had their one and only Top 40 hit – what was it called?

QUIZ 163

Q1
Matt Bianco

Q2
'Dreams'

Q3
I Monster

Q4
'Tears on my Pillow'

Q5
The Police

Q6
Faithless

Q7
'Stop Your Sobbing'

Q8
Busted

Q9
Sandman

Q10
'I'm Only Sleeping' (a double 'A' side with a song called 'Off On Holiday')

POPMASTER QUIZ 166

WEATHER WITH YOU

QUESTION 1
Which girl group wanted to 'Blame It On The Weatherman' in 1999?

QUESTION 2
What single marked Robbie Williams' return to Take That in 2010?

QUESTION 3
Two chart acts had Top 10 singles in the 1980s with different songs called 'Walking On Sunshine'. Name either of them

QUESTION 4
What was the title of Bruno Mars' 2011 single taken from the soundtrack of "The Twilight Saga: Breaking Dawn, Part 1"?

QUESTION 5
Born Norman Smith, under what name did this singer have Top 5 songs in the early Seventies called 'Don't Let It Die' and 'Oh Babe, What Would You Say'?

QUESTION 6
The rock group Rainbow had three Top 10 singles – 'Since You've Been Gone' was the first in 1979. The other two came in 1980 and 1981. Name either.

QUESTION 7
Over the course of their chart career, which group has released Top 3 albums called "Final Straw", "A Hundred Million Suns" and "Fallen Empires" and No 1 album with "Eyes Open"?

QUESTION 8
Which hit by the Electric Light Orchestra ends with the words 'Please Turn Me Over'?

QUESTION 9
What does the wind 'cry' according to the title of the 1967 Top 10 song by The Jimi Hendrix Experience?

QUESTION 10
Which former BBC TV weatherman was the subject of a novelty hit at Christmas 1988?

QUIZ 164

Q1
Vincent Price

Q2
'19'

Q3
Les Crane

Q4
'The Look Of Love'

Q5
Baz Luhrmann

Q6
'Deck Of Cards' (a spoken tale of a soldier who used playing cards as his 'bible')

Q7
Elvis Presley

Q8
'O Superman'

Q9
Yin and Yan

Q10
'Oops , I Did It Again'

QUIZ 165

Q1
'Crazy Horses'

Q2
Kings of Leon (three brothers and a cousin)

Q3
'Fire'

Q4
Pearson

Q5
Gone

Q6
Matt & Luke

Q7
I'll Take You There', 'If You're Ready Come Go With Me'

Q8
Cleopatra

Q9
'Breathless'

Q10
'Wam Bam' (Reached No 30 and spent 7 weeks on the chart)

QUIZ 167 POPMASTER

WHAT'S IN A NAME? (1)

Artists' real names or how they chose their stage names

QUESTION 1
How did ABBA get their name?

QUESTION 2
Which group used an adaptation of a character in the Jane Fonda film "Barbarella" as their group name?

QUESTION 3
Bono reportedly chose his stage name from a hearing-aid shop called Bonavox, but what is Bono's real name?

QUESTION 4
Which Scottish band, formed in the mid-Eighties, took its name from the title of a song on Steely Dan's album "Aja"?

QUESTION 5
The Thompson Twins took their name from characters in a comic strip by a Belgian cartoonist. Name both the cartoonist and his comic strip?

QUESTION 6
One of Britain's most successful female singers in the 1960s was born Mary O'Brien. Under what name did she record

QUESTION 7
Madness chose their band name as homage to one of their favourite ska/reggae artists who had recorded a song by that name in the Sixties – who is he?

QUESTION 8
Which group used an adaptation of a WWII aircraft pilot term to describe UFOs and unknown aircraft as their band name?

QUESTION 9
Bernard Jewry changes his name to Shane Fenton to record hits in the 1960s, but changed his name again for further hits in the 1970s and 1980s. What was his third name?

QUESTION 10
Which group got their name from a line in David Bowie's song 'Jean Genie'?

POPMASTER QUIZ 168

WHAT'S IN A NAME? (2)

Artists' real names or how they chose their stage names

QUESTION 1
Tom Fletcher, Danny Jones, Dougie Poynter and Harry Judd chose their band name after a charter in the film "Back To The Future" Under what name do they record?

QUESTION 2
Name the Scottish alt-rock band that reached the Top 5 in 1990 with the song 'I'm Free' and took its name from a character in the children's programme "The Clangers"?

QUESTION 3
Right Said Fred got their name from the title of a 1962 Top 10 single recorded by which British actor?

QUESTION 4
Which rapper's real name is Shawn Corey Carter?

QUESTION 5
Which character from the Charles Dickens novel "David Copperfield" provided the name for a British rock band that had 12 chart albums in the Seventies and Eighties?

QUESTION 6
Adam Tinley had a Top 10 hit in 1990 with 'The Space Jungle'. Under what stage name did he record this hit?

QUESTION 7
What is the real name of U2 guitarist The Edge?

QUESTION 8
Is Curtis James Jackson III better known as Lil Wayne, 50 Cent or Ludacris?

QUESTION 9
What is Alice Cooper's real name?

QUESTION 10
'Step Into My Office Baby', 'I'm A Cuckoo' and 'Books' were hits in the Noughties for which Glaswegian group, whose name came from a French book by Cécile Aubry and its companion TV series?

A answers

QUIZ 166

Q1
*B*Witched*

Q2
'The Flood'

Q3
Rocker's Revenge (feat. Donnie Calvin, No. 4 in 1982), Katrina & The Waves (No. 8 in 1985)

Q4
'It Will Rain'

Q5
Hurricane Smith

Q6
'All Night Long', 'I Surrender'

Q7
Snow Patrol

Q8
'Mr Blue Sky'

Q9
Mary ('The Wind Cries Mary' reached No. 6)

Q10
John Kettley; 'John Kettley (Is A Weatherman)' was a hit for Tribe of Toffs)

QUIZ 167

Q1 *The initials of the four members' first names (Agnetha, Björn, Benny, Anna-Frid)*

Q2 *Duran Duran (Milo O'Shea plays the villain Dr. Durand Durand)*

Q3 *Paul Hewson*

Q4 *Deacon Blue (the third track is called 'Deacon Blues')*

Q5 *Hergé, (The Adventures Of) Tintin*

Q6 *Dusty Springfield*

Q7 *Prince Buster*

Q8 *Foo Fighters*

Q9 *Alvin Stardust*

Q10 *Simple Minds ("so simple minded he can't drive his module")*

QUIZ 169 POPMASTER

WHO AM I?

Countdown the ten clues to reveal a name! The fewer the number of clues you need the better...

QUESTION 1
I was born in Nashville, Tennessee, and my middle name is Randall.

QUESTION 2
My first major break was with a boy band financed by American impresario Lou Pearlman, who was convicted in 2007 of conspiracy and money laundering.

QUESTION 3
As a child I appeared in the American TV shows "The New Mickey Mouse Club" and "Star Search".

QUESTION 4
I met fellow cast member Britney Spears whilst appearing in "The New Mickey Mouse Club" and she became my girlfriend.

QUESTION 5
I was the voice of Prince Artie Pendragon in the 2007 animated film "Shrek The Third".

QUESTION 6
In 2008, I was a guest vocalist on Madonna's No 1 hit '4 Minutes.'

QUESTION 7
I began dating actress Jessica Biel in 2007. We separated in 2011, only to reconcile and marry the following year in Italy.

QUESTION 8
In 1997, I made my first Top 40 appearance in boy band 'NSync' with a record called 'Tearin' Up My Heart'.

QUESTION 9
When performing with Janet Jackson during the interval at the 2004 Super Bowl-broadcast to over 140 million viewers, I tore off part of her black leather costume to reveal part of one of her breasts.

QUESTION 10
My first solo hit after leaving NSync reached No 2 in the UK chart and was titled 'Like I Love You'.

POPMASTER QUIZ 170

WHO'S THAT GIRL? (1)

Which female is missing from each of these line-ups?

QUESTION 1
Una Foden, Rochelle Humes, Mollie King, Vanessa White...?

QUESTION 2
Vicki Peterson, Debbie Peterson, Michael Steele…?

QUESTION 3
Shaznay Lewis, Nicole Appleton, Natalie Appleton…?

QUESTION 4
Butch Vig, Duke Erikson, Steve Marker…?

QUESTION 5
Jim Corr, Andrea Corr, Caroline Corr…?

QUESTION 6
Mick Fleetwood, John McVie, Stevie Nicks, Lindsay Buckingham… (classic 70s & 80s line-up)?

QUESTION 7
Perrie Edwards, Jade Thirwall, Leigh-Anne Peacock…?

QUESTION 8
Noel Hogan, Mike Hogan, Fergal Lawler…?

QUESTION 9
Mark Richardson, Ace, Cass…?

QUESTION 10
Bobby G, Cheryl Baker, Mike Nolan… (from 1981 to 1985)?

A answers

QUIZ 168

Q1
McFly (Michael J Fox's character was called Marty McFly)

Q2
The Soup Dragons

Q3
Bernard Cribbins

Q4
Jay-Z

Q5
Uriah Heep

Q6
Adamski

Q7
David Evans

Q8
50 Cent

Q9
Vincent Furnier

Q10
Belle & Sebastian (book called "Belle et Sébastien")

QUIZ 169

Justin Timberlake

QUIZ 171 POPMASTER

WHO'S THAT GIRL? (2)

Which female is missing from each of these line-ups?

QUESTION 1
Chris Stein, Jimmy Destri, Nigel Harrison, Clem Burke…?

QUESTION 2
Easther Bennett, Vernie Bennett, Kéllé Bryan… (1992 to 1995)?

QUESTION 3
Tom Dumont, Tony Kanal, Adrian Young…?

QUESTION 4
Lars-Olof Johansson, Bengt Lagerberg, Magnus Sveningsson, Peter Svensson…?

QUESTION 5
Nicole Scherzinger, Melody Thornton, Jessica Sutta, Carmit Bachar, Kimberley Wyatt…?

QUESTION 6
Lindsay Armaou, Edele Lynch, Sinéad O'Carroll…?

QUESTION 7
Hannah Blilie, Nathan "Brace Paine" Howdeshell…?

QUESTION 8
Liz McClarnon, Natasha Hamilton… (reformed original hit line-up)?

QUESTION 9
Geoff Barrow, Adrian Utley, Dave McDonald…?

QUESTION 10
Sarah Dallin, Keren Woodward… (from 1988 to 1991)?

POPMASTER QUIZ 172

WINE, WOMEN AND SONG

QUESTION 1
Which legendary singer had a Top 20 hit in 1971 with the Paul Ryan song 'I Will Drink The Wine'?

QUESTION 2
Who had a No 1 hit in 2014 with his single 'Sing'?

QUESTION 3
Can you name the female singer who was featured on Tears for Fears' 1989 Top 40 hit 'Woman In Chains'?

QUESTION 4
In 1957, two versions of the song 'Kisses Sweeter Than Wine' made the UK Top 10. One was by Jimmy Rodgers. Who sang the successful British cover version?

QUESTION 5
Can you name the female singer who had a Top 3 hit in 2008 with 'Womanizer'?

QUESTION 6
Which singer and songwriter achieved an American No 1 and a UK Top 20 hit in 1962 with 'Song Sung Blue'?

QUESTION 7
Can you name the American singer who in 1991 successfully revived Percy Sledge's biggest hit, 'When A Man Loves A Woman'?

QUESTION 8
In 1978, which female singer achieved a Top 20 hit with the song 'Lilac Wine'?

QUESTION 9
Which successful group reached No 2 in 1997 with their hit single 'Song 2'?

QUESTION 10
Can you name the performer who made the Top 5 in 1978 with his almost totally instrumental hit 'Song For Guy'?

QUIZ 170

Q1 *Frankie Bridge (The Saturdays)*

Q2 *Susanna Hoffs (The Bangles)*

Q3 *Melanie Blatt (All Saints)*

Q4 *Shirley Manson (Garbage)*

Q5 *Sharon Corr (The Corrs)*

Q6 *Christine McVie (Fleetwood Mac)*

Q7 *Jesy Nelson (Little Mix)*

Q8 *Dolores O'Riordan (The Cranberries)*

Q9 *Skin, aka Deborah Anne Dyer (Skunk Anansie)*

Q10 *Jay Aston (Bucks Fizz original line-up)*

QUIZ 171

Q1
Debbie Harry (Blondie)

Q2
Louise Nurding (later Louise Redknapp) (Eternal)

Q3
Gwen Stefani (No Doubt)

Q4
Nina Persson (The Cardigans)

Q5
Ashley Roberts (Pussycat Dolls)

Q6
*Keavy Lynch (B*Witched)*

Q7
Beth Ditto (Gossip)

Q8
Kerry Katona (Atomic Kitten)

Q9
Beth Gibbons (Portishead)

Q10
Jacqui O'Sullivan (Bananarama second line-up)

QUIZ 173 POPMASTER

YOUNG AT HEART

Chart acts by teenagers... or younger

QUESTION 1
What was the title of 15 year-old-Vanessa Paradis' 1988 UK chart debut?

QUESTION 2
When Craig David reached No 1 in 2000 with 'Fill Me In', he became the youngest British male artist to write and sing a No 1. How old was he?

QUESTION 3
Who made his UK debut in 1966 at the age of 15 with 'Uptight (Everything's Alright)'?

QUESTION 4
The singer Lena Zavaroni was only ten years old when she had her two hit singles in 1974. Name either of them.

QUESTION 5
Who had a Top 20 hit in 1986 with 'It's 'Orrible Being In Love (When You're $8^{1}/_{2}$)'?

QUESTION 6
Justin Bieber had his first UK hit in 2010 when he was just fifteen – what was it called?

QUESTION 7
Released in 2004, who had a No 1 album when she was just 17½ called "Mind, Body & Soul"?

QUESTION 8
When Hanson reached No 1 in June 1997 with 'MMMBop', Isaac Hanson was 16, Taylor Hanson was just 13, but what was the name and age of the third and youngest brother?

QUESTION 9
What is the name of Kim Wilde's brother, who had an unsuccessful UK chart career in the early Seventies but went on to be hugely successful as the writer and producer of many of his sister's hits?

QUESTION 10
After 'Long Haired Lover From Liverpool', Little Jimmy Osmond had two further hit singles – one billed as Little Jimmy Osmond, the other just as Jimmy Osmond. Name either of them.

POPMASTER QUIZ 174

ZOO STORY

QUIZ 172

QUESTION 1
What was the title of the 1982 No 1 by Tight Fit?

QUESTION 2
The 2001 debut single by Gorillaz had a famous American actor and director as its title. Name that actor?

QUESTION 3
'Monkey' was a 1988 Top 20 single and American No 1 for which singer?

QUESTION 4
Which 'big cat' featured in the title of Lulu's Top 10 single from 1968?

QUESTION 5
Which of these groups had a Top 5 hit at Christmas 1984 with 'Nellie the Elephant'? Was it Toy Dolls, Splodgenessabounds, or Tenpole Tudor?

QUESTION 6
What type of animal was Rocky, according to the title of the Beatles' song from their "White Album"?

QUESTION 7
The American band The Turtles had three UK hits in the late Sixties. Name one of them?

QUESTION 8
Released in 1980, which Liverpudlian group's first album was called "Crocodiles"?

QUESTION 9
'Can't Fight The Moonlight' was a No 1 for LeAnn Rimes in 2000. In which feature film did that song appear?

QUESTION 10
The group Blue Zoo had its only Top 40 hit in 1982. What was it called?

Q1 *Frank Sinatra*

Q2 *Ed Sheeran*

Q3 *Oleta Adams*

Q4 *Frankie Vaughan*

Q5 *Britney Spears*

Q6 *Neil Diamond*

Q7 *Michael Bolton*

Q8 *Elkie Brooks*

Q9 *Blur*

Q10 *Elton John*

QUIZ 173

Q1 *Joe Le Taxi*

Q2 *18*

Q3 *Stevie Wonder*

Q4 *'Ma! (He's Making Eyes At Me)', '(You've Got) Personality'*

Q5 *Claire and Friends*

Q6 *One Time*

Q7 *Joss Stone*

Q8 *Zac (11) (born October 1985)*

Q9 *Ricky Wilde*

Q10 *Tweedlee Dee (some pressings Have 'Tweedle Dee', I'm Gonna Knock On Your Door (billed as Jimmy Osmond)*

QUIZ 175 POPMASTER

RECORD PRODUCERS

Can you name the record producer or production team at the controls of the following singles?

QUESTION 1

'Get Ready' by The Temptations, 'My Guy' by Mary Wells, 'Floy Joy' by The Supremes?

QUESTION 2

'Human' by Human League, 'Miss You Much' by Janet Jackson, 'Just Be Good To Me' by S.O.S. Band?

QUESTION 3

'Parklife' by Blur, 'Linger' by The Cranberries, 'I Predict A Riot' by Kaiser Chiefs?

QUESTION 4

'Watching The Detectives' by Elvis Costello, 'Stop Your Sobbing' by The Pretenders, 'New Rose' by The Damned?

QUESTION 5

'She's Gone' by Daryl Hall & John Oates, 'Waiting For A Star To Fall' by Boy Meets Girl, 'Wood Beez (Pray Like Aretha Franklin)' by Scritti Politti?

QUESTION 6

'Why' by Annie Lennox, 'Leave Right Now' by Will Young, 'It's Raining Men' by Geri Halliwell?

QUESTION 7

'Space Oddity' by David Bowie, 'Your Song' by Elton John, 'Streets Of London' by Ralph McTell?

QUESTION 8

'When Will I See You Again' by The Three Degrees, 'Me and Mrs Jones' by Billy Paul, 'Back Stabbers' by The O'Jays?

QUESTION 9

'Come On Eileen' by Dexy's Midnight Runners, 'Our House' by Madness, 'Reward' by The Teardrop Explodes?

QUESTION 10

'Sultans Of Swing' by Dire Straits, 'This Town Ain't Big Enough For Both Of Us' by Sparks, 'Love Me Like I Love You' by Bay City Rollers?

POPMASTER QUIZ 176

MISSING WORDS

Here is a list of ten songs each with one word missing from the title. Can you name the performer and fill in the blank?

QUESTION 1
The Importance Of Being--------'? (From 2005)

QUESTION 2
'One ---- Woman' (from 1980)

QUESTION 3
'Let The ------Control Your Body'? (From 1994)

QUESTION 4
'My------Is Coming In'? (From 1965)

QUESTION 5
'--- For The Weekend'? (From 2016)

QUESTION 6
'I'll Put You ---------Again'? (From 1979)

QUESTION 7
'Have You Ever--------Loved A Woman'? (From 1995)

QUESTION 8
'--- Of Our Lives' (from 1999)

QUESTION 9
'I Will Never Let You------'? (From 2014)

QUESTION 10
'Banana---' (from 1975)

A answers

QUIZ 174

Q1 *The Lion Sleeps Tonight*

Q2 *Clint Eastwood*

Q3 *George Michael*

Q4 *Tiger (I'm A Tiger reached No. 9 in December '68)*

Q5 *Toy Dolls*

Q6 *Raccoon (the White Album is officially called 'The Beatles')*

Q7 *'Happy Together', 'She'd Rather Be With Me', 'Elenore' (the latter two were both Top 10 hits)*

Q8 *Echo & The Bunnymen*

Q9 *Coyote Ugly*

Q10 *Cry Boy Cry*

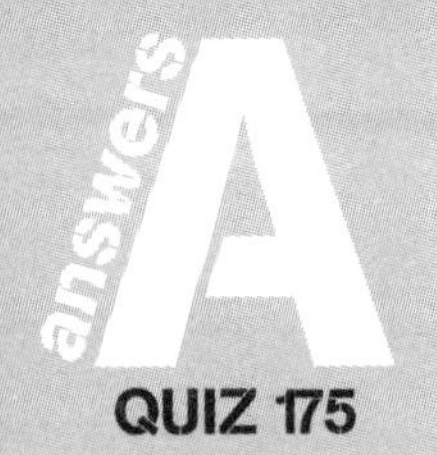

QUIZ 175

Q1
Smokey Robinson (billed just as "Smokey" on the original American releases)

Q2
Jimmy Jam & Terry Lewis

Q3
Stephen Street

Q4
Nick Lowe

Q5
Arif Mardin

Q6
Stephen Lipson

Q7
Gus Dudgeon

Q8
Kenny Gamble & Leon Huff

Q9
Clive Langer & Alan Winstanley

Q10
Muff Winwood

QUIZ 177 POPMASTER

QUESTION 1
Who sang about 'Nutbush City Limits' in 1973?

QUESTION 2
The Darkness reached the Top 10 in 2003 with the song 'I Believe in…' what?

QUESTION 3
Who reached the Top 10 in 1992 with his cover version of 'The Days of Pearly Spencer'?

QUESTION 4
Dusty Springfield's only No 1 single was a 1966 song called 'You Don't…' what?

QUESTION 5
What three-word song title has provided different hits for Dead or Alive in 1985, Genesis in 1986 and Belinda Carlisle in 1996?

QUESTION 6
Which Welsh band's Top 10 singles in the Noughties included 'Madame Helga', 'Maybe Tomorrow' and 'Moviestar'?

QUESTION 7
The Australian group Icehouse had its biggest UK hit in 1983. What was it called?

QUESTION 8
The songs 'Action', 'The Lies in Your Eyes' and 'The Six Teens' were all hits in the mid-Seventies for which group?

QUESTION 9
Natalie Cole had her only two Top 10 singles in the late Eighties – name either of these songs.

QUESTION 10
Which of Terry Hall's groups had a hit in 1985 with the song 'Thinking of You'?

POPMASTER QUIZ 178

QUIZ 176

QUESTION 1
Who reached No 1 in 2014 with her single 'Crazy Stupid Love' (featuring Tinie Tempah)?

QUESTION 2
The duo Jon and Vangelis had two Top 10 singles at the beginning of the 1980s. Name either of them.

QUESTION 3
Who reached No 1 in 1969 with 'Israelites'?

QUESTION 4
Which 2002 No 1 by Gareth Gates has the subtitle '(Stupid Mistake)'?

QUESTION 5
Which group of comedians had a Top 10 hit in 1973 with 'Ying Tong Song'?

QUESTION 6
Which U2 song was a Top 3 hit for Mary J Blige with U2 in 2006?

QUESTION 7
What are the names of both of the members of the duo The Communards?

QUESTION 8
The 1991 single 'Radio Wall of Sound' was the final original Top 40 hit single for which group?

QUESTION 9
During the course of their chart career, the group Secret Affair had three Top 40 singles. Name one of them.

QUESTION 10
Who won the 'Best British Female Solo Artist' award at the 2015 BRIT Awards?

Q1 *'Idle'* *Oasis*

Q2 *'Man'* *Sheena Easton*

Q3 *'Beat'* *2 Unlimited*

Q4 *'Ship'* *The Walker Brothers*

Q5 *'Hymn'* *Coldplay feat. Beyonce (uncredited)*

Q6 *'Together'* *Hot Chocolate*

Q7 *'Really'* *Bryan Adams*

Q8 *'Summertime'* *A1*

Q9 *'Down'* *Rita Ora*

Q10 *'Rock'* *The Wombles*

QUIZ 177

Q1
Ike & Tina Turner

Q2
A Thing Called Love

Q3
Marc Almond

Q4
Have to Say You Love Me

Q5
'In Too Deep'

Q6
Stereophonics

Q7
'Hey Little Girl'

Q8
The Sweet

Q9
'Pink Cadillac' (No.5 in 1988), 'Miss You Like Crazy' (No.2 in 1989)

Q10
The Colourfield

QUIZ 179 POPMASTER

QUESTION 1
Which group's No 1 singles in the 1960s included 'You Really Got Me' and 'Sunny Afternoon'?

QUESTION 2
The songs 'Forgive Me', 'Better in Time' and 'Happy' were all hits in the Noughties for which singer?

QUESTION 3
What shared one-word title has provided different Top 10 hits for Roy Orbison and Julee Cruise, a Top 20 hit for Ant & Dec and Top 40 hits for Cathy Dennis and McAlmont & Butler?

QUESTION 4
Which former American president featured in the title of a 2004 Top 3 single by Manic Street Preachers?

QUESTION 5
Who had hit cover versions in 1993 with the songs 'Ruby Tuesday', 'Shotgun Wedding' and 'Have I Told You Lately'?

QUESTION 6
Released in 1977, what is the title of the Steve Gibbons Band's only Top 40 hit?

QUESTION 7
What is the first name of the singer in Goldfrapp?

QUESTION 8
With whom did Sarah Brightman have a Top 3 hit in 1997 called 'Time to Say Goodbye (Con te Partiro)'?

QUESTION 9
The group Liverpool Express had three Top 40 hits in the mid-Seventies. Name one of them.

QUESTION 10
Which vocal group had Top 10 singles in 2006 called 'Whole Lotta History', 'Something Kinda Ooooh' and 'I Think We're Alone Now'?

POPMASTER QUIZ 180

QUESTION 1
Coldplay had their very first No 1 single in June 2008 – what was it called?

QUESTION 2
The song 'Happenin' All Over Again' was a Top 5 hit in 1990 for the American singer Lonnie… who?

QUESTION 3
In 1966, The Lovin' Spoonful had their only two Top 10 singles. Name one of them.

QUESTION 4
One of the most successful groups of the first half of the 1980s reached the Top 10 with 'Victims', 'The War Song' and 'It's a Miracle'. Who are they?

QUESTION 5
What was the title of the song by Rednex that spent three weeks at No 1 in 1995?

QUESTION 6
Songs sharing the title 'After the Love Has Gone' have provided different Top 40 hits for three chart acts – in 1979, 1985 and 1999. Name one of them.

QUESTION 7
What type of 'Divorce' did Steely Dan sing about on their 1976 single?

QUESTION 8
Which punk group has included Dave Vanian, Rat Scabies, Captain Sensible and Brian James amongst its line-up?

QUESTION 9
What is the title of the only Spice Girls No 1 to have the word 'Spice' in the title?

QUESTION 10
Which Liverpool group made its Top 40 debut in 1996 with 'Female of the Species'?

QUIZ 178

Q1
Cheryl Cole

Q2
'I Hear You Now', 'I'll Find My Way Home'

Q3
Desmond Dekker & The Aces

Q4
'Anyone of Us'

Q5
The Goons

Q6
'One'

Q7
Jimmy Somerville, Richard Coles

Q8
Slade

Q9
'Time for Action', 'Let Your Heart Dance', 'My World'

Q10
Paloma Faith

QUIZ 181 POPMASTER

QUESTION 1
Which chart act reached No 2 in 1979 with the song 'Pop Muzik'?

QUESTION 2
Which Small Faces song did M People cover in 1995?

QUESTION 3
One of the most successful UK groups of the first half of the 1980s had a Top 10 double 'A' side in 1981 with 'Musclebound' and 'Glow'. Who are they?

QUESTION 4
Which American singer had hits in the mid-Fifties with the songs 'Indian Love Call', 'China Doll' and 'Tumbling Tumbleweeds'?

QUESTION 5
What one-word title has provided different hits for The Who in 1966 and 1976, Clout in 1978 and Liquid Gold in 1980?

QUESTION 6
Beginning with the earliest, put these three songs by Depeche Mode in the order they were originally hits: 'Personal Jesus', 'See You', 'Barrel of a Gun'?

QUESTION 7
What type of 'Rose' did Sting sing about in 2000 on his Top 20 single featuring raï singer Cheb Mami?

QUESTION 8
The 1980 Top 10 song 'You Gave Me Love' was recorded by Crown... what... Affair?

QUESTION 9
The songs 'My Sweet Rosalie', 'Oh Boy (The Mood I'm In)' and 'Beautiful Lover' were all hits in the Seventies for which vocal group?

QUESTION 10
Which of these 1960s singers is associated with the group The Dakotas – Johnny Kidd, Billy J Kramer or Freddie Garrity?

QUIZ 179

Q1
The Kinks

Q2
Leona Lewis

Q3
'Falling'

Q4
Richard Nixon ('The Love of Richard Nixon')

Q5
Rod Stewart

Q6
'Tulane'

Q7
Alison

Q8
Andrea Bocelli

Q9
'You Are My Love', 'Every Man Must Have a Dream', 'Dreamin''

Q10
Girls Aloud

POPMASTER QUIZ 182

QUIZ 180

Q1
'Viva la Vida'

Q2
Gordon

Q3
'Daydream', 'Summer in the City'

Q4
Culture Club

Q5
'Cotton Eye Joe'

Q6
Earth, Wind & Fire, Princess, Steps (Damage's 2001 cover only reached 42)

Q7
Haitian

Q8
The Damned

Q9
'Spice Up Your Life'

Q10
Space

QUESTION 1
Which group made its chart debut in 1987 with the song 'Don't Dream It's Over'?

QUESTION 2
What shared one-word title has provided different hits for Rita Coolidge in 1978, F.R. David in 1983 and The Christians in 1989?

QUESTION 3
Which Australian singer reached the Top 10 in the early summer of 2008 with her single 'Sweet About Me'?

QUESTION 4
The theme tune to which Spaghetti Western film gave Hugo Montenegro, his Orchestra and Chorus a No 1 in 1968?

QUESTION 5
Name the American female country trio who made their UK chart debut in 1999 with the single 'There's Your Trouble'.

QUESTION 6
Two of the six Top 10 singles for Wizzard in the 1970s had the word 'Rock' somewhere in the title. Name one of these two songs.

QUESTION 7
What is the name of the male member of the duo Yazoo?

QUESTION 8
What do the chart acts The Honeycombs, Carpenters and The White Stripes have in common?

QUESTION 9
The 1986 debut hit for Mel & Kim had the subtitle '(Get Fresh at the Weekend)'. What was its full title?

QUESTION 10
The 1977 single 'Oh, Lori' was the only UK hit for which pair of American brothers?

QUIZ 181

Q1
M

Q2
'Itchycoo Park'

Q3
Spandau Ballet

Q4
Slim Whitman

Q5
'Substitute'

Q6
'See You' ('82), 'Personal Jesus' ('89), 'Barrel of a Gun' ('97)

Q7
'Desert Rose'

Q8
Heights

Q9
Brotherhood of Man

Q10
Billy J Kramer

QUIZ 183 POPMASTER

QUESTION 1
Curt Smith is one of the two main members of Tears for Fears – who is the other?

QUESTION 2
Which of these three songs marked the chart debut of the group Toto – was it 'Africa', 'Hold the Line' or 'Rosanna'?

QUESTION 3
The singer who spent four weeks at No 1 in 1994 with 'Baby Come Back' is called Pato... who?

QUESTION 4
Name the American vocal group who had hits in the early 1970s with 'Didn't I (Blow Your Mind this Time)' and 'La-La Means I Love You'?

QUESTION 5
Which shared three-word title has provided different Top 40 hits for The Animals in 1965, Talk Talk in 1990, Dr Alban in 1992 and Bon Jovi in 2000?

QUESTION 6
Who had solo hits in the early 1980s called 'King's Call' and 'Yellow Pearl'?

QUESTION 7
Who am I? I was born in New Jersey in 1949, my songs have provided hits for Patti Smith, Manfred Mann's Earth Band and The Pointer Sisters. My own albums include "Devils & Dust" and "The Rising"?

QUESTION 8
The Script had a Top 3 single in the Noughties called 'The Man Who Can't…' what?

QUESTION 9
Beginning with the earliest, put these three singles by David Bowie in the order they were originally hits: 'Hallo Spaceboy', 'Loving the Alien','Starman'?

QUESTION 10
Which politician featured in the video for Tracey Ullman's 1984 single 'My Guy'?

POPMASTER QUIZ 184

QUESTION 1
Which group reached the Top 5 in 1978 with the song 'With a Little Luck', taken from their Top 5 album London Town?

QUESTION 2
Complete the title of this 1981 single by Madness – 'The Return of the...' what?

QUESTION 3
The American group who had chart singles in the Noughties with 'Girl All the Bad Guys Want' and '1985' is called Bowling for... what?

QUESTION 4
George Harrison had three Top 40 solo hits in the 1980s – 'All Those Years Ago' was the first of these. Name one of the other two.

QUESTION 5
'Make it Easy on Yourself' was No 1 in 1965 for which group?

QUESTION 6
The group Razorlight had its only No 1 single in 2006 – what is it called?

QUESTION 7
Which of these groups had their only hit in 1983 with 'The Safety Dance'. Was it Roman Holliday, Men Without Hats or It's Immaterial?

QUESTION 8
What comes next in this sequence of albums released by Radiohead: Pablo Honey ('93), The Bends ('95), OK Computer ('97)...?

QUESTION 9
The American singer who had a hit in 1973 with 'Pillow Talk' had the same name as a Swedish singer who had a hit in 1974 with 'Y Viva Espana'. What is that shared name?

QUESTION 10
Released in 1982, which actor features in the title of the first and biggest hit for the duo Haysi Fantayzee?

QUIZ 182

Q1
Crowded House

Q2
'Words'

Q3
Gabriella Cilmi

Q4
'The Good, The Bad and The Ugly'

Q5
Dixie Chicks

Q6
'Rock 'N' Roll Winter (Loony's Tune), 'Are You Ready to Rock'

Q7
Vince Clarke

Q8
A female drummer

Q9
'Showing Out (Get Fresh at the Weekend)'

Q10
Alessi

QUIZ 183

Q1
Roland Orzabal

Q2
'Hold the Line' (1979; the other two are from 1983)

Q3
Banton

Q4
The Delfonics

Q5
'It's My Life'

Q6
Phil Lynott

Q7
Bruce Springsteen

Q8
Be Moved

Q9
'Starman' ('72), 'Loving the Alien' ('85), 'Hallo Spaceboy' ('96)

Q10
Neil Kinnock

QUIZ 185 POPMASTER

QUESTION 1
Which group had hits in 1978 with the songs 'Nice 'N' Sleazy' and '5 Minutes'?

QUESTION 2
According to Pat Benatar's 1985 Top 20 hit, 'Love is a…' what?

QUESTION 3
Who am I? Born Arnold Dorsey in 1936, my first three hits were in 1967, I recorded the song 'Les Bicyclettes de Belsize' in '68 and I hit the Top 40 in 1999 with 'Quando Quando Quando'. I sang the UK's 2012 Eurovision entry.

QUESTION 4
Beginning with the earliest, put these three songs by Kate Bush in the order they were originally hits: 'Moments of Pleasure', 'King of the Mountain' and 'Cloudbusting'?

QUESTION 5
One of the biggest UK groups of the early 1980s had their only Top 10 hit of the '90s in 1995 with 'Tell Me When'. Name the group.

QUESTION 6
What was the title of the 2002 No 1 by Nelly featuring Kelly Rowland?

QUESTION 7
In which decade did Cliff Richard have Top 10 singles with 'True Love Ways', 'Please Don't Fall in Love' and 'Daddy's Home'?

QUESTION 8
Which hit guitar-pop trio of the Noughties consisted of James Bourne, Charlie Simpson and Matt Willis?

QUESTION 9
The actor Bruce Willis had two Top 10 cover versions in 1987. Name one of them.

QUESTION 10
Which American vocal group's hits in the early Seventies included 'Elmo James', 'I'm on My Way to a Better Place' and 'Finders Keepers'?

POPMASTER QUIZ 186

QUIZ 184

QUESTION 1
Which 1969 single by The Who was also a chart hit in the Seventies for The New Seekers and Elton John?

QUESTION 2
Which one-time teen idol of the 1970s had his only Top 40 hit of the Eighties in 1985 with the Top 5 song 'The Last Kiss'?

QUESTION 3
What is the title of the 2014 No 1 song by Jessie J, Ariana Grande and Nicki Minaj?

QUESTION 4
Which group, featuring singer Miles Hunt, had Top 10 EPs in the early Nineties called 'Welcome to the Cheap Seats' and 'On the Ropes'?

QUESTION 5
Name the song originally by Wham! that gave Shane Richie a Top 3 single in 2003.

QUESTION 6
Fourteen years before their only UK No 1, which American group made its chart debut in 1976 with the song 'Rock N' Me'?

QUESTION 7
In 1980, the Canadian group Rush had its biggest UK single with 'The Spirit of...' what?

QUESTION 8
The song 'This Kiss' was the 1998 chart debut by which American country singer?

QUESTION 9
In 1981, Fred Wedlock declared he was the 'Oldest... what... in Town'?

QUESTION 10
Although it failed to be a Top 40 hit, which American jazz instrumental group is best known for their 1977 single 'Birdland'?

Q1
Wings

Q2
Los Palmas Seven

Q3
Soup

Q4
'Got My Mind Set on You' ('87), 'When We was Fab' ('88)

Q5
The Walker Brothers

Q6
'America'

Q7
Men Without Hats

Q8
Kid A (2000)

Q9
Sylvia

Q10
John Wayne ('John Wayne is Big Leggy')

QUIZ 185

Q1
The Stranglers

Q2
Battlefield

Q3
Engelbert Humperdinck

Q4
'Cloudbusting' ('85), 'Moments of Pleasure' ('93), 'King of the Mountain' (05)

Q5
Human League

Q6
'Dilemma'

Q7
1980s

Q8
Busted

Q9
'Respect Yourself', 'Under the Boardwalk'

Q10
The Chairmen of the Board

QUIZ 187 POPMASTER

QUESTION 1
Which critically acclaimed American group is led by Donald Fagen and Walter Becker?

QUESTION 2
The American singer Lobo had two hits in the 1970s and both were Top 5 singles. Name either of them.

QUESTION 3
...and a Dutch singer also called Lobo had a Top 10 hit in 1981 with which song?

QUESTION 4
Which group had hits in 2004 with 'Matinee' and 'Michael'?

QUESTION 5
The songs 'Duel' and 'Dr Mabuse' were hits in the mid-1980s for Propaganda. Did the group come from The Netherlands, Germany or Sweden?

QUESTION 6
In 1992, Annie Lennox was 'Walking on…' what?

QUESTION 7
The Greek group Aphrodite's Child had its only UK hit in 1968 with 'Rain and Tears', but two of its members went on to have British solo success in the 1970s and 1980s. Name either of these members.

QUESTION 8
Which Beatles studio album includes the songs 'With a Little Help from My Friends', 'When I'm Sixty-Four', 'Lucy in the Sky with Diamonds' and 'Being for the Benefit of Mr Kite'?

QUESTION 9
In 1993, the film composer David Arnold had a hit with 'Play Dead' that featured vocals by which female singer?

QUESTION 10
The singer Curtis Stigers' first two chart singles were also his only Top 10 hits. Name either of these 1992 Top 10 songs.

POPMASTER QUIZ 188

QUIZ 186

QUESTION 1
Which singer-songwriter had both a hit single and album in 1980 called 'Me Myself I'?

QUESTION 2
With nearly three years on the chart, what was the title of the 1995 debut album by The Lighthouse Family that contained the singles 'Lifted', 'Goodbye Heartbreak' and 'Loving Every Minute'?

QUESTION 3
Which group was 'Bringing on Back the Good Times' in 1969?

QUESTION 4
What type of 'Weekend' did The Stylistics sing about on their 1976 Top 10 single?

QUESTION 5
Which American group released the No 1 albums Only by the Night in 2008, Come Around Sundown in 2010 and Mechanical Bull in 2014?

QUESTION 6
What nationality was the group Freiheit, who had a hit in the late Eighties with 'Keeping the Dream Alive' – were they German, Austrian or Swiss?

QUESTION 7
Who made her chart debut in 1978 with 'I'm Every Woman'?

QUESTION 8
Two of The Jam's hit singles had the word 'Town' somewhere in the title – 'Town Called Malice' was one, what was the other?

QUESTION 9
Which group had a Top 10 hit in 2007 with 'How to Save a Life'?

QUESTION 10
Having had three hits (including a No 1) in 1979, which American vocal group began the 1980s with a Top 20 single called 'Can't Stop the Music'?

Q1 *'Pinball Wizard' (The New Seekers' version paired the song with 'See Me, Feel Me')*

Q2 *David Cassidy*

Q3 *'Bang Bang'*

Q4 *The Wonder Stuff*

Q5 *'I'm Your Man'*

Q6 *Steve Miller Band*

Q7 *Radio*

Q8 *Faith Hill*

Q9 *Swinger*

Q10 *Weather Report*

QUIZ 187

Q1
Steely Dan

Q2
'Me and You and a Dog Named Boo', 'I'd Love You to Want Me'

Q3
'The Caribbean Disco Show'

Q4
Franz Ferdinand

Q5
Germany

Q6
Broken Glass

Q7
Demis Roussos, Vangelis

Q8
Sgt Pepper's Lonely Hearts Club Band

Q9
Björk

Q10
'I Wonder Why', 'You're All that Matters to Me'

QUIZ 189 POPMASTER

QUESTION 1
The 2001 chart debut by Nelly Furtado was called 'I'm Like a...' what?

QUESTION 2
The 1996 Top 3 single 'If You Ever' was recorded as a duet by one of the most successful boy bands and one of the most successful British female singers of the time. Name either the boy band or the singer.

QUESTION 3
What song, written by George Gershwin with lyrics by DuBose Heyward, was taken into the chart in 1982 by Fun Boy Three?

QUESTION 4
The singer who reached No 2 in 1979 with 'Silly Games' is called Janet… who?

QUESTION 5
Which of Coldplay's albums contains the singles 'Shiver' and 'Trouble'?

QUESTION 6
What is the name of the drummer in U2?

QUESTION 7
The Queen songs 'Now I'm Here', 'Bicycle Race'/'Fat Bottomed Girls' and 'Save Me' all just missed the Top 10 by peaking at number 11, but which of these three singles was the first to make the chart?

QUESTION 8
Which American singer had a Top 30 hit in 1966 with 'Born a Woman' and a Top 20 hit in 1967 with 'Single Girl'?

QUESTION 9
What was the title of the 1997 chart debut by Finley Quaye?

QUESTION 10
Name the male vocalist who reached the Top 5 in 1983 with his single 'Calling Your Name'.

POPMASTER QUIZ 190

QUIZ 188

QUESTION 1
Who made her chart debut in 1973 with the song 'Can the Can'?

Q1 *Joan Armatrading*

QUESTION 2
Characters from the TV series *The X Files* provided Catatonia with the title of their first Top 10 single in 1998. What was the song called?

Q2 *Ocean Drive*

QUESTION 3
The Australian group who had its only UK Top 40 hit in 1983 with the Top 10 song 'Waiting for a Train' is called Flash and… what?

Q3 *Love Affair*

QUESTION 4
The American vocal group The Tymes had two chart hits in the 1960s called 'So Much in Love' and 'People'. They had two further Top 40 hits in the 1970s. Name one of these.

Q4 *'Funky Weekend'*

QUESTION 5
Name the Canadian singer who made his debut on the singles chart in 2005 with the song 'Home', taken from his Top 5 album It's Time.

Q5 *Kings of Leon*

QUESTION 6
What type of '...Stomp' did Hamilton Bohannon sing about on his Top 10 hit in the mid-Seventies?

Q6 *German*

QUESTION 7
Who is the one-time lead singer with Japan who had solo hits in 1984 called 'Red Guitar' and 'The Ink in the Well'?

Q7 *Chaka Khan*

QUESTION 8
The Motown group Boyz II Men made its chart debut in 1992 with a song that spent three weeks at No 1 and five months on the chart. What is it called?

Q8 *'Strange Town'*

QUESTION 9
The 1986 single 'My Favourite Waste of Time' was the only hit single for which singer?

Q9 *The Fray*

QUESTION 10
How do you pronounce the titles of the Ed Sheeran albums released in 2011 and 2014?

Q10 *The Village People*

QUIZ 189

Q1
Bird

Q2
East 17, Gabrielle

Q3
'Summertime'

Q4
Kay

Q5
Parachutes

Q6
Larry Mullen Jr

Q7
'Now I'm Here'

Q8
Sandy Posey

Q9
'Sunday Shining'

Q10
Marilyn

QUIZ 191 POPMASTER

QUESTION 1
Which American group made its debut Top 40 appearance in 1989 with the song 'Orange Crush'?

QUESTION 2
Which 1974 single by the Carpenters has the subtitle '(On the Bayou)'?

QUESTION 3
Who reached the Top 3 with her singles 'Don't be a Stranger' in 1993 and 'Escaping' in 1996?

QUESTION 4
Which shared five-word song title has provided different hits for Roxy Music in 1974, U2 in 1989, Bryan Adams in 1992 and 911 in 1998?

QUESTION 5
In 1983, in between Yazoo and Erasure, Vince Clarke reached the Top 5 with a song called 'Never Never', which featured Feargal Sharkey as vocalist. But under what name did they record it?

QUESTION 6
Released in 2009, what is the title of the debut No 1 album by Florence + the Machine, which spent almost three years in the Top 75?

QUESTION 7
In 1980, the American musician Tom Browne reached the Top 10 with 'Funkin' for Jamaica (N.Y.)', but did he play saxophone, trumpet or trombone?

QUESTION 8
What is the name of Daniel Bedingfield's sister, who reached No 1 in 2004 with the song 'These Words'?

QUESTION 9
Name the group that had its only Top 40 hit in 1979 with 'Back of My Hand'.

QUESTION 10
The Associates made their only three Top 40 appearances in 1982. Name one of these three singles.

POPMASTER QUIZ 192

QUIZ 190

QUESTION 1
Name the Australian group that had hit singles in 1990 called 'Suicide Blonde' and 'Disappear', both taken from their hit album X.

QUESTION 2
The 1910 Fruitgum Co. made its only chart appearance in 1968 with a song that reached No 2 and spent four months on the chart - what was it called?

QUESTION 3
Having had a run of hits in the 1970s, which soul singer's only UK Top 40 hit of the 1980s was the 1987 single 'Sho' You Right'?

QUESTION 4
Released in 1976, the one and only hit for The Climax Blues Band was a Top 10 single in the autumn of that year - what was it called?

QUESTION 5
Which British female vocalist wanted to 'Keep this Fire Burning' in 2005?

QUESTION 6
Which American rapper, producer and entrepreneur had a No 1 soundtrack album in the summer of 2015 called Compton?

QUESTION 7
What was the title of the 1990 No 1 by Beats International featuring Lindy Layton that reworked a former SOS Band hit from 1984?

QUESTION 8
The song 'In a Lifetime' was a Top 20 hit in both 1986 and 1989 for Clannad. It featured guest vocals from the lead singer of another Irish band. Who was the guest vocalist?

QUESTION 9
Which instrument did Dave Clark play in The Dave Clark Five?

QUESTION 10
Was the 1978 Top 10 song 'Let's All Chant' the only hit for Narada Michael Walden, Michael Zager Band or Nick Straker Band?

Q1 *Suzi Quatro*

Q2 *'Mulder and Scully'*

Q3 *The Pan*

Q4 *'You Little Trustmaker', 'Ms Grace'*

Q5 *Michael Bublé*

Q6 *'Disco Stomp'*

Q7 *David Sylvian*

Q8 *'End of the Road'*

Q9 *Owen Paul*

Q10 *Plus (+) Multiply (x)*

QUIZ 191

Q1
R.E.M.

Q2
'Jambalaya'

Q3
Dina Carroll

Q4
'All I Want is You'

Q5
The Assembly

Q6
Lungs

Q7
Trumpet

Q8
Natasha

Q9
The Jags

Q10 *'Party Fears Two', 'Club Country', '18 Carat Love Affair'/'Love Hangover' (double 'A' side)*

QUIZ 193 POPMASTER

QUESTION 1
Brian Eno, Paul Thompson, Andy Mackay and Eddie Jobson have all been members of which group?

QUESTION 2
The band Whitesnake had its only two UK Top 10 singles in 1987. Name either of them.

QUESTION 3
Which female vocal group had a Top 10 hit in 2014 with their cover version of Cameo's hit 'Word Up'?

QUESTION 4
The 1970 No 2 song 'Patches' was the title of the only hit single for the American singer Clarence… who?

QUESTION 5
According to the title of their only Top 10 single in 1982, The Mobiles were doing what in Berlin?

QUESTION 6
Name the American female vocal group whose British Top 10 singles in the 1990s included 'My Lovin'', 'Don't Let Go (Love)' and 'Hold On'.

QUESTION 7
What was the title of the 2010 Top 10 song by Enrique Iglesias that featured Nicole Scherzinger?

QUESTION 8
Which band reached the Top 5 in 1989 with 'She Drives Me Crazy'?

QUESTION 9
Which member of S Club 7 made her solo debut in 2005 with the Top 20 single 'What Hurts the Most'?

QUESTION 10
The Commodores reached the Top 3 in 1985 with a song that pays tribute to both Jackie Wilson and Marvin Gaye. What was it called?

POPMASTER QUIZ 194

QUESTION 1
Which group was credited alongside Lloyd Cole on his recordings during the 1980s?

QUESTION 2
Beginning with the earliest, put these three songs by Elvis Presley in the order they were originally hits: 'All Shook Up', 'Moody Blue', 'Love Letters'.

QUESTION 3
A 1992 Top 10 version of Alice Cooper's '(I Want to be) Elected' was recorded by Mr Bean and Smear Campaign and featured which rock vocalist?

QUESTION 4
What was the title of the 1986 Top 3 duet by Patti LaBelle and Michael McDonald?

QUESTION 5
Which British rock group had a Top 3 single in 1995 called 'When Love and Hate Collide'?

QUESTION 6
Released in 1969 and 1970, which group's last Top 10 single of the Sixties was 'Viva Bobby Joe' and first of the Seventies 'Black Skin Blue Eyed Boys'?

QUESTION 7
The American vocal group The Whispers had their two UK Top 10 singles in the early '80s. Name either of them.

QUESTION 8
'King' is the title of a 2015 No 1 by a London-based electronica band fronted by Olly Alexander. What is the band called?

QUESTION 9
Which 1996 Top 10 single by Radiohead has the subtitle '(Fade Out)'?

QUESTION 10
Barbra Streisand's 1988 Top 20 duet 'Till I Loved You (Love Theme from 'Goya')' was recorded with an actor from one of the most successful American TV series of the Eighties. Who is he?

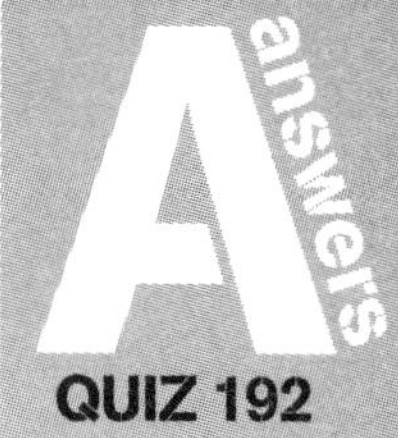

QUIZ 192

Q1
INXS

Q2
'Simon Says'

Q3
Barry White

Q4
'Couldn't Get it Right'

Q5
Beverley Knight

Q6
Dr Dre

Q7
'Dub be Good to Me' (the SOS Band original was called 'Just be Good to Me')

Q8
Bono (U2)

Q9
Drums

Q10
Michael Zager Band

QUIZ 193

Q1 *Roxy Music*

Q2 *'Is this Love, 'Here I Go Again' (re-mix)*

Q3 *Little Mix (recorded for Sport Relief)*

Q4 *Carter*

Q5 *'Drowning in Berlin'*

Q6 *En Vogue*

Q7 *'Heartbeat'*

Q8 *Fine Young Cannibals*

Q9 *Jo O'Meara*

Q10 *'Nightshift'*

QUIZ 195 POPMASTER

QUESTION 1
Who had hits in 1986 with the singles 'What Have You Done for Me Lately', 'Nasty' and 'When I Think of You'?

QUESTION 2
Which 2014 No 1 by Clean Bandit featuring Jess Glynne has become a musical favourite of advertising companies?

QUESTION 3
Which Scottish group had hits in the 1990s with 'Nothing Ever Happens', 'Always the Last to Know' and 'Driving with the Brakes On'?

QUESTION 4
The 1984 hit duet by Julio Iglesias and Willie Nelson was called 'To All the…' what?

QUESTION 5
Name the American vocal group who sang about 'The Rubberband Man' in 1976?

QUESTION 6
One of the final original hits for ABBA mentions the author Marilyn French, Chinese food and the TV series *Dallas* in its lyrics. What is it called?

QUESTION 7
Which group had Top 10 singles in 1964 with 'Just One Look', 'Here I Go Again' and 'We're Through'?

QUESTION 8
The Swiss duo Double reached the Top 10 in 1986 with their only Top 40 hit single. What was it called?

QUESTION 9
The songs 'Skinny Genes' and 'Pack Up' were hits in 2010 for the daughter of West End star Frances Ruffelle and granddaughter of Sylvia Young, founder of the famous theatre school. Who is she?

QUESTION 10
Which two drinks featured in the title of Dr Feelgood's 1979 Top 10 single?

POPMASTER QUIZ 196

QUIZ 194

Q1 *The Commotions*

Q2 *'All Shook Up' ('57), 'Love Letters' ('66), 'Moody Blue' ('77)*

Q3 *Bruce Dickinson*

Q4 *'On My Own'*

Q5 *Def Leppard*

Q6 *The Equals*

Q7 *'And the Beat Goes On', 'It's a Love Thing'*

Q8 *Years & Years*

Q9 *'Street Spirit'*

Q10 *Don Johnson (from Miami Vice)*

QUESTION 1
Which song by Ian Dury & The Blockheads mentions the Marx Brothers, a hit song by Little Richard and the director of the film *Annie Hall* in its lyrics?

QUESTION 2
Which band had hits in the mid '90s called 'Staying out for the Summer' and 'Good Enough'?

QUESTION 3
Which early Eighties hit for Leo Sayer was written by Barry and Robin Gibb and produced by Arif Mardin?

QUESTION 4
Brothers Howard and Guy Lawrence released a No 1 album called Settle in 2013 and had a Top 20 single in 2015 with 'Omen', featuromg vocals by Sam Smith. Under what name do they record?

QUESTION 5
Manfred Mann's Paul Jones had two solo Top 10 singles in the 1960s. Name either of them.

QUESTION 6
Which group of the early 1980s had its final Top 40 hits in 1983 with the songs 'Don't Talk to Me About Love' and 'Bring Me Closer'?

QUESTION 7
Christina Aguilera made her chart debut in 1999 with her first No 1 single. What was it called?

QUESTION 8
'Bonfire Heart' was a Top 5 single in 2013 for which singer-songwriter?

QUESTION 9
What is the title of the Top 3 single from 2000 credited to Tom Jones and Mousse T?

QUESTION 10
Having had success with three different chart groups, who had solo hit singles in 1973 with 'Dear Elaine' and 'Forever'?

QUIZ 195

Q1
Janet Jackson

Q2
'Rather Be'

Q3
Del Amitri

Q4
Girls I've Loved Before

Q5
The Detroit Spinners

Q6
'The Day Before You Came'

Q7
The Hollies

Q8
'The Captain of Her Heart'

Q9
Eliza Doolittle

Q10
'Milk and Alcohol'

QUIZ 197 POPMASTER

QUESTION 1
Which Swedish group's hits in the 1990s included 'Happy Nation', 'Always Have, Always Will' and 'Life is a Flower'?

QUESTION 2
What was the title of Owl City's 2010 No 1 debut hit?

QUESTION 3
Who am I? I had my first hits as a member of the American teen group New Edition in 1983, my first UK Top 10 song was 'My Prerogative' in 1988, and I married Whitney Houston in 1992?

QUESTION 4
Name the Ray Davies song released as part of a double 'A' side single with "A' Bomb in Wardour Street' by The Jam in 1978.

QUESTION 5
What type of 'Game' did Chris Isaak sing about on his 1990 chart debut?

QUESTION 6
Name two of the three members of A-ha.

QUESTION 7
'Ring out Solstice Bells' was a Christmas hit in 1976 for which folk-rock group?

QUESTION 8
Which U2 single from the Eighties featured a guest appearance from B.B. King?

QUESTION 9
The 1978 single 'I Love the Nightlife (Disco 'Round)' was the only Top 40 hit for the American singer Alicia... who?

QUESTION 10
What was the title of The Script's 2012 No 1 that featured will.i.am?

POPMASTER QUIZ 198

QUIZ 196

QUESTION 1
What was the title of the 1986 chart debut by Bruce Hornsby & The Range?

QUESTION 2
Which of these chart acts reached the Top 10 in 1978 with 'Supernature' – was it Eruption, Cerrone or Crown Heights Affair?

QUESTION 3
In 1994, the duo Corona spent 18 weeks on the chart and reached No 2 with 'The Rhythm of…' what?

QUESTION 4
Which British singer-songwriter had hits in the first half of the 1970s with 'Getting a Drag', 'Sugar Me' and 'Won't Somebody Dance with Me'?

QUESTION 5
Craig David had a Top 3 hit in 2003 with a song that featured Sting as a guest vocalist – what was it called?

QUESTION 6
The American singer who had his only two UK hits in 1980 with 'Escape (The Pina Colada Song)' and 'Him' is called Rupert… ?

QUESTION 7
What was Robin Gibb 'Saved by…', according to the title of his 1969 solo hit?

QUESTION 8
What was the surname of Mac and Katie, who had hits in 1975 with 'Sugar Candy Kisses', 'Don't Do it Baby' and 'Like a Butterfly'?

QUESTION 9
In 1985, David Grant and Jaki Graham had a Top 5 hit with a cover of a Detroit Spinners hit from 1973. What was it called?

QUESTION 10
Released in 2005, which member of Blue began his solo career with the Top 5 singles 'Lay Your Hands' and 'No Worries'?

Q1
'Reasons to be Cheerful (Pt.3)'

Q2
Dodgy

Q3
'Heart (Stop Beating in Time)'

Q4
Disclosure

Q5
'High Time', 'I've Been a Bad, Bad Boy'

Q6
Altered Images

Q7
'Genie in a Bottle'

Q8
James Blunt

Q9
'Sex Bomb'

Q10
Roy Wood (The Move, ELO's '10538 Overture', Wizzard)

QUIZ 197

Q1
Ace of Base

Q2
'Fireflies'

Q3
Bobby Brown

Q4
David Watts

Q5
'Wicked Game'

Q6
Morten Harket, Pal Waaktaar-Savoy, Mags (Magne Furuholmen)

Q7
Jethro Tull

Q8
'When Love Comes to Town'

Q9
Bridges

Q10
'Hall of Fame'

QUIZ 199 POPMASTER

QUESTION 1
'Suedehead' is the title of the 1988 debut solo single by which artist?

QUESTION 2
The American rock band Boston reached the singles chart in 1977 with the song 'More than a…' what?

QUESTION 3
Which group had hits in 2012 called 'Survival' and 'Madness' – both taken from their No 1 album The 2nd Law?

QUESTION 4
Which James Bond theme song was covered by Guns N' Roses for a Top 5 hit in 1991?

QUESTION 5
The group that had all three of its Top 40 hits in 1980, with 'Living by Numbers', 'This World of Water' and 'Sanctuary', was called New… what?

QUESTION 6
Which 1968 hit for Union Gap featuring Gary Puckett reached the chart again in 1974, but this time credited as Gary Puckett and the Union Gap?

QUESTION 7
Which singer comes next in this sequence – Steve Brookstein, Shayne Ward, Leona Lewis, Leon Jackson... ?

QUESTION 8
...and what is the name of the only group to win the UK version of *The X Factor* in the first 10 years of its run?

QUESTION 9
The songs 'You're Lying' and 'Intuition' were hits at the start of the 1980s for which of these groups – Beggar and Co, Linx or Loose Ends?

QUESTION 10
Name the EastEnders actress who had hits in the 1990s with 'Looking Up', 'Happy Just to be with You' and 'Do You Know'.

POPMASTER QUIZ 200

QUESTION 1
Graham Gouldman and Lol Creme were two of the four members of the original 10cc. Who were the other two?

QUESTION 2
Released in 1979, what was the title of the first and biggest hit for the group Sad Cafe?

QUESTION 3
Which family group released albums in the 1990s called Forgiven Not Forgotten and Talk on Corners?

QUESTION 4
What word appears in the titles of different hit singles in the Seventies by The Goodies, Wild Cherry and KC & The Sunshine Band?

QUESTION 5
Which Nashville group had a Top 30 hit in 2010 and a Top 20 hit in 2012 with the song 'Need You Now'?

QUESTION 6
The group Mr Mister had two hit singles in the mid-Eighties. Name either of them.

QUESTION 7
Name the soul singer who had hits in 1966 with 'Fa Fa Fa Fa Fa (Sad Song)' and a cover of '(I Can't Get No) Satisfaction' and a posthumous hit in 1968 with 'Hard to Handle'.

QUESTION 8
In the summer of 2008, The Ting Tings had a Top 10 single called 'Shut Up and…' what?

QUESTION 9
What do the initials 'PJ' stand for in PJ Harvey?

QUESTION 10
The duo Candy Flip had its only Top 40 hit in 1990 with a Top 3 cover version of which Beatles song?

QUIZ 198

Q1
'The Way it Is'

Q2
Cerrone

Q3
'The Rhythm of the Night'

Q4
Lynsey De Paul

Q5
'Rise & Fall'

Q6
Holmes

Q7
'Saved by the Bell'

Q8
Kissoon

Q9
'Could it Be I'm Falling in Love'

Q10
Simon Webbe

QUIZ 201 POPMASTER

QUESTION 1
Who wrote all of the hit singles by the American group Bread?

QUESTION 2
What is the title of the 1984 Top 3 single by Giorgio Moroder and Phil Oakey?

QUESTION 3
Name the Danish group that had its biggest UK hit in 2008 with 'Fascination', but has also had hits with '10,000 Nights of Thunder', 'Boyfriend' and 'The Spell'.

QUESTION 4
Lenny Kravitz had his only No 1 single in 1999 – what was it called?

QUESTION 5
Which of these groups had a Top 20 hit in 1983 with the song 'Don't Try to Stop It' – Halo James, Roman Holliday or Jo Boxers?

QUESTION 6
What were OneRepublic 'Counting…' according to the title of their 2013 No 1?

QUESTION 7
What are the names of the two members of Roxette?

QUESTION 8
The group 5000 Volts had two hits in the mid-1970s. Name either of them.

QUESTION 9
Having had Top 10 hits in the Sixties, Seventies and Eighties, which group had further Top 10 singles in the Nineties with 'Secret Love', 'Alone' and 'For Whom the Bell Tolls'?

QUESTION 10
Two hit singles in 2004 by Scissor Sisters had female names as their titles – name both of them.

QUIZ 199

Q1
Morrissey

Q2
'More than a Feeling'

Q3
Muse

Q4
'Live and Let Die'

Q5
Musik

Q6
'Young Girl'

Q7
Alexandra Burke (the first five winners of The X Factor, from 2004 to 2008)

Q8
Little Mix (2011)

Q9
Linx

Q10
Michelle Gayle

POPMASTER QUIZ 202

QUIZ 200

QUESTION 1
What are the first names of the two Everly Brothers?

QUESTION 2
The singer Fontella Bass had her biggest hit with a song that reached the chart in 1965. What is it called?

QUESTION 3
Jazzie B is the founder, leader and producer of which British hit group of the Eighties and Nineties?

QUESTION 4
What was the title of David Essex's 1973 chart debut?

QUESTION 5
Which group reached the Top 10 in 2008 singing about 'Violet Hill'?

QUESTION 6
What was 'Kinky…', according to the title of the Happy Mondays' 1990 Top 5 single?

QUESTION 7
'Into the Blue' was a Top 20 hit in 2014 for which Australian singer?

QUESTION 8
What word appears in the titles of different hit singles by Emerson Lake & Palmer, Paul Young and Pulp?

QUESTION 9
Who comes next in this sequence of artists – The New Seekers, Cliff Richard, Olivia Newton-John, The Shadows... ?

QUESTION 10
The 1989 Top 10 duet 'Wait' was recorded by Kym Mazelle along with the lead singer of The Blow Monkeys. What is he called?

Q1
Kevin Godley, Eric Stewart

Q2
'Everyday Hurts' (produced and engineered by Eric Stewart of 10cc)

Q3
The Corrs

Q4
Funky ('Funky Gibbon', 'Play that Funky Music', 'Sound Your Funky Horn')

Q5
Lady Antebellum

Q6
'Broken Wings', 'Kyrie' (both No.1 in the USA)

Q7
Otis Redding

Q8
'Shut Up and Let Me Go'

Q9
Polly Jean

Q10
'Strawberry Fields Forever'

QUIZ 203 POPMASTER

QUIZ 201

Q1
David Gates

Q2
'Together in Electric Dreams'

Q3
Alphabeat

Q4
'Fly Away'

Q5
Roman Holliday

Q6
Stars

Q7
Per Gessle, Marie Fredriksson

Q8
'I'm on Fire', 'Doctor Kiss-Kiss'

Q9
Bee Gees

Q10
'Laura', 'Mary'

QUESTION 1
Both of the lead singers with Genesis in the 1970s have also had successful solo careers. Name both of them.

QUESTION 2
'Billy-Ray' was the subject of the lyrics of Dusty Springfield's final Top 10 hit of the 1960s. What was it called?

QUESTION 3
One of the most successful UK groups of the Noughties consisted of Tom Fletcher, Danny Jones, Dougie Poynter and Harry Judd. Name the group.

QUESTION 4
What one word has provided the title for different hit songs by Tears for Fears in 1983, Lisa Stansfield in 1991 and The Lightning Seeds in 1995?

QUESTION 5
Which American band made its debut on the UK singles chart in 2012 with 'Radioactive', taken from their album Night Visions, a Top 3 hit in 2013?

QUESTION 6
Which group had hits in the mid-Seventies with 'Only You Can', 'Imagine Me Imagine You' and 'S-S-S-Single Bed'?

QUESTION 7
Which Rolling Stones song gave Susan Boyle a Top 10 single in December 2009?

QUESTION 8
Name the American singer who had Top 10 hits in the '90s called 'Breathe Again', 'Un-Break My Heart' and 'I Don't Want To'.

QUESTION 9
Leapy Lee had 'Little…' ones, ABC had a 'Poison…' one, and Pixie Lott had a 'Broken…' one. What are they?

QUESTION 10
'Take Me to the Mardi Gras' was a hit in 1973 for which American singer-songwriter?

POPMASTER QUIZ 204

QUESTION 1
Which influential Manchester band had Top 10 singles in 1990 with 'Elephant Stone' and 'One Love'?

QUESTION 2
The 2002 debut hit by Darius was also the singer's only No 1 single – what was it called?

QUESTION 3
Which group had hits in the first half of the Seventies with 'One and One is One', 'Rising Sun' and 'Slip and Slide'?

QUESTION 4
The American group Mr Big had its biggest hit in 1992 with a song that was Top 3 in the UK and No 1 in the States. What is it called?

QUESTION 5
Prior to announcing a group hiatus, which member of One Direction reduced the group from a five-piece to a quartet?

QUESTION 6
Which group sang about a 'Honaloochie Boogie' in 1973?

QUESTION 7
Who was the lead singer with The Stranglers during the 1970s and 1980s?

QUESTION 8
Released in 2010 and 2012, Ellie Goulding's first two albums both reached No 1. Name either of them.

QUESTION 9
Who was Nile Rodgers' writing and production partner on hits for Sister Sledge, Chic, Diana Ross and Sheila & B. Devotion?

QUESTION 10
When The Beatles' Anthology series was released in the mid-'90s, two John Lennon songs were reworked by the remaining Beatles and released as singles. Name either of these Top 5 hits.

QUIZ 202

Q1 *Phil, Don*

Q2 *'Rescue Me'*

Q3 *Soul II Soul*

Q4 *'Rock On'*

Q5 *Coldplay*

Q6 *Afro*

Q7 *Kylie Minogue*

Q8 *Common ('Fanfare for the Common Man', 'Love of the Common People', 'Common People')*

Q9 *Brotherhood of Man (UK Eurovision Song Contest entries, 1972-1976)*

Q10 *Robert Howard (known as Dr Robert in The Blow Monkeys)*

QUIZ 203

Q1
Peter Gabriel, Phil Collins

Q2
'Son of a Preacher Man'

Q3
McFly

Q4
'Change'

Q5
Imagine Dragons

Q6
Fox

Q7
'Wild Horses'

Q8
Toni Braxton

Q9
Arrows ('Little Arrows', 'Poison Arrow', 'Broken Arrow')

Q10
Paul Simon

QUIZ 205 POPMASTER

QUESTION 1
Talking Heads made their UK singles chart debut in 1981 with the song 'Once in a…' what?

QUESTION 2
The 2001 Top 5 song 'Nobody Wants to be Lonely' was recorded by Ricky Martin and which American female singer?

QUESTION 3
What girls name provided the title of Blondie's 1999 comeback No 1 single?

QUESTION 4
The 1979 single 'King Rocker' was the biggest hit for a group that featured Billy Idol as lead singer. What were they called?

QUESTION 5
Gordon Haskell made his only Top 40 appearance with a 2001 song that reached No 2. What was it called?

QUESTION 6
The group Freeez had two Top 10 singles in the early 1980s. Name either of them.

QUESTION 7
Which Canadian singer reached No 1 in 2006 with her single 'Maneater'?

QUESTION 8
What was '…in Your Soul', according to the title of the 1990 Top 10 single by They Might be Giants?

QUESTION 9
The songs 'All of Me Loves All of You', 'Summerlove Sensation' and 'Love Me Like I Love You' were all Top 10 songs in the mid-1970s for which group?

QUESTION 10
Black Sabbath had a No 1 album in 1970 with Paranoid, the group's second studio album. Their next No 1 album came in 2013 with their 19th studio album. What was this album called?

POPMASTER QUIZ 206

QUESTION 1
Which American city features in the title of songs in the Seventies by T.Rex, Hello and Darts?

QUESTION 2
The 2006 hits 'You Give Me Something', 'Wonderful World' and 'The Pieces Don't Fit Anymore' all featured on the No 1 album Undiscovered by which singer-songwriter?

QUESTION 3
Released in 1983, which Top 10 single by Mike Oldfield featured vocals by Maggie Reilly?

QUESTION 4
Who sang about 'Galveston' in 1969?

QUESTION 5
What was the one-word title of the 1995 Top 3 duet by Michael Jackson and Janet Jackson?

QUESTION 6
Who released Top 5 albums in 2011 called Director's Cut and 50 Words for Snow?

QUESTION 7
Released in 1975, what is the title of the only Top 10 single by Pete Wingfield?

QUESTION 8
Who comes next in this sequence – Tina Turner, Sheryl Crow, Garbage, Madonna... ?

QUESTION 9
The Housemartins had a No 1 single during their chart career in the 1980s. What was it called?

QUESTION 10
Name the Scottish group that had hits in the mid-1970s with 'This Flight Tonight', 'Bad Bad Boy' and 'My White Bicycle'.

QUIZ 204

Q1 *The Stone Roses*

Q2 *'Colourblind'*

Q3 *Medicine Head*

Q4 *'To be with You'*

Q5 *Zayn Malik*

Q6 *Mott the Hoople*

Q7 *Hugh Cornwell*

Q8 *Lights ('10), Halcyon ('12)*

Q9 *Bernard Edwards*

Q10 *'Free as a Bird', 'Real Love'*

QUIZ 207 POPMASTER

QUESTION 1
Which hit by The Beatles that topped the chart for six weeks in 1969 credited Billy Preston on the label?

QUESTION 2
Can you name the singer who first made the top forty in 1993 with 'Caught in the Middle' who then reached the top twenty the following year after being re-mixed?

QUESTION 3
'No More (Baby I'ma do Right)' was a Top 10 hit in 2001 for which American vocal group?

QUESTION 4
Can you name the singer whose second of four top forty hits from 2005 was titled 'Other Side of the World'?

QUESTION 5
Which 1969 top twenty hit by Jackie Wilson was successfully re-issued in 1975 as part of a double 'A' side with 'I Get the Sweetest Feeling'?

QUESTION 6
Who topped the UK singles chart in 2015 with a song called 'Marvin Gaye' that featured vocals by Meghan Trainor?

QUESTION 7
Can you name the act that topped the chart for four weeks in 1995 with 'Boom Boom Boom'?

QUESTION 8
In 1969, after achieving two Top 10 hits, which group just failed to make the top forty with 'Are You Growing Tired of My Love', but later went on to have dozens more hits?

QUESTION 9
What is the title of the song that was a top twenty hit in 1964 for The Ronettes and a Top 10 hit in 1980 for the Ramones?

QUESTION 10
Which famous actor joins Sharleen Spiteri and Texas in the video for their 2000 Top 10 hit song 'In Demand'?

QUIZ 205

Q1
Lifetime

Q2
Christina Aguilera

Q3
'Maria'

Q4
Generation X

Q5
'How Wonderful You Are'

Q6
'Southern Freeez', 'I.O.U.'

Q7
Nelly Furtado

Q8
Birdhouse

Q9
Bay City Rollers

Q10
13

POPMASTER QUIZ 208

QUESTION 1
'Running Bear' was one of two Top 3 hits for Johnny Preston in 1960. What was the other?

QUESTION 2
Who topped the chart for the fourth time with his 2011 single 'The Lazy Song'?

QUESTION 3
Can you name the duo who recorded the 1975 Top 10 hit 'Blue Guitar'?

QUESTION 4
Can you name the Spanish singer who topped the singles chart for four weeks in 2002 with 'Hero'?

QUESTION 5
Which group took Dan Hartman's 1978 Top 10 hit 'Instant Replay' back into the chart in 1990?

QUESTION 6
What song title is shared by a Top 10 hit from 1983 by Musical Youth and a 1987 No 1 by Rick Astley?

QUESTION 7
According to Lieutenant Pigeon's 1972 No 1 hit, what was 'Mouldy'?

QUESTION 8
Can you name the group that topped the chart in 2010 with 'This Ain't a Love Song'?

QUESTION 9
Which legendary female singer achieved Top 5 hits in the Fifties with 'Mr Wonderful' and 'Fever'?

QUESTION 10
Can you name the crooner who made the Top 10 in 1962 with a song called 'Softly as I Leave You'?

QUIZ 206

Q1
New York ('New York City', 'New York Groove', 'Boy from New York City')

Q2
James Morrison

Q3
'Moonlight Shadow'

Q4
Glen Campbell

Q5
'Scream'

Q6
Kate Bush

Q7
'Eighteen with a Bullet'

Q8
Chris Cornell (James Bond theme songs, 1997-2006)

Q9
'Caravan of Love'

Q10
Nazareth

QUIZ 207

Q1 'Get Back'

Q2 Juliet Roberts

Q3 3LW

Q4 KT Tunstall

Q5 '(Your Love Keeps Lifting Me) Higher and Higher'

Q6 Charlie Puth

Q7 The Outhere Brothers

Q8 Status Quo

Q9 'Baby, I Love You'

Q10 Alan Rickman

QUIZ 209 POPMASTER

QUESTION 1
From 1973, what was the title of the only Top 5 hit by The Hotshots that was a cover of the original 1967 hit by The Royal Guardsmen?

QUESTION 2
Can you name the Andrew Lloyd Webber and Tim Rice musical that provided Boyzone with their 1998 chart-topping single 'No Matter What'?

QUESTION 3
Petula Clark achieved two No 1 hits in the Sixties. The first was called 'Sailor', but what was the title of the other?

QUESTION 4
Can you name the singer who topped the chart in 2011 with his hit single 'Dance with Me Tonight'?

QUESTION 5
In 1980, which duo topped the American chart and achieved their only UK Top 10 hit with 'Do that to Me One More Time'?

QUESTION 6
Which female singer achieved a top twenty hit in 1997 with the title song to the James Bond movie *Tomorrow Never Dies*?

QUESTION 7
Which rock band topped the albums chart in 1992 with Automatic for the People?

QUESTION 8
According to her 1993 Top 10 hit, which female singer was looking in 'All the Right Places'?

QUESTION 9
In 1985, Aled Jones reached the Top 10 with the song 'Walking in the Air' that came from which famous animated movie?

QUESTION 10
What was the title of Paul Simon's first solo Top 5 hit in 1972 after his break-up with Art Garfunkel?

POPMASTER QUIZ 210

QUIZ 208

QUESTION 1
Which legendary rock and roll singer scored a top twenty hit in 1961 with a song called 'Weekend'?

QUESTION 2
Shakatak scored two Top 10 hits in the Eighties. The first was 'Night Birds', but what was the title of the other?

QUESTION 3
What song title is shared by a Top 10 hit from 1973 by The O'Jays and a 1989 Top 5 hit by Holly Johnson?

QUESTION 4
Under what name did British male producer Dave Lee release 'American Dream', his mainly instrumental debut Top 3 hit from 2001?

QUESTION 5
Can you name the group that topped the chart in 1976 with 'Forever and Ever' and included Midge Ure in their line-up?

QUESTION 6
From 1969, Zager and Evans became the only duo to date whose name begins with a 'Z' to top both the UK and American charts. What was the title of their No 1 hit?

QUESTION 7
Can you name the female vocal group that made their chart debut in 2008 with 'If This is Love'?

QUESTION 8
What was the title of the 1999 top twenty hit by The Three Amigos that was also featured in the movie *American Pie*?

QUESTION 9
Who wrote the 1982 top twenty hit 'Ziggy Stardust', by Northampton group Bauhaus?

QUESTION 10
In 1969, which group achieved the last of their four top twenty hits with 'In the Bad Bad Old Days (Before You Loved Me)'?

Q1 *'Cradle of Love'*

Q2 *Bruno Mars*

Q3 *Justin Hayward and John Lodge*

Q4 *Enrique Iglesias*

Q5 *Yell!*

Q6 *'Never Gonna Give You Up'*

Q7 *Old Dough*

Q8 *Scouting for Girls*

Q9 *Peggy Lee*

Q10 *Matt Monro*

QUIZ 209

Q1
'Snoopy vs The Red Baron'

Q2
Whistle Down the Wind

Q3
'This is My Song'

Q4
Olly Murs

Q5
Captain and Tennille

Q6
Sheryl Crow

Q7
R.E.M.

Q8
Lisa Stansfield

Q9
The Snowman

Q10
'Mother and Child Reunion'

QUIZ 211 POPMASTER

QUESTION 1
Australian group The Easybeats achieved two top twenty hits in the Sixties – the first was 'Friday on My Mind', but what was the title of the other song?

QUESTION 2
Which successful act made the Top 10 in 2004 with their hit single 'Comfortably Numb'?

QUESTION 3
Can you name the group that achieved a Top 10 hit in 1971 with 'What are You Doing Sunday'?

QUESTION 4
Which band made their 1990 top forty chart debut with 'The Groovy Train'?

QUESTION 5
Which Birmingham ska band made their 1979 Top 10 chart debut with the double 'A'-sided hit 'Tears of a Clown' and 'Ranking Full Stop'?

QUESTION 6
Can you name the female singer who topped the chart in 2013 with 'We Can't Stop'?

QUESTION 7
From 1988, which group achieved their 11th top forty hit with 'King of Emotion'?

QUESTION 8
In which 1962 movie did Elvis Presley first feature his double 'A'-sided No 1 hits 'Rock-a-Hula-Baby' and 'Can't Help Falling in Love'?

QUESTION 9
According to their 1980 Top 10 hit, which legendary group experienced an 'Emotional Rescue'?

QUESTION 10
Can you name the American rock band that made the Top 5 in 2001 with a cover of Erasure's 1988 hit 'A Little Respect'?

POPMASTER QUIZ 212

QUIZ 210

QUESTION 1
According to her 2008 top twenty hit, which female singer gave us the 'Cold Shoulder'?

QUESTION 2
From 1960, can you name the only Top 10 hit achieved by the Danish husband and wife duo Nina and Frederik?

QUESTION 3
American group The Manhattans scored two Top 10 hits in 1976 – the first was 'Kiss and Say Goodbye', but what was the title of the other hit?

QUESTION 4
In 2005, which female singer made the Top 5 with 'Nine Million Bicycles'?

QUESTION 5
From 1980, what was the title of the only top forty hit by Australian duo Air Supply?

QUESTION 6
'Black or White' by Michael Jackson topped both the UK and American charts in 1991, but which famous musician was featured playing the guitar solo?

QUESTION 7
Which Swiss singer and songwriter scored a top twenty hit in 1978 with 'I Love America'?

QUESTION 8
According to their 1991 No 2 hit, which group climbed aboard the 'Last Train to Trancentral'?

QUESTION 9
In which 1962 movie did Elvis Presley first feature his No 1 hit 'Return to Sender'?

QUESTION 10
Can you name the British group that made their Top 10 chart debut in 2004 with 'Pressure Point...'?

Q1
Eddie Cochran

Q2
'Down on the Street'

Q3
'Love Train'

Q4
Jakatta

Q5
Slik

Q6
'In the Year 2525 (Exordium and Terminus)'

Q7
The Saturdays

Q8
'Louie Louie'

Q9
David Bowie

Q10
The Foundations

QUIZ 211

Q1
'Hello, How Are You'

Q2
Scissor Sisters

Q3
Dawn featuring Tony Orlando

Q4
The Farm

Q5
The Beat

Q6
Miley Cyrus

Q7
Big Country

Q8
Blue Hawaii

Q9
The Rolling Stones

Q10
Wheatus

QUIZ 213 POPMASTER

QUESTION 1
In what year did Go West make their chart debut with 'We Close Our Eyes'?

QUESTION 2
Which group achieved two Top 10 hits in 1998 with 'Come Back to What You Know' and 'My Weakness is None of Your Business'?

QUESTION 3
In 1985, which singer, songwriter and drummer's ninth solo top twenty hit was titled 'Take Me Home'?

QUESTION 4
Can you remember the title of the song by Geraldine – aka Peter Kay – that crashed into the chart at No 2 in 2008?

QUESTION 5
In 1993, a single by Take That featuring Lulu entered the chart at No 1. Can you remember the title?

QUESTION 6
Desmond Dekker & The Aces topped the singles chart in 1969 with 'Israelites', and the follow-up also made the Top 10. Can you name it?

QUESTION 7
Can you name the group that reached the Top 3 in 1984 mainly due to the popularity of their record 'Agadoo' in holiday resorts abroad?

QUESTION 8
Apart from their No 1 with Baddiel & Skinner, can you name the only other single by The Lightning Seeds to make the Top 10 in the Nineties?

QUESTION 9
Can you name the group that achieved a No 1 album in 1969 with On the Threshold of a Dream?

QUESTION 10
Which singer topped the chart for four weeks in 2003 with his single 'Ignition'?

POPMASTER QUIZ 214

QUESTION 1
Which legendary easy listening singer achieved his last solo top twenty hit of the Seventies with the disco-flavoured 'Gone, Gone, Gone'?

QUESTION 2
Can you name the group that had their first UK Top 10 hit in 1995 with 'I've Got a Little Something for You'?

QUESTION 3
In 1995, and with the help of Vic Reeves and Bob Mortimer, which group successfully revived The Monkees' 1967 chart-topper 'I'm a Believer'?

QUESTION 4
Can you name the group that made the top twenty in 1981 with 'Sgt Rock (Is Going to Help Me)'?

QUESTION 5
Which female singer reached the top twenty in 1973 with her version of John Denver's song 'Take Me Home Country Roads'?

QUESTION 6
In 1985, German keyboard player Harold Faltermeyer reached No 2 in the chart with 'Axel F', but can you name the group that took the song back into the Top 10 in 1995?

QUESTION 7
In 1980, The Jam scored a double 'A'-sided No 1 hit. 'Going Underground' was on one side, but what was on the other?

QUESTION 8
Can you name the female singer who once sang with Soul II Soul and scored her own top twenty hit in 1990 with 'Livin' in the Light'?

QUESTION 9
Fairground Attraction topped the chart in 1988 with 'Perfect', and their follow-up also made the Top 10 in the same year. What was the title?

QUESTION 10
Can you name the group that achieved a top twenty hit in 1999 with a hit called 'The Kids Aren't Alright' that was featured in the movie *The Faculty* the same year?

QUIZ 212

Q1 *Adele*

Q2 *'Little Donkey'*

Q3 *'Hurt'*

Q4 *Katie Melua*

Q5 *'All out of Love'*

Q6 *Slash from Guns N' Roses*

Q7 *Patrick Juvet*

Q8 *The KLF*

Q9 Girls! Girls! Girls!

Q10 *The Zutons*

QUIZ 215 POPMASTER

QUIZ 213

Q1
1985

Q2
Embrace

Q3
Phil Collins

Q4
'The Winner's Song'

Q5
'Relight My Fire'

Q6
'It Miek'

Q7
Black Lace

Q8
'You Showed Me'

Q9
The Moody Blues

Q10
R Kelly

QUESTION 1
Which successful boy band scored a Top 5 hit in 1996 with 'Coming Home Now'?

QUESTION 2
Apart from singer and actor David Soul's two No 1 hits, 'Don't Give Up on Us' and 'Silver Lady', can you name either of his other two Top 10 hits?

QUESTION 3
Can you name the comedy actor who reached the top forty in 2001 with 'Are You Lookin' at Me'?

QUESTION 4
Which female singer recorded a 1985 Top 5 cover version of Michael Jackson's hit from 1972 called 'Ben'?

QUESTION 5
The Drifters scored debut hits in the Sixties with songs that both included the word 'Dance' in the title – one was 'Save the Last Dance for Me', but what was the title of their first chart entry?

QUESTION 6
Can you name the group that achieved their first Top 10 hit in 1993 with 'Too Young to Die'?

QUESTION 7
What was the name of the Australian singer who reached the Top 10 in 2008 with 'Black and Gold'?

QUESTION 8
According to his 1983 Top 3 hit, which Guyanan-born performer was walking down 'Electric Avenue'?

QUESTION 9
Can you name the band whose album Are You Experienced made the Top 10 in 1967?

QUESTION 10
Which duo made the Top 3 in 1997 with the theme tune to the movie *The Saint*?

POPMASTER QUIZ 216

QUIZ 214

QUESTION 1
Which 1954 Johnnie Ray No 1 did Elvis Presley successfully revive in 1964?

Q1 *Johnny Mathis*

QUESTION 2
Can you name the female singer who achieved a Top 10 hit in 2007 with 'No One'?

Q2 *MN8*

QUESTION 3
In 1991, Scritti Politti – with more than a little help from Shabba Ranks – made the top twenty with which Lennon and McCartney song?

Q3 *EMF*

QUESTION 4
Released in 1980, what was the title of the only top forty hit by American singer Stacy Lattisaw?

Q4 *XTC*

QUESTION 5
Can you name the group whose single 'All I Need is a Miracle' was first released in 1986 but failed to make the top forty until re-issued and re-mixed in 1996?

Q5 *Olivia Newton-John*

QUESTION 6
The duo Hudson-Ford had two top twenty hits in the Seventies. The first was 'Pick Up the Pieces' – what was the title of the second?

Q6 *Clock*

QUESTION 7
Which group's first Top 10 hit came in 1996 with 'Stupid Girl', which contained a sample of 'Train in Vain' by The Clash?

Q7 *'Dreams of Children'*

QUESTION 8
Which legendary guitarist and singer had a No 1 album in 1994 called From the Cradle?

Q8 *Caron Wheeler*

QUESTION 9
In 2008, Leona Lewis achieved a No 2 hit with a double 'A'-sided release. One of the songs was 'Better in Time', but what was the title of the religious-themed ballad on the other side?

Q9 *'Find My Love'*

QUESTION 10
Name the singer who made his top 40 debut in 1960 with 'Lucky Devil' – more than two years before he scored his first No 1.

Q10 *The Offspring*

QUIZ 215

Q1
Boyzone

Q2
'Going in with My Eyes Open', 'Let's Have a Quiet Night In'

Q3
Ricky Tomlinson

Q4
Marti Webb

Q5
'Dance with Me'

Q6
Jamiroquai

Q7
Sam Sparro

Q8
Eddy Grant

Q9
The Jimi Hendrix Experience

Q10
Orbital

QUIZ 217 POPMASTER

QUESTION 1
From which successful movie did the 1994 Top 10 hit single 'All for Love', by Bryan Adams, Rod Stewart and Sting, come?

QUESTION 2
In 1980, The Tourists scored a Top 10 hit with 'So Good to be Back Home', but which more successful act did they evolve into?

QUESTION 3
Can you name the Top 10 hit from 1967 by Herman's Hermits that was successfully revived in 1976 by the Carpenters?

QUESTION 4
Which 1997 No 1 hit by Eternal featured vocals by Bebe Winans?

QUESTION 5
What is the song title shared by a Top 3 hit by Racey in 1979, a Top 10 hit by Ultimate Kaos in 1994 and a No 2 hit by Rachel Stevens, also from 2004?

QUESTION 6
In the Eighties, Wham! achieved four consecutive Top 10 hits with their first four releases. Can you name the first?

QUESTION 7
According to his 1975 top twenty hit, which singer-songwriter claimed 'I Don't Love You but I Think I Like You'?

QUESTION 8
From 1985, what was the title of the top twenty hit recorded by Lisa Lisa and Cult Jam with Full Force?

QUESTION 9
Can you name the rock band that topped the albums chart in 1971 with Fireball?

QUESTION 10
What was the title of the official song of the England World Cup football squad from 2002 that became a Top 10 hit for Ant & Dec?

POPMASTER QUIZ 218

QUIZ 216

Q1 *'Such a Night'*

Q2 *Alicia Keys*

Q3 *'She's a Woman'*

Q4 *'Jump to the Beat'*

Q5 *Mike & The Mechanics*

Q6 *'Burn Baby Burn'*

Q7 *Garbage*

Q8 *Eric Clapton*

Q9 *'Footprints in the Sand'*

Q10 *Frank Ifield*

QUESTION 1
In 1974, Johnny Bristol achieved his only hit as a performer with 'Hang on in There Baby' – the same year he wrote the only No 1 for The Osmonds. What was the title?

QUESTION 2
Procol Harum topped the chart in 1967 with 'A Whiter Shade of Pale' and their follow-up became their only other Top 10 hit. Can you remember the title?

QUESTION 3
What is the song title shared by Anita Ward's 1979 No 1 hit and the 1991 top twenty hit by Monie Love vs Adeva?

QUESTION 4
Can you name the female group that achieved a Top 10 hit in 2001 with 'All Hooked Up'?

QUESTION 5
Which group made their top forty debut in 2001 with a song called 'Red'?

QUESTION 6
The late Bobby Darin achieved two No 1 hits in 1959 – the first was 'Dream Lover', what was the second?

QUESTION 7
McFly scored a No 1 in 2007 with their double 'A'-sided hit 'Baby's Coming Back'. What was the other song on the release?

QUESTION 8
Which family group's only No 1 album was their 1986 release Silk and Steel?

QUESTION 9
Can you name the female singer who achieved a Top 10 hit in 2003 with 'Mixed Up World'?

QUESTION 10
Fine Young Cannibals achieved a number of hits in the Eighties, but only one of their records made the top twenty in the Nineties. Can you name it?

QUIZ 219 POPMASTER

QUESTION 1
Which 1978 top twenty hit by Billy Joel did Barry White take back into the chart towards the end of the same year?

QUESTION 2
What was the title of Marty Wilde's 1961 Top 10 hit that was an even bigger hit in the same year for the original American version by Bobby Vee?

QUESTION 3
'Doo Wop (That Thing)' was the first solo Top 10 hit by Lauryn Hill, who had previously been a member of two successful groups. Can you name either of them?

QUESTION 4
Can you name the group that topped the albums chart in 1993 with Walthamstow?

QUESTION 5
In 1961, two versions of the title theme to the movie *Pepe* made the top twenty. The bigger hit was by Duane Eddy, but who recorded the other version?

QUESTION 6
In 1990, Twenty 4 Seven featuring Captain Hollywood achieved two top twenty hits – the second was 'Are You Dreaming', but what was the title of the first?

QUESTION 7
In 1981, which group reached the Top 10 for the first time in nearly six years with 'We'll Bring the House Down'?

QUESTION 8
Can you name the rapper who topped the chart in 2000 with his single 'Stan'?

QUESTION 9
The title track of Lemar's second album was a Top 10 single for the singer in 2005 – what was it called?

QUESTION 10
Can you name the singer-songwriter who had his only top forty hit in 1979 with 'Just When I Needed You Most'?

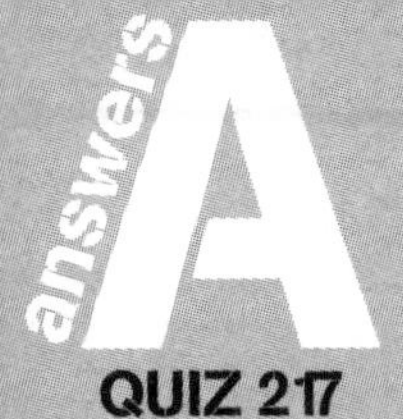

QUIZ 217

Q1
The Three Musketeers

Q2
Eurythmics

Q3
'There's a Kind of Hush'

Q4
'I Wanna be the Only One'

Q5
'Some Girls'

Q6
'Young Guns (Go for It)'

Q7
Gilbert O'Sullivan

Q8
'I Wonder if I Take You Home'

Q9
Deep Purple

Q10
'We're on the Ball'

POPMASTER QUIZ 220

QUESTION 1
The American R&B group Raydio achieved two top forty hits in the Seventies – the first was 'Jack and Jill', but can you name the second?

QUESTION 2
What was the title of Bitty McLean's 1994 Top 10 hit that had originally been a hit in 1967 for The Mamas and The Papas?

QUESTION 3
Which successful group made their final appearance in the Top 10 with 'Big Apple'?

QUESTION 4
In 1979, which Jamaican singer made the top twenty for the first and only time in his career with 'Money in My Pocket'?

QUESTION 5
From the year 2000, can you name the French group who topped the UK chart with 'Lady (Hear Me Tonight)'?

QUESTION 6
Can you name the singer-songwriter who topped the albums chart in 1987 with ...Nothing Like the Sun?

QUESTION 7
In 1979, which soul group made their final appearance in the top forty with 'Sing a Happy Song'?

QUESTION 8
What hit song title is shared by Billy Fury in 1961, Pet Shop Boys in 1991 and Will Young in 2011?

QUESTION 9
Which rock band had a Top 10 hit in 1995 with 'This Ain't a Love Song'?

QUESTION 10
As a duo, what was the collective name with which David Grant and Peter "Sketch" Martin scored their only Top 10 hit with 'Intuition' in 1981?

QUIZ 218

Q1 *'Love Me for a Reason'*

Q2 *'Homburg'*

Q3 *'Ring My Bell'*

Q4 *All Saints*

Q5 *Elbow*

Q6 *'Mack the Knife'*

Q7 *'Transylvania'*

Q8 *Five Star*

Q9 *Sophie Ellis-Bextor*

Q10 *'The Flame'*

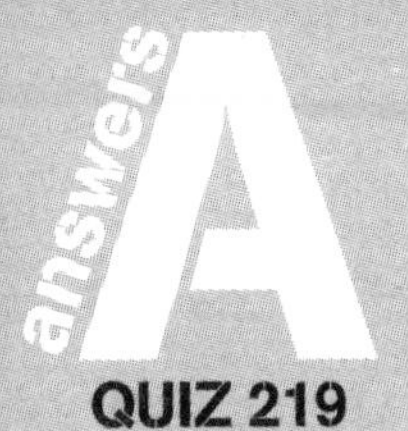

QUIZ 219

Q1
'Just the Way You Are'

Q2
'Rubber Ball'

Q3
Fugees, Refugee All Stars

Q4
East 17

Q5
Russ Conway

Q6
'I Can't Stand It'

Q7
Slade

Q8
Eminem

Q9
'Time to Grow'

Q10
Randy Vanwarmer

QUIZ 221 POPMASTER

QUESTION 1
Which group's only Top 10 hit came in 1970 with a revival of The Animals' 1964 No 1 'The House of the Rising Sun'?

QUESTION 2
Can you name the Irish female singer who had Top 5 hits in the Fifties with 'Softly, Softly',' 'Let Me Go Lover' and 'Evermore'?

QUESTION 3
Harold Melvin & The Blue Notes scored two Top 10 hits in the Seventies. The first was 'If You Don't Know Me by Now', but what was the title of the second?

QUESTION 4
In 1993, which group achieved a Top 3 hit with 'Exterminate!' that was featured in the movie *Batman Returns*?

QUESTION 5
Can you name the band that topped the albums chart in 2015 with How Big, How Blue, How Beautiful?

QUESTION 6
Under what name did Linda Green and Herbert Feemster record their 1979 Top 5 hit 'Reunited'?

QUESTION 7
'It's Your Day Today' became the last of 11 top forty entries for this singer in the Sixties. Can you name him?

QUESTION 8
Which female singer topped the singles chart for two weeks in 2009 with 'Fight for this Love'?

QUESTION 9
From 1978, what was the title of the only top twenty hit by Blue Öyster Cult?

QUESTION 10
Which hit song made the top forty in 1978 for Rose Royce, Jimmy Nail in 1985 and Double Trouble featuring Janette Sewell and Carl Brown in 1990?

POPMASTER QUIZ 222

QUESTION 1
Anthony Newley achieved two No 1 hits in 1960. The first was called 'Why', but what was the title of the second?

QUESTION 2
Can you name the vocal trio who topped the chart in 2004 with 'Baby Cakes'?

QUESTION 3
Released at the end of 1979, what is the title of the Top 3 hit duet by Billy Preston and Syreeta that was featured in the movie *Fastbreak*?

QUESTION 4
Which group had a top twenty hit in the early Seventies with the song 'Come Softly to Me' that had previously been a Top 10 hit for both The Fleetwoods and Frankie Vaughan and The Kaye Sisters in 1959?

QUESTION 5
Can you name the act that topped the albums chart in 2015 with Wilder Mind?

QUESTION 6
From 1978, what was the title of the only top twenty hit achieved by Australian singer John Paul Young?

QUESTION 7
Which legendary pop star released the single 'Golden' in 2015 in celebration of his 75th birthday?

QUESTION 8
Can you name the female singer who made the Top 10 in 2004 with 'Don't Tell Me' and 'My Happy Ending'?

QUESTION 9
What was the title of the 1973 top twenty hit by New York City that The Pasadenas took into the Top 5 in 1992?

QUESTION 10
Which 1964 top twenty hit by Elvis Presley did ZZ Top take all the way into the Top 10 in 1992?

QUIZ 220

Q1 *'Is this a Love Thing'*

Q2 *'Dedicated to the One I Love'*

Q3 *Kajagoogoo*

Q4 *Dennis Brown*

Q5 *Modjo*

Q6 *Sting*

Q7 *The O'Jays*

Q8 *'Jealousy'*

Q9 *Bon Jovi*

Q10 *Linx*

QUIZ 221

Q1
Frijid Pink

Q2
Ruby Murray

Q3
'Don't Leave Me this Way'

Q4
Snap! (featuring Niki Haris)

Q5
Florence + The Machine

Q6
Peaches and Herb

Q7
P.J. Proby

Q8
Cheryl Cole

Q9
'(Don't Fear) the Reaper'

Q10
'Love Don't Live Here Anymore'

QUIZ 223 POPMASTER

QUESTION 1
In 1966, which female singer achieved her eighth consecutive top forty hit with 'Nothing Comes Easy'?

QUESTION 2
From 1980, what was the title of the only No 1 hit achieved by American R&B group Odyssey?

QUESTION 3
Which American singer-songwriter achieved his only Top 10 hit in 1978 with 'Lucky Star'?

QUESTION 4
Can you name the group that achieved two top twenty hits in the Nineties with 'Sixty Mile Smile' and 'Beautiful Day'?

QUESTION 5
What was the title of the 1987 Top 3 hit by Mental as Anything that was featured in the movie *Crocodile Dundee*?

QUESTION 6
Which Canadian singer was featured on Chris Brown's 2011 top twenty hit 'Next to You'?

QUESTION 7
Over the years, whose group, The Bluesbreakers, has included Eric Clapton, Peter Green and Mick Taylor in its line-up?

QUESTION 8
The Bee Gees achieved two No 1 hits in the Sixties – 'Massachusetts' was the first one, what was the other?

QUESTION 9
Can you name the band that topped the albums chart in 2002 with Heathen Chemistry?

QUESTION 10
What was the title of the 1979 chart hit by Patrick Hernandez, the one-time backing singer for Madonna?

POPMASTER QUIZ 224

QUIZ 222

QUESTION 1
In 1970, the soul act The Chairmen of the Board scored two Top 10 hits – the first was 'Give Me Just a Little More Time', but what was the title of the second?

QUESTION 2
Can you name the group that achieved their first top twenty hit in 1982 with 'Promised You a Miracle'?

QUESTION 3
In 1972, Andy Williams released a song with the subtitle '(Speak Softly Love)' that was the love theme from which classic movie?

QUESTION 4
What is the name of the actress who has been a cast regular in *Coronation Street* since the Eighties (playing Audrey Roberts) who had a Top 10 hit in 1968 with 'Where Will You Be'?

QUESTION 5
Can you name the rock band that topped the albums chart in 2011 with Wasting Light?

QUESTION 6
What was the title of the 1995 top twenty hit by Jimmy Somerville that had previously been a 1975 Top 5 hit for Susan Cadogan?

QUESTION 7
Which group released their single 'Lucky You' in 1994 but didn't see it make the top forty until its re-issue the following year?

QUESTION 8
Can you name the French duo that made their chart debut in 1998 with 'Sexy Boy'?

QUESTION 9
Released in 1963, what was the title of the only No 1 hit achieved by The Dave Clark Five, at the start of 1964?

QUESTION 10
Which legendary female singer topped both the American and UK charts in 1980 with the Barry and Robin Gibb song 'Woman in Love'?

Q1 *'Do You Mind'*

Q2 *3 of a Kind*

Q3 *'With You I'm Born Again'*

Q4 *The New Seekers*

Q5 *Mumford & Sons*

Q6 *'Love is in the Air'*

Q7 *Cliff Richard*

Q8 *Avril Lavigne*

Q9 *'I'm Doin' Fine Now' (spelt 'Doing' on the Pasadenas version)*

Q10 *'Viva Las Vegas'*

QUIZ 223

Q1
Sandie Shaw

Q2
'Use it Up and Wear it Out'

Q3
Dean Friedman

Q4
3 Colours Red

Q5
'Live it Up'

Q6
Justin Bieber

Q7
John Mayall

Q8
'I've Gotta Get a Message to You'

Q9
Oasis

Q10
'Born to be Alive'

QUIZ 225 POPMASTER

QUESTION 1
Which group reached the Top 5 in 1967 with their hit single 'Zabadak!'?

QUESTION 2
In 1978, Glasgow-born Frankie Miller achieved his only UK Top 10 hit. What was the title?

QUESTION 3
Can you name the pianist and orchestra leader whose only hit made the Top 5 in 1963 with the theme from the movie *The Legion's Last Patrol*?

QUESTION 4
Which rock performer's Top 10 album, released in 1983, was called Midnight at the Lost and Found?

QUESTION 5
Can you name the Lionel Bart musical which featured Harry Secombe's 1963 top twenty hit 'If I Ruled the World'?

QUESTION 6
What was the title of the 1991 Top 10 duet by Kylie Minogue and Keith Washington?

QUESTION 7
Can you name the *X Factor* winner who had the 2010 Christmas No 1 with 'When We Collide'?

QUESTION 8
As featured in the Seventies TV series *Rock Follies*, what was the only chart hit for its stars – Julie Covington, Rula Lenska, Charlotte Cornwell and Sue Jones-Davies?

QUESTION 9
Which group ended a run of five consecutive Top 10 hits in the Nineties with 'Sun Hits the Sky'?

QUESTION 10
First released in the Sixties, which Tamla Motown single by The Elgins failed to chart until it was re-issued in 1971, making the Top 3?

POPMASTER QUIZ 226

QUESTION 1
According to their 1979 hit album and single, which group were enjoying 'Breakfast in America'?

QUESTION 2
What was the title of Junior's 1982 chart debut and only solo Top 10 hit?

QUESTION 3
Which country and western singer topped the chart for 11 weeks in 1955 with 'Rose Marie'?

QUESTION 4
In 1972, David Cassidy achieved his first solo hit – a double 'A' side that peaked at No 2. One of the songs was 'Could it be Forever' – what was the other?

QUESTION 5
In the year 2000, Coldplay had their first top twenty hit. What was the title?

QUESTION 6
Between 1996 and 1997, Alisha's Attic had three consecutive hits that all peaked at number 12 in the chart. Can you name one of these hits?

QUESTION 7
What was the name of the group that reached the Top 10 in 1980 with the revival of the 1958 No 2 hit 'Tom Hark', by Elias and His Zigzag Jive Flutes?

QUESTION 8
Despite their popularity, folk duo Peter, Paul and Mary only achieved one Top 10 hit. What was it called?

QUESTION 9
Can you remember the name of the German studio group that topped the singles chart in 2000 with 'Toca's Miracle'?

QUESTION 10
In 1978, which legendary rock band had a Top 3 album called And Then There Were Three?

QUIZ 224

Q1
'You've Got Me Dangling on a String'

Q2
Simple Minds

Q3
The Godfather

Q4
Sue Nicholls

Q5
Foo Fighters

Q6
'Hurt So Good'

Q7
The Lightning Seeds

Q8
Air

Q9
'Glad All Over'

Q10
Barbra Streisand

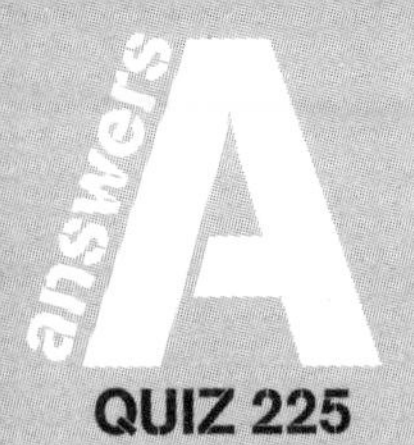

QUIZ 225

Q1 *Dave Dee, Dozy, Beaky, Mick & Tich*

Q2 *'Darlin''*

Q3 *Ken Thorne*

Q4 *Meat Loaf*

Q5 *Pickwick*

Q6 *'If You Were with Me Now'*

Q7 *Matt Cardle*

Q8 *'OK?'*

Q9 *Supergrass*

Q10 *'Heaven Must Have Sent You'*

QUIZ 227 POPMASTER

QUESTION 1
Can you name the Jamaican reggae star who achieved a top twenty hit in 1967 with 'Al Capone'?

QUESTION 2
Which of these Rod Stewart records remained at the top of the chart the longest: 'Baby Jane', 'Da Ya Think I'm Sexy?' or 'Sailing'?

QUESTION 3
American soul singer Donna Allen released two Top 10 hits in the Eighties. One was 'Joy and Pain', but what was the title of the other?

QUESTION 4
Which female singer topped the chart in 2006 with 'Smile', and in 2009 with 'The Fear'?

QUESTION 5
Can you name the group whose third hit in a run of five Top 5 singles in the early Eighties was 'Say Hello, Wave Goodbye'?

QUESTION 6
Tom Jones enjoyed a Top 5 hit in 1988 that featured Art of Noise and a song called 'Kiss', but do you know who wrote it?

QUESTION 7
Can you name the group that made their 1990 top twenty chart debut with 'Loaded'?

QUESTION 8
What was the title of the only solo top forty hit recorded by David Ruffin following his departure from The Temptations?

QUESTION 9
On which 1975 album by Wings did their hit single 'Listen to What the Man Said' first appear?

QUESTION 10
Can you name the legendary soul singer who in 1966 took 'Land of a Thousand Dances' into the top forty?

POPMASTER QUIZ 228

QUESTION 1
Who topped the chart in 1953 for two weeks with 'Hey Joe'?

QUESTION 2
Can you name the female singer who was featured on Quincy Jones's 1981 top twenty hit 'Razzamatazz'?

QUESTION 3
Which American group made the Top 10 in 1997 with a cover of The Ohio Players' US No 1 'Love Rollercoaster'?

QUESTION 4
Which of these Donny Osmond hits remained at No 1 for the most weeks: 'Puppy Love', 'The Twelfth of Never' or 'Young Love'?

QUESTION 5
Which 1965 No 1 hit by The Rolling Stones featured the Jagger and Richards song 'Play with Fire' on the 'B' side?

QUESTION 6
Can you name the American singer-songwriter whose only top twenty hit was his 1976 cover of Unit 4 + 2's 1965 No 1 'Concrete and Clay'?

QUESTION 7
Which UK No 1 by the Spice Girls was their only record to top the American chart?

QUESTION 8
In 1991, George Michael made the top forty with 'Heal the Pain' that he re-recorded for his 2006 greatest hits album. Can you remember who sang with him on the new version?

QUESTION 9
Which 'sensational' band made the Top 10 of the albums chart in 1975 with Tomorrow Belongs to Me?

QUESTION 10
American singer Debbie Gibson achieved two Top 10 hits in the Eighties. One was 'Shake Your Love', but what was the other called?

QUIZ 226

Q1
Supertramp

Q2
'Mama Used to Say'

Q3
Slim Whitman

Q4
'Cherish'

Q5
'Yellow'

Q6
'Alisha Rules the World', 'Indestructible', 'Air We Breathe'

Q7
The Piranhas

Q8
'Leaving on a Jet Plane'

Q9
Fragma

Q10
Genesis

QUIZ 227

Q1
Prince Buster

Q2
'Sailing' (4 weeks)

Q3
'Serious'

Q4
Lily Allen

Q5
Soft Cell

Q6
Prince

Q7
Primal Scream

Q8
'Walk Away from Love'

Q9
Venus and Mars

Q10
Wilson Pickett

QUIZ 229 POPMASTER

QUESTION 1
Which band topped the chart for two weeks in 1983 with 'Is There Something I Should Know'?

QUESTION 2
Can you name the female singer who made her top forty chart debut in 1992 with 'Feel So High'?

QUESTION 3
In 1974, Donny and Marie Osmond reached No 2 with their first hit duet, 'I'm Leaving It (All) Up to You'. It was a revival of a 1963 American No 1 by which other duo?

QUESTION 4
Which of these Shakin' Stevens hits remained at the top of the singles chart the longest: 'Green Door', 'This Ole House' or 'Merry Christmas Everyone'?

QUESTION 5
Which 1965 No 1 hit by The Beatles featured the Lennon and McCartney song 'I'm Down' on the 'B' side?

QUESTION 6
Can you name the act that successfully revived Roger Miller's 1965 No 1 'King of the Road' on their 1990 Top 10 EP with that title?

QUESTION 7
Which American female singer made the Top 3 of the albums chart in 1989 with The Other Side of the Mirror?

QUESTION 8
After a number of minor hits, which band finally made the top twenty in 2004 with 'The Bucket'?

QUESTION 9
In 1993, House of Pain achieved their only UK Top 10 hit with a double 'A'-sided hit. One of the songs was called 'Top o' the Morning to Ya' – what was the other?

QUESTION 10
Which two singers achieved a Top 10 duet in 1992 with the theme song to the musical Beauty and the Beast?

POPMASTER QUIZ 230

QUIZ 228

QUESTION 1
In 1969, which group had a hit with '(Call Me) No 1' – but only made it to No 2?

Q1
Frankie Laine

QUESTION 2
According to their 2006 Top 10 hit, which successful duo claimed 'I'm with Stupid'?

Q2
Patti Austin

QUESTION 3
Can you name the singer who achieved a No 1 album in 1984 with 'Human's Lib'?

Q3
Red Hot Chili Peppers

QUESTION 4
Which 1978 Top 10 hit by Third World was successfully covered in 1991 by Heavy D & The Boys?

Q4
'Puppy Love' (5 weeks)

QUESTION 5
According to their 1983 top twenty hit, which legendary band invited us to 'Come Dancing'?

Q5
'The Last Time'

QUESTION 6
Can you name the American singer who, in 2004, achieved her 11th consecutive UK top forty hit with 'Welcome to My Truth'?

Q6
Randy Edelman

QUESTION 7
In 1993, which band made their chart debut when they reached No 2 with 'The Key the Secret'?

Q7
'Wannabe'

QUESTION 8
As a solo performer, Midge Ure scored two Top 10 hits in the Eighties. The second of these was his No 1 'If I Was', but what was the title of the first?

Q8
Paul McCartney

QUESTION 9
Which of these Madonna hits remained at the top of the chart the longest: 'Into the Groove', 'Papa Don't Preach' or 'Like a Prayer'?

Q9
The Sensational Alex Harvey Band

QUESTION 10
Can you name the Beatles album on which their song 'Carry that Weight' first appeared?

Q10
'Foolish Beat'

QUIZ 231 POPMASTER

QUESTION 1
In 1961, which American female singer reached the Top 5 with the title song to the movie in which she starred, *Where the Boys Are*?

QUESTION 2
Can you name the actor who reached No 2 in the singles chart in 1978 with 'Sandy'?

QUESTION 3
Which Salvation Army pop group achieved a top forty hit in 1964 with 'It's an Open Secret'?

QUESTION 4
Featured in the Eighties movie *Footloose*, which female singer found herself 'Holding out for a Hero'?

QUESTION 5
Which of these hits by Slade remained at the top of the chart the longest: 'Mama Weer All Crazee Now', Skweeze Me Pleeze Me' or 'Coz I Luv You'?

QUESTION 6
Can you name the female Jamaican singer who in 1994 made the Top 3 with 'You Don't Love Me (No No No)' but never managed to repeat her success?

QUESTION 7
Which 2003 Top 5 hit by P!nk featured William Orbit and could be heard in the movie *Charlie's Angels: Full Throttle*?

QUESTION 8
Can you name the group that topped the albums chart in 1980 with Flesh and Blood?

QUESTION 9
In 2002, which successful male vocalist joined Jakatta on his Top 10 hit 'My Vision'?

QUESTION 10
American rapper Robert Van Winkle scored two big UK hits when 'Ice Ice Baby' topped the chart and 'Play that Funky Music' made the Top 10. Under what name did he release the records?

QUIZ 229

Q1
Duran Duran

Q2
Des'ree

Q3
Dale & Grace

Q4
'Green Door' (4 weeks)

Q5
'Help!'

Q6
The Proclaimers

Q7
Stevie Nicks

Q8
Kings of Leon

Q9
'Jump Around'

Q10
Celine Dion & Peabo Bryson

POPMASTER QUIZ 232

QUESTION 1
Which American female singer graced the top twenty for the final time in 1988 with 'Radio Romance'?

QUESTION 2
Part of a run of seven consecutive top twenty hits during the Eighties, who considered himself a 'Wide Boy'?

QUESTION 3
In 1991, which legendary group made the Top 10 for the first time in just over eight years with 'No Son of Mine'?

QUESTION 4
Two versions of the song 'Answer Me' topped the chart in 1953 – one was by Frankie Laine, but who recorded the other?

QUESTION 5
Under what collective name did the UK pop-folk act that comprised of Luke Concannon and John Parker achieve their 2005 No 1 with 'JCB Song'?

QUESTION 6
Can you name the Brazilian musician who reached the Top 10 in 1973 with his jazz version of 'Also Sprach Zarathustra (2001)' but never made the chart again?

QUESTION 7
In 1985, which female singer topped the albums chart for two weeks with Promise?

QUESTION 8
Who, according to his 1990 Top 10 hit, checked in at the 'Blue Hotel'?

QUESTION 9
Which of these David Bowie hits remained at No 1 the longest: 'Space Oddity', 'Let's Dance' or 'Ashes to Ashes'?

QUESTION 10
In 1994, which American group reached No 2 with 'Baby I Love Your Way' but never bothered the top forty again?

QUIZ 230

Q1
The Tremeloes

Q2
Pet Shop Boys

Q3
Howard Jones

Q4
'Now that We've Found Love'

Q5
The Kinks

Q6
Anastacia

Q7
Urban Cookie Collective

Q8
'No Regrets'

Q9
'Into the Groove' (4 weeks)

Q10
Abbey Road

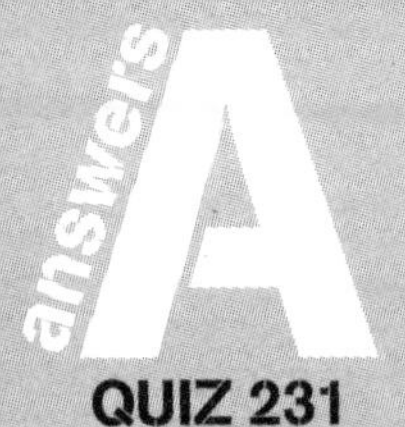

QUIZ 231

Q1
Connie Francis

Q2
John Travolta

Q3
The Joy Strings

Q4
Bonnie Tyler

Q5
'Coz I Luv You' (4 weeks)

Q6
Dawn Penn

Q7
'Feel Good Time'

Q8
Roxy Music

Q9
Seal

Q10
Vanilla Ice

QUIZ 233 POPMASTER

QUESTION 1
From 1973, what was the title of Clifford T Ward's only top 40 hit?

QUESTION 2
On which album did Heart's 1987 American No 1 and UK Top 3 hit 'Alone' first appear?

QUESTION 3
Ricky Ross, who achieved his only solo top forty hit in 1996 with 'Radio On', was once a member of which successful band?

QUESTION 4
Can you name the instrumental outfit that topped the chart in 1958 for three weeks with 'Hoots Mon'?

QUESTION 5
Which of these Elvis Presley hits spent the longest time at No 1: 'The Wonder of You', 'Way Down' or 'Crying in the Chapel'?

QUESTION 6
What hit song title is shared by a 1994 top forty hit by Killing Joke and a 1994 No 1 by Robbie Williams?

QUESTION 7
Richard Melville Hall made the Top 10 in 1997 with 'James Bond Theme', featured in the movie *Tomorrow Never Dies*. Under what name did he release the hit?

QUESTION 8
From 1967, what was the title of the only top forty hit achieved by Simon Dupree & The Big Sound?

QUESTION 9
Can you name the UK rock band that achieved No 1 albums in the Seventies with 'Houses of the Holy, The Song Remains the Same and In Through the Out Door?

QUESTION 10
Which Canadian group topped the American chart and made the UK Top 5 in 1999 with 'One Week'?

POPMASTER QUIZ 234

QUESTION 1
On which Moody Blues album did their 1970 No 2 hit 'Question' first appear as the opening track?

QUESTION 2
A 1960 Top 3 hit by Elvis Presley has the same title as a 1984 top twenty hit by Lionel Richie and Trevor Walters' Top 10 cover of Richie's song that same year. What is that shared song title?

QUESTION 3
The lead singer of which successful rock band achieved solo Top 10 hits in 1997 with 'Midnight in Chelsea' and 'Queen of New Orleans'?

QUESTION 4
Can you name the group whose hits between 1970 and 1973 included 'Good Morning Freedom', 'The Banner Man' and 'Randy'?

QUESTION 5
In 1992, which group topped the chart for four weeks with 'Ebeneezer Goode'?

QUESTION 6
Which American vocalist reached No 2 on the albums chart in 1979 with Fate for Breakfast?

QUESTION 7
What was the name of the American singer who topped the singles chart in early 1959 with 'The Day the Rains Came'?

QUESTION 8
In 1983, JoBoxers achieved two consecutive Top 10 hits. The first was 'Boxer Beat', but what was the second?

QUESTION 9
X Factor winner Joe McElderry topped the chart for just one week with his debut single – his only No 1 to date. Can you name it?

QUESTION 10
Which of these Cliff Richard hits remained at No 1 for the longest period of time: 'Congratulations', 'Summer Holiday' or 'The Young Ones'?

QUIZ 232

Q1
Tiffany

Q2
Nik Kershaw

Q3
Genesis

Q4
David Whitfield

Q5
Nizlopi

Q6
Deodato

Q7
Sade

Q8
Chris Isaak

Q9
'Let's Dance' (3 weeks)

Q10
Big Mountain

QUIZ 235 POPMASTER

QUIZ 233

Q1 *'Gaye'*

Q2 *Bad Animals*

Q3 *Deacon Blue*

Q4 *Lord Rockingham's XI*

Q5 *'The Wonder of You' (6 weeks)*

Q6 *'Millennium'*

Q7 *Moby*

Q8 *'Kites'*

Q9 *Led Zeppelin*

Q10 *Barenaked Ladies*

QUESTION 1
With which successful group of the Sixties and Seventies was Junior Campbell once a member?

QUESTION 2
Can you name the Jamaican singer who achieved his one and only top forty hit in the mid-Seventies with a cover of The Allman Brothers song 'Midnight Rider'?

QUESTION 3
The disco band Shalamar achieved four Top 10 hits in the Eighties: 'I Can Make You Feel Good', 'A Night to Remember', 'There it Is' and which other single?

QUESTION 4
Which of these hits by The Police spent the most weeks at No 1 on the UK singles chart: 'Message in a Bottle', 'Walking on the Moon' or 'Don't Stand So Close to Me'?

QUESTION 5
Can you name the American duo that topped the chart for five weeks in 1958 with 'When'?

QUESTION 6
By what name is British singer Dominique Atkins, who achieved a Top 10 hit in 1995 with 'Not Over Yet', better known?

QUESTION 7
Can you name the American group whose only Top 10 album was their 1977 release Aja?

QUESTION 8
Which Irish rock band achieved top twenty hits in the Nineties with 'Linger', 'Salvation' and 'Promises'?

QUESTION 9
What song title is shared by a top twenty hit from 1966 by The Mindbenders, a No 1 from 1980 by David Bowie and a top twenty from 1997 by Faith No More?

QUESTION 10
Can you name the group who took Grandmaster Flash and Melle Mel's 1983 Top 10 hit 'White Lines (Don't Don't do It)' back into the top twenty in 1995, minus one of the 'Don't''s?

POPMASTER QUIZ 236

QUIZ 234

QUESTION 1
Can you name the 1967 No 1 album by The Monkees on which their chart-topping single 'I'm a Believer' was the closing track?

QUESTION 2
Which one-time member of the Spice Girls topped the chart in 2000 with 'I Turn to You'?

QUESTION 3
What song title is shared by a 1962 top twenty hit by Nat 'King' Cole and George Shearing, a Top 10 hit from 1991 by Simple Minds and a No 2 hit from 2005 by Oasis?

QUESTION 4
Which 1969 Marvin Gaye Top 5 hit featured the song 'Wherever I Lay My Hat' on the 'B' side?

QUESTION 5
In 2005, the Kaiser Chiefs re-issued their debut top forty hit 'I Predict a Riot' with which song to make it a double 'A' side?

QUESTION 6
Which group had Top 10 albums in the Seventies with Sheet Music, The Original Soundtrack and Deceptive Bends?

QUESTION 7
Which famous orchestra leader and composer wrote the theme tune to the successful Sixties movie and cartoon series *The Pink Panther*?

QUESTION 8
Can you name the group that made their 1980 top twenty chart debut with 'Messages'?

QUESTION 9
'I Should Coco' was a 1995 No 1 album for which successful band?

QUESTION 10
Which of these Michael Jackson hits spent the most weeks at No 1: 'One Day in Your Life', 'Earth Song' or 'I Just Can't Stop Loving You'?

Q1
A Question of Balance

Q2
'Stuck on You'

Q3
Jon Bon Jovi

Q4
Blue Mink

Q5
The Shamen

Q6
Art Garfunkel

Q7
Jane Morgan

Q8
'Just Got Lucky'

Q9
'The Climb'

Q10
'The Young Ones' (6 weeks)

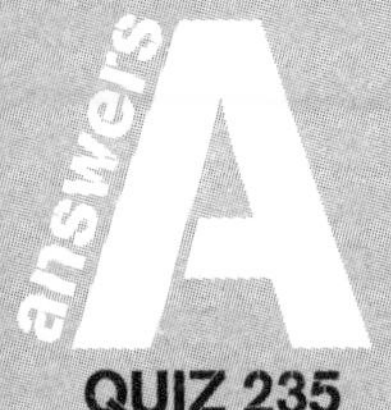

QUIZ 235

Q1
Marmalade

Q2
Paul Davidson

Q3
'Dead Giveaway'

Q4
'Don't Stand So Close to Me' (4 weeks)

Q5
The Kalin Twins

Q6
Grace

Q7
Steely Dan

Q8
The Cranberries

Q9
'Ashes to Ashes'

Q10
Duran Duran

QUIZ 237 POPMASTER

A BITE OF THE APPLE

These are questions about artists that were signed or had records released on The Beatles' Apple label.

QUESTION 1
What was the title of the only solo hit single release on the Apple label by Billy Preston?

QUESTION 2
Which female singer had Top 10 hits on Apple with 'Goodbye' and 'Temma Harbour'?

QUESTION 3
Can you name the singer and songwriter who released his debut eponymous album, produced by Peter Asher, on the Apple label in 1968?

QUESTION 4
Which member of The Beatles achieved an American No 1 and a UK Top 10 hit in 1973 with 'Give Me Love (Give Me Peace on Earth)'?

QUESTION 5
From 1971, what was the title of Paul McCartney's first solo hit on the Apple label?

QUESTION 6
What was the name of the group that scored two top forty hits on Apple, 'Hare Krishna Mantra' in 1969 and 'Govinda' the following year?

QUESTION 7
Although not a hit, which member of The Ronettes released just one single on Apple in 1971 - the George Harrison composition 'Try Some, Buy Some'?

QUESTION 8
Can you name the group who achieved their one and only top 40 hit in 1969 with a medley of 'Golden Slumbers' and 'Carry that Weight'?

QUESTION 9
Featuring Paul McCartney on kazoo and Harry Nilsson on backing vocals, which member of The Beatles made the Top 5 in 1974 with the revival of Johnny Burnette's 1961 hit 'You're Sixteen'?

QUESTION 10
Which group achieved three Top 10 hits on Apple in the early Seventies - 'Come and Get It', 'No Matter What' and 'Day After Day'?

POPMASTER QUIZ 238

ALTERNATIVE ARTISTS

QUESTION 1
Members of Duran Duran released a Top 10 single called 'Election Day' in 1985, but under what name did they record this hit?

QUESTION 2
...Other Duran Duran members recorded a Top 20 debut single with singer Robert Palmer and Chic drummer Tony Thompson, as The Power Station. What was it called?

QUESTION 3
Under what name did Siouxsie Sioux and Budgie of Siouxsie & The Banshees have hits with the songs 'Right Now' and 'Miss the Girl'?

QUESTION 4
Electronic, Monaco and The Other Two have all been alternative chart acts by members of which group?

QUESTION 5
Which two members of Talking Heads began the group Tom Tom Club in 1981?

QUESTION 6
Name all five of the musicians who, alongside successful individual careers, came together to form The Traveling Wilburys.

QUESTION 7
David Bowie put his solo career to one side in the late Eighties to form a band with Reeves Gabrels and brothers Hunt and Tony Sales. What were they called?

QUESTION 8
Sir John Johns, The Red Curtain, Lord Cornelius Plum and E.I.E.I. Owen were the 'members' of The Dukes of Stratosphear – a pseudonym used by which British band?

QUESTION 9
Alex Turner of The Last Shadow Puppets is also lead singer with a band whose five studio albums to date have all reached No 1. What is that group?

QUESTION 10
When Motörhead teamed up with Girlschool to record the 1981 Top 5 EP 'St Valentine's Day Massacre', they were jointly known by what name?

QUIZ 236

Q1 *More of The Monkees*

Q2 *Melanie C*

Q3 *'Let there be Love'*

Q4 *'Too Busy Thinking 'bout My Baby'*

Q5 *'Sink that Ship'*

Q6 *10cc*

Q7 *Henry Mancini*

Q8 *Orchestral Manoeuvres in the Dark*

Q9 *Supergrass*

Q10 *'Earth Song' (6 weeks)*

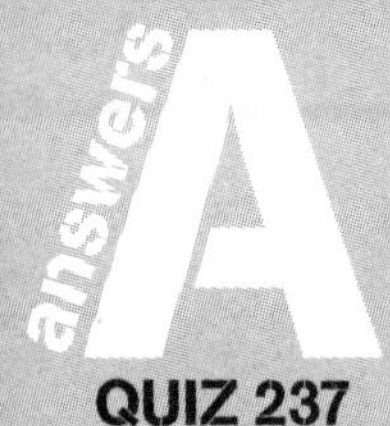

QUIZ 237

Q1
'That's the Way God Planned It'

Q2
Mary Hopkin

Q3
James Taylor

Q4
George Harrison

Q5
'Another Day'

Q6
The Radha Krishna Temple

Q7
Ronnie Spector

Q8
Trash

Q9
Ringo Starr

Q10
Badfinger

QUIZ 239 POPMASTER

ALTERNATIVE VERSIONS

QUESTION 1
Tracey Ullman's 1984 hit 'My Guy' was her gender-reversed version of the song 'My Girl', which was a hit in 1980 for which group?

QUESTION 2
Following the success of The Simon Park Orchestra's 1973 No 1 'Eye Level', Matt Monro had a Top 40 hit with a vocal version of that tune. What was it called?

QUESTION 3
Name both the groups that have reached No 1 with versions of the song 'The Tide is High'.

QUESTION 4
Having co-written and produced the song 'China Girl' for Iggy Pop's 1977 album The Idiot, David Bowie decided to record his own version of the song for which 1983 No 1 album?

QUESTION 5
Having reached No.69 for one week in 1994 with the song 'Missing', which duo reached the Top 3 in 1995 and spent 22 weeks on the chart with a remixed version of that same song?

QUESTION 6
In the same week in September 1978, The Jacksons and a singer called Mick Jackson both entered the Top 40 with their versions of which song?

QUESTION 7
'Do They Know it's Christmas?' has been No 1 for Band Aid, Band Aid II, Band Aid 20 and Band Aid 30, but who sings the opening line on each of the versions?

QUESTION 8
In 1993, Barry Manilow had a Top 40 hit with a dance version of a song that had been a Top 30 hit for him in the late Seventies. What is the song?

QUESTION 9
'He was Beautiful' was a 1979 Top 20 vocal version of the theme from *The Deer Hunter*. It was recorded by Iris who?

QUESTION 10
Ron and Russell Mael of Sparks featured in the video of a cover of their song 'This Town Ain't Big Enough for Both of Us', a 2005 Top 10 hit for Justin Hawkins of The Darkness recording under what name?

POPMASTER QUIZ 240

ANAGRAMOPHONES (1)

Unpick the names of these chart artists and their No 1 singles; the year is given as a clue.

QUESTION 1
"Icier Hellhole Loin" (1984)

QUESTION 2
"Masquerade in Hype on Hob" (1975)

QUESTION 3
"Bewailing Crass Pen" (1996)

QUESTION 4
"Bracketed Toilet Ties" (1965)

QUESTION 5
"Exorbitant Spies Cry" (2004)

QUESTION 6
"Naive Bicycle Ace Alibi" (1990)

QUESTION 7
"Beanbag and Quince" (1976)

QUESTION 8
"Dim Clamps Bled Filthiness" (1989)

QUESTION 9
"Flared Yoga Package" (2009)

QUESTION 10
"Do Be Soothsaying Vicar Bob" (1966)

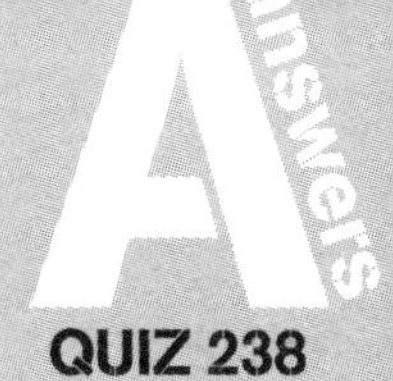

QUIZ 238

Q1
Arcadia

Q2
'Some Like it Hot'

Q3
The Creatures

Q4
New Order

Q5
Tina Weymouth and Chris Frantz

Q6
Bob Dylan, George Harrison, Jeff Lynne, Roy Orbison, Tom Petty

Q7
Tin Machine

Q8
XTC

Q9
Arctic Monkeys

Q10
Headgirl

QUIZ 239

Q1
Madness

Q2
'And You Smiled'

Q3
Blondie, Atomic Kitten

Q4
Let's Dance

Q5
Everything but the Girl

Q6
'Blame it on the Boogie' (Mick Jackson was one of the song's co-writers)

Q7
Paul Young, Kylie Minogue, Chris Martin (Coldplay), One Direction

Q8
'Could it be Magic'

Q9
Iris Williams

Q10
British Whale

QUIZ 241 POPMASTER

ANAGRAMOPHONES (2)

Unpick the names of these chart artists and their No 1 singles; the year is given as a clue.

QUESTION 1
"Wasted Migratory Game" (1971)

QUESTION 2
"Despairingly for Drum" (1995)

QUESTION 3
"Hot Pest Bows Depressingly" (1986)

QUESTION 4
"We Involuntarily Howl Egg" (2003)

QUESTION 5
"Nosh Toll on Networking Monkeys" (1969)

QUESTION 6
"Adaptable Nuts Rule" (1983)

QUESTION 7
"Barnstorm Warp Tattoo" (1978)

QUESTION 8
"Beer Vehicle" (1998)

QUESTION 9
"Cry Milk Leakage" (2007)

QUESTION 10
"Incompatible Eagles Toes" (1979)

POPMASTER QUIZ 242

ANAGRAMOPHONES (3)

Unpick the names of these chart artists and their No 1 singles; the year is given as a clue.

QUESTION 1
"Carefree Mania" (1982)

QUESTION 2
"Ably Compose Bonanza" (1996)

QUESTION 3
"Uneasy Weedily Honoree" (1977)

QUESTION 4
"Alien Yells Mill" (2006)

QUESTION 5
"Drab Matrimony Numbers" (1965)

QUESTION 6
"Extreme Malt Rags" (1972)

QUESTION 7
"Garnishes Eden" (2014)

QUESTION 8
"Forget Lamp Damn Infantrymen" (1966)

QUESTION 9
"Goodbye Loftier Whole Workstations" (1984)

QUESTION 10
"Yellowing Identical Hormone" (1998)

A answers

QUIZ 240

Q1
Lionel Richie, 'Hello'

Q2
Queen, 'Bohemian Rhapsody'

Q3
Spice Girls, 'Wannabe'

Q4
Beatles, 'Ticket to Ride'

Q5
Britney Spears, 'Toxic'

Q6
Vanilla Ice, 'Ice Ice Baby'

Q7
ABBA, 'Dancing Queen'

Q8
Simple Minds, 'Belfast Child'

Q9
Lady Gaga, 'Poker Face'

Q10
Beach Boys, 'Good Vibrations'

QUIZ 241

Q1
Rod Stewart, 'Maggie May'

Q2
Simply Red, 'Fairground'

Q3
Pet Shop Boys, 'West End Girls'

Q4
Will Young, 'Leave Right Now'

Q5
Rolling Stones, 'Honky Tonk Women'

Q6
Spandau Ballet, 'True'

Q7
Boomtown Rats, 'Rat Trap'

Q8
Cher, 'Believe'

Q9
Mika, 'Grace Kelly'

Q10
Police, 'Message in a Bottle'

QUIZ 243 POPMASTER

AND YOUR BIRD CAN SING

QUESTION 1
Which album by the Eagles includes the songs 'New Kid in Town', 'Life in the Fast Lane' and 'The Last Resort'?

QUESTION 2
The songs 'There Goes the Fear' and 'Black and White Town' were Top 10 hits in the Noughties for which group?

QUESTION 3
Which song has been a hit for both Inez & Charlie Foxx in 1969 and Carly Simon and James Taylor in 1974?

QUESTION 4
Who had her debut Top 40 hit in 1992 with the Top 5 song 'All I Wanna Do'?

QUESTION 5
Which of our feathered friends features in the title of a 1982 Top 10 hit by Kid Creole & The Coconuts?

QUESTION 6
Children from the Abbey Hey Junior School had a Top 20 hit in 1979 with 'The Sparrow', which they recorded under what name?

QUESTION 7
Lemon Jelly reached the Top 20 in 2003 with the track 'Nice Weather for…' what?

QUESTION 8
Gerry Rafferty sang about a 'Night Owl' on his 1979 solo hit, but with which group did he have three Top 40 hits earlier that decade?

QUESTION 9
The song 'L'Oiseau et L'Enfant' won the 1977 Eurovision Song Contest. It was sung by Marie Myriam, but did she win for Belgium, France, Luxembourg or Switzerland?

QUESTION 10
The theme song to the children's TV programme *Magpie* was recorded by The Murgatroyd Band – a pseudonym for members of which Sixties hit group?

POPMASTER QUIZ 244

BALL AND CHAIN

QUIZ 242

QUESTION 1
In 1960, which American singer achieved his first UK Top 10 hit with 'Chain Gang'?

QUESTION 2
Which group scored a 1982 top twenty hit in the UK with 'Back on the Chain Gang', which was featured in the movie *King of Comedy*?

QUESTION 3
Which musical featured the 1989 UK No 2 hit for Michael Ball, 'Love Changes Everything'?

QUESTION 4
Which vocal group successfully revived Diana Ross's 1986 No 1 hit, 'Chain Reaction', in 2001?

QUESTION 5
Can you name the female pianist who successfully recorded a medley of old standards that made the UK Top 5 in 1957 under the title 'Let's Have a Ball'?

QUESTION 6
Which duo made the top twenty in 1988 with 'Chains of Love'?

QUESTION 7
Released in 1970, which Motown group achieved their third UK Top 10 hit with 'Ball of Confusion'?

QUESTION 8
Can you name the well-known trumpeter who achieved a number of hits with his jazz band including 'Midnight in Moscow', 'March of the Siamese Children' and 'The Green Leaves of Summer'?

QUESTION 9
In 1990, which successful reggae band from Birmingham made the top forty with their single 'Wear You to the Ball'?

QUESTION 10
What was the title of the 1972 debut Top 10 hit for Roy Wood's group, Wizzard?

Q1
Irene Cara, 'Fame'

Q2
Babylon Zoo, 'Spaceman'

Q3
Leo Sayer, 'When I Need You'

Q4
Lily Allen, 'Smile'

Q5
Byrds, 'Mr Tambourine Man'

Q6
T.Rex, 'Telegram Sam'

Q7
Ed Sheeran, 'Sing'

Q8
Manfred Mann, 'Pretty Flamingo'

Q9
Frankie Goes to Hollywood, 'Two Tribes'

Q10
Celine Dion, 'My Heart Will Go On'

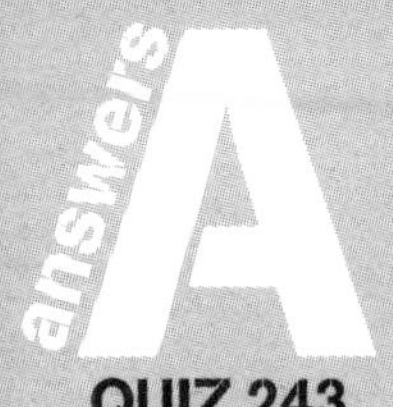

QUIZ 243

Q1
Hotel California

Q2
Doves

Q3
'Mockingbird'

Q4
Sheryl Crow

Q5
Pigeon ('Stool Pigeon' reached number 7 in the summer of '82)

Q6
The Ramblers

Q7
Ducks

Q8
Stealers Wheel

Q9
France

Q10
The Spencer Davis Group

QUIZ 245 POPMASTER

BEAT THE INTRO (1)

Can you name the hit single from the artist, year and description of how the song starts?

QUESTION 1
Kraftwerk – 1975 – a lorry or large vehicle starting up and pulling away

QUESTION 2
Kate Bush – 1989 – the sound of peeling church bells

QUESTION 3
Take That – 1995 – the 'Tuba Mirum' trumpet fanfare from Verdi's 'Requiem'

QUESTION 4
Madonna featuring Justin Timberlake – 2008 – the brief ticking of a watch or clock

QUESTION 5
Duran Duran – 1981 – the sound of a fast motor drive of a camera

QUESTION 6
Jonathan Richman – 1977 – counting up to 6

QUESTION 7
Michael Jackson – 1983 – a creaky door or coffin lid opening and some footsteps

QUESTION 8
A-ha – 1990 – a muffled thunder storm

QUESTION 9
Bobby Goldsboro – 1973 – the sound of waves on a beach

QUESTION 10
Mika – 2007 – a satisfied slurping through a straw

POPMASTER QUIZ 246

BEAT THE INTRO (2)

Can you name the hit single from the artist, year and description of how the song starts?

QUESTION 1
The Sweet – 1974 – a crowd chanting "We Want Sweet"

QUESTION 2
George Michael – 1987 – the introduction to an old Wham! song played on an organ

QUESTION 3
Madonna – 2005 – a ticking clock or watch (again, very brief!)

QUESTION 4
Blondie – 1978 – the sound of a phone ringing in the earpiece

QUESTION 5
Malcolm McLaren – 1983 – the sound of a skipping rope

QUESTION 6
Electric Light Orchestra – 1978 – a weather report on the radio

QUESTION 7
The Monkees – 1967 – the studio saying that the 'take' is 7A

QUESTION 8
The Specials – 1981 – the sound of howling wind

QUESTION 9
Roxy Music – 1975 – the sound of someone walking along and opening a car door

QUESTION 10
Lady Gaga – 2009 – a solo violin playing with the sound of wind and the sea in the background

A answers

QUIZ 244

Q1 *Sam Cooke*

Q2 *The Pretenders*

Q3 *Aspects of Love*

Q4 *Steps*

Q5 *Winifred Atwell*

Q6 *Erasure*

Q7 *The Temptations*

Q8 *Kenny Ball*

Q9 *UB40*

Q10 *'Ball Park Incident'*

QUIZ 245

Q1
'Autobahn'

Q2
'The Sensual World'

Q3
'Never Forget'

Q4
'4 Minutes'

Q5
'Girls on Film'

Q6
'Roadrunner'

Q7
'Thriller'

Q8
'Crying in the Rain'

Q9
'Summer (The First Time)'

Q10
'Big Girl (You Are Beautiful)'

QUIZ 247 POPMASTER

BELL RINGERS

QUESTION 1
Showaddywaddy's final Bell release became their only No 1, previously an American hit in the Sixties for Curtis Lee. What was the title?

QUESTION 2
Can you name the female American group who achieved their only top twenty hit in 1968 with a song called 'Captain of Your Ship'?

QUESTION 3
The Bell label had quite a reputation for creating one-off hits, such was the case with a UK studio group named Mardi Gras who covered a 1969 Top 5 Marvin Gaye hit in 1972. Can you name it?

QUESTION 4
In 1973, David Cassidy achieved his second and final No 1 with a double 'A'-sided hit. One song was 'The Puppy Song', but what was the other?

QUESTION 5
What was the name of the made-up group that scored a major hit in 1971 with 'Johnny Reggae'?

QUESTION 6
The all-girl group from Philadelphia, First Choice, achieved two top twenty hits on Bell in 1973. The first was 'Armed and Extremely Dangerous', what was the second?

QUESTION 7
Also in 1973, Barry Blue achieved two Top 10 hits on Bell - the first was 'Dancin' (On a Saturday Night)', what was the other?

QUESTION 8
Can you name the first hit for The Box Tops from 1967 that topped the American chart for four weeks?

QUESTION 9
After his 1962 hit 'Hey Baby', American singer Bruce Channel had to wait over six years before he next made the chart, with his only hit on Bell. What was the title?

QUESTION 10
From 1975, what was the title of the Bay City Rollers' first No 1 - a revival of a 1965 song by The Four Seasons?

POPMASTER QUIZ 248

BIG STARS LITTLE HITS (1)

Can you name these famous artists or bands from the titles of three of their smaller Top 40 hits?

QUESTION 1
'New Amsterdam' in 1980, 'Veronica' in 1989, 'Sulky Girl' in 1994

QUESTION 2
'Sunny' in 1966, 'Dark Lady' in 1974, 'Not Enough Love in the World' in 1996

QUESTION 3
'Missionary Man' in 1987, 'Angel' in 1990, '17 Again' in 2000

QUESTION 4
'Rock 'n' Roll Damnation' in 1978, 'Shake Your Foundations' in 1986, 'Hard as a Rock' in 1995

QUESTION 5
'Thinking of You' in 2009, 'The One that Got Away' in 2011, 'Birthday' in 2014

QUESTION 6
'Blowin' in the Wind' in 1966, 'We Can Work it Out' in 1971, 'That Girl' in 1982

QUESTION 7
'Living in Sin' in 1989, 'Misunderstood' in 2002, 'Because We Can' in 2013

QUESTION 8
'Sign of the Times' in 1978, 'The Right Stuff' in 1987, 'Will You Love Me Tomorrow' in 1993

QUESTION 9
'Wild Honey' in 1967, 'Rock and Roll Music' in 1976, 'Here Comes the Night' in 1979

QUESTION 10
'Treat Her Like a Lady' in 1999, 'Goodbye's (The Saddest Word)' in 2002, 'Loved Me Back to Life' in 2013

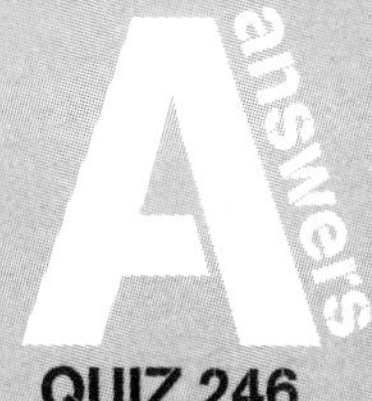

QUIZ 246

Q1 *'Teenage Rampage'*

Q2 *'Faith' (organ is playing a slow version of Wham!'s Freedom)*

Q3 *'Hung Up'*

Q4 *'Hanging on the Telephone'*

Q5 *'Double Dutch'*

Q6 *'Mr Blue Sky'*

Q7 *'Daydream Believer'*

Q8 *'Ghost Town'*

Q9 *'Love is the Drug'*

Q10 *'Alejandro'*

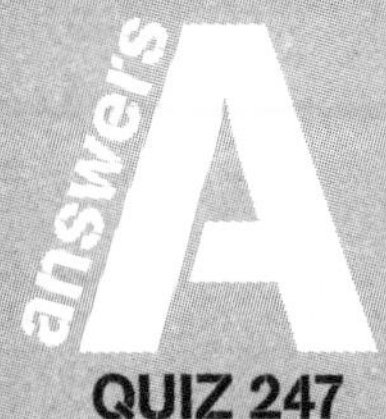

QUIZ 247

Q1
'Under the Moon of Love'

Q2
Reparata & The Delrons

Q3
'Too Busy Thinking 'bout My Baby'

Q4
'Daydreamer'

Q5
The Piglets

Q6
'Smarty Pants'

Q7
'Do You Wanna Dance?'

Q8
'The Letter'

Q9
'Keep On'

Q10
'Bye Bye Baby'

QUIZ 249 POPMASTER

BIG STARS LITTLE HITS (2)

Can you name these famous artists or bands from the titles of three of their smaller Top 40 hits?

QUESTION 1
'Wow' in 1979, 'The Big Sky' in 1986, 'Moments of Pleasure' in 1993

QUESTION 2
'Love in Itself' in 1983, 'Policy of Truth' in 1990, 'Wrong' in 2009

QUESTION 3
'Heaven' in 1985, 'Do I Have to Say the Words?' in 1992, 'Flying' in 2004

QUESTION 4
'Loving You is Sweeter than Ever' in 1966, 'Just Seven Numbers (Can Straighten out My Life)' in 1971, 'Don't Walk Away' in 1981

QUESTION 5
'Modern Girl' in 1984, 'Runnin' for the Red Light (I Gotta Life)' in 1996, 'Couldn't Have Said it Better' in 2003

QUESTION 6
'Popscene' in 1992, 'MOR' in 1997, 'Good Song' in 2003

QUESTION 7
'Movin' Out (Anthony's Song)' in 1978, 'The Longest Time' in 1984, 'All About Soul' in 1993

QUESTION 8
'Careless Memories' in 1981, 'Meet El Presidente' in 1987, 'Electric Barbarella' in 1999

QUESTION 9
'(Ain't That) Just Like Me' in 1963, 'King Midas in Reverse' in 1967, 'Long Cool Woman in a Black Dress' in 1972

QUESTION 10
'Shapes that Go Together' in 1994, 'Summer Moved On' in 2000, 'Cosy Prisons' in 2006

POPMASTER QUIZ 250

BIG STARS LITTLE HITS (3)

Can you name these famous artists or bands from the titles of three of their smaller Top 40 hits?

QUESTION 1
'Love Loves to Love Love' in 1967, 'Take Your Mama for a Ride' in 1975, 'Where the Poor Boys Dance' in 2000

QUESTION 2
'La Tristesse Durera (Scream to a Sigh)' in 1993, 'Let Robeson Sing' in 2001, '(It's Not War) Just the End of Love' in 2010

QUESTION 3
'Get Down and Get with It' in 1971, 'My Baby Left Me - That's All Right' in 1977, 'All Join Hands' in 1984

QUESTION 4
'Being Boring' in 1990, 'I Get Along' in 2002, 'It Doesn't Often Snow at Christmas' in 2009

QUESTION 5
'Thieves Like Us' in 1984, 'Spooky' in 1993, 'Waiting for the Sirens' Call' in 2005

QUESTION 6
'Think' in 1968, 'Angel' in 1973, 'A Rose is Still a Rose' in 1998

QUESTION 7
'You Could Have Been a Lady' in 1971, 'Are You Getting Enough of What Makes You Happy' in 1980, 'Tears on the Telephone' in 1983

QUESTION 8
'Word is Out' in 1991, 'Some Kind of Bliss' in 1997, 'Timebomb' in 2012

QUESTION 9
'America' in 1974, 'Imperial Wizard' in 1979, 'Falling Angels Riding' in 1985

QUESTION 10
'Infidelity' in 1987, 'Thrill Me' in 1992, 'Fake' in 2003

Answers

QUIZ 248

Q1 *Elvis Costello*

Q2 *Cher*

Q3 *Eurythmics*

Q4 *AC/DC*

Q5 *Katy Perry*

Q6 *Stevie Wonder*

Q7 *Bon Jovi*

Q8 *Bryan Ferry*

Q9 *The Beach Boys*

Q10 *Celine Dion*

QUIZ 249

Q1
Kate Bush

Q2
Depeche Mode

Q3
Bryan Adams

Q4
The Four Tops

Q5
Meat Loaf

Q6
Blur

Q7
Billy Joel

Q8
Duran Duran

Q9
The Hollies

Q10
A-ha

QUIZ 251 POPMASTER

BOY BANDS

QUESTION 1
Which 1996 No 1 by Take That was a cover of a Bee Gees song?

QUESTION 2
Which member of The Jonas Brothers had a Top 3 solo single in 2015 with 'Jealous'?

QUESTION 3
Which Christmas carol formed part of a Christmas double 'A' side Top 3 single by Bros in 1988?

QUESTION 4
Lee, Jimmy and Spike had a run of 13 hit singles in the Nineties, recorded under what name?

QUESTION 5
Which 1974 single by the Bay City Rollers was also the title of their 1975 TV series?

QUESTION 6
Which boy band had Top 10 hits in 2014 with the songs 'Tonight (We Live Forever)' and 'You Got it All'?

QUESTION 7
What was the title of the 1983 No 1 by New Edition?

QUESTION 8
The songs 'Anything', 'Why' and 'I Need You' were Top 10 hits for Michael Jackson's nephews Taj, Taryll and TJ in the mid-Nineties. What was the name of this trio?

QUESTION 9
A1 reached No 1 in 2000 with their version of which A-ha song?

QUESTION 10
'You Just Might See Me Cry' was the title of a Top 3 hit in 1976 for Our Kid, who found success having appeared on which TV talent show?

POPMASTER QUIZ 252

CARTOON HEROES

Questions about animated and puppet pop stars

QUESTION 1
Which two puppet pigs released their first single in 1958 and just failed to reach the Top 40 in 1993 with their version of Jackie Wilson's 'Reet Petite'?

QUESTION 2
Which character, a fixture of Saturday TV in the early '90s, knocked Take That's 'Babe' off No 1 to have the Christmas No 1 in 1993 with an eponymously titled single?

QUESTION 3
Which favourite seasonal song scraped the bottom of the Top 40 as a cover version for Keith Harris and Orville the duck at Christmas in 1985?

QUESTION 4
Roland Rat Superstar had two Top 40 hits in the Eighties. Name either of them.

QUESTION 5
What was the name of Kermit the Frog's nephew who sang the Top 10 Muppet hit 'Halfway Down the Stairs' in 1977?

QUESTION 6
The Smurfs' entire singles chart career in the Top 40 has been in just two years – three hits in 1978 and two in 1996. 'The Smurf Song' was the 1978 Top 3 debut. Name one of the other four songs.

QUESTION 7
Under what name did American rap duo James Alpem and Richard Usher record their 1990 No 1 'Turtle Power'?

QUESTION 8
Who was the voice of Chef from *South Park*, who reached No 1 in 1999 with 'Chocolate Salty Balls (PS I Love You)'?

QUESTION 9
Only one of The Wombles' Top 10 singles did not include a derivation of the furry creatures' name in the title – what was it called?

QUESTION 10
Although they never had a UK hit single, what was the name of Hanna-Barbera's early Seventies cartoon about an all-girl mystery-solving pop group?

A answers

QUIZ 250

Q1 *Lulu*

Q2 *Manic Street Preachers*

Q3 *Slade*

Q4 *Pet Shop Boys*

Q5 *New Order*

Q6 *Aretha Franklin*

Q7 *Hot Chocolate*

Q8 *Kylie Minogue*

Q9 *David Essex*

Q10 *Simply Red*

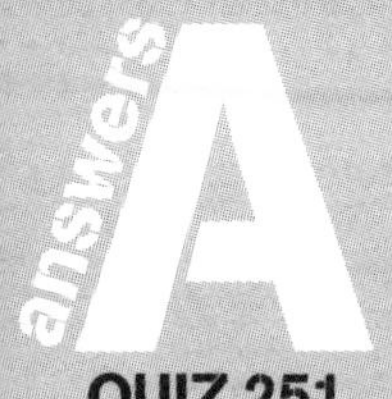

QUIZ 251

Q1
'How Deep is Your Love'

Q2
Nick Jonas

Q3
'Silent Night' (double 'A' side with 'Cat Among the Pigeons')

Q4
911

Q5
'Shang-a-Lang'

Q6
Union J

Q7
'Candy Girl'

Q8
3T

Q9
'Take on Me'

Q10
New Faces

QUIZ 253 POPMASTER

CHRISTMAS LIST

This round is about hit Christmas songs that made the UK top forty between 1955 and 2003.

QUESTION 1
Can you name the singer who achieved a No 1 hit in 1985 with 'Merry Christmas Everyone' and a top forty hit in 1991 with 'I'll be Home this Christmas'?

QUESTION 2
Which legendary singer-songwriter found himself in the Top 10 in 1985 with his version of 'Santa Claus is Coming to Town'?

QUESTION 3
In 1973, which group (featuring contributions from The Suedettes, The Stockland Green Bilateral School First Year Choir, Miss Snob and Class 3C) were in the Top 5 with 'I Wish it Could be Christmas Everyday'?

QUESTION 4
Can you name the crooner who topped the singles chart in 1955 for three weeks with 'Christmas Alphabet' and made the Top 10 in 1956 with 'Christmas Island'?

QUESTION 5
Which rock band scored a No 2 hit in 2003 with 'Christmas Time (Don't Let the Bells End)'?

QUESTION 6
What was the title of Greg Lake's 1975 solo Christmas No 2 hit?

QUESTION 7
Can you name the Cuban female singer who made the Top 10 in 1992 with 'Christmas Through Your Eyes'?

QUESTION 8
Although never a major hit, which Chris Rea Yuletide song has gained steady sales since its initial release in 1988?

QUESTION 9
Which successful glam-rock band topped the chart in 1974 for four weeks with 'Lonely this Christmas'?

QUESTION 10
Which classic 1962 Brenda Lee hit was successfully revived by Mel Smith and Kim Wilde in 1987?

POPMASTER QUIZ 254

CLASSIC POP

These are hit singles with a link to classical music

QUESTION 1
Eric Carmen's only UK hit – later covered by Celine Dion – contains a portion of Rachmaninoff's 'Piano Concerto No.2'. What is it called?

QUESTION 2
The Farm's 'Altogether Now', Coolio's 'C U When U Get There' and 'Welcome to the Black Parade' by My Chemical Romance are all inspired by a canon written by which 17th-century German composer?

QUESTION 3
The melody of the late 19th-century song ''O Sole Mio' was used for which Elvis Presley No 1?

QUESTION 4
Tchaikovsky's '1812 Overture' is referenced in the riff and bassline of the 1967 debut hit by The Move. What is the song called?

QUESTION 5
David Shire's 'Night on Disco Mountain', from *Saturday Night Fever*, is his take on 'Night on Bald Mountain' by which composer?

QUESTION 6
In 1984, Malcolm McLaren had a Top 20 hit with song subtitled '(Un Bel di Vedremo)' – the name of the aria by Puccini which features in the single. What was it called?

QUESTION 7
'Jupiter, the Bringer of Jollity', from Holst's Planets suites, is used as the basis of the melody for which 1973 hit by Manfred Mann's Earth Band?

QUESTION 8
The guitar riff in the 2001 Muse hit 'Plug in Baby' has often been compared to part of 'Toccata and Fugue in D minor' by which Baroque composer?

QUESTION 9
Mozart's 'Symphony No.41' features in which of The Wombles' hit singles?

QUESTION 10
Which 2001 single by Janet Jackson includes a small section of one of Erik Satie's 'Gymnopédies'?

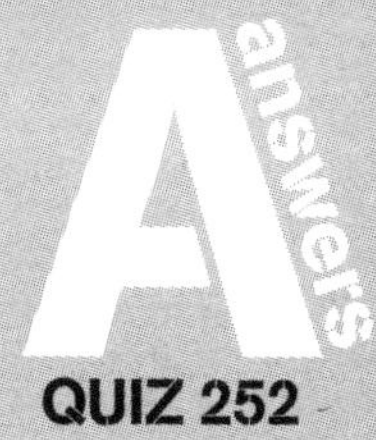

QUIZ 252

Q1 *Pinky & Perky*

Q2 *Mr Blobby*

Q3 *'White Christmas'*

Q4 *'Rat Rapping', 'Love Me Tender'*

Q5 *Robin*

Q6 *'Dippety Day', 'Christmas in Smurfland', 'I've Got a Little Puppy', 'Your Christmas Wish'*

Q7 *Partners in Kryme*

Q8 *Isaac Hayes*

Q9 *'Banana Rock'*

Q10 *Josie & The Pussycats*

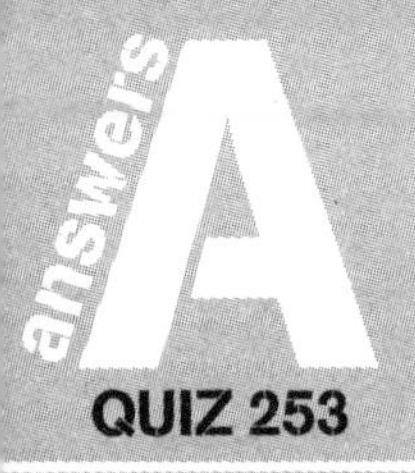

QUIZ 253

Q1
Shakin' Stevens

Q2
Bruce Springsteen

Q3
Wizzard

Q4
Dickie Valentine

Q5
The Darkness

Q6
'I Believe in Father Christmas'

Q7
Gloria Estefan

Q8
'Driving Home for Christmas'

Q9
Mud

Q10
'Rockin' Around the Christmas Tree'

QUIZ 255 POPMASTER

CONNECTIONS (1)

In each case, what is the common link between these three bands, songs or artists?

QUESTION 1
Madness, Bananarama, Gorillaz

QUESTION 2
'Someday' by The Gap Band, 'I Feel for You' by Chaka Khan, 'There Must be an Angel (Playing with My Heart)' by Eurythmics

QUESTION 3
Martin Fry of ABC, Shaun Ryder of Happy Mondays, Phil Oakey of Human League

QUESTION 4
'Miss Sarajevo' by Passengers, 'True' by Spandau Ballet, 'Where Do You Go to (My Lovely)' by Peter Sarstedt

QUESTION 5
'Street Life' by The Crusaders, 'Killer' by Adamski, 'In a Broken Dream' by Python Lee Jackson

QUESTION 6
New Order's 'True Faith', The Police's 'Synchronicity II', Bastille's 'Pompeii'

QUESTION 7
ABBA's 'Does Your Mother Know', Oasis' 'Don't Look Back in Anger', Eagles' 'Take it to the Limit'

QUESTION 8
The chart acts Wah, Wham & Yell

QUESTION 9
'Walking in the Rain with the One I Love' by Love Unlimited, 'Heartache' by Pepsi & Shirley, 'Central Park Arrest' by Thunderthighs

QUESTION 10
'My Way' by Frank Sinatra, 'Amoureuse' by Kiki Dee, 'Seasons in the Sun' by Terry Jacks

POPMASTER QUIZ 256

CONNECTIONS (2)

In each case, what is the common link between these three bands, songs or artists?

QUESTION 1
Madness, U2, The Police

QUESTION 2
Dave Edmunds' 'Girls Talk', Lulu's 'The Man Who Sold the World', Sinead O'Connor's 'Nothing Compares 2 U'

QUESTION 3
Cher, Denise Marsa, Sheena Easton

QUESTION 4
Shayne Ward, Sarah Harding of Girls Aloud, Davy Jones of The Monkees

QUESTION 5
'Unchained Melody', 'Bohemian Rhapsody', 'The Ballad of John and Yoko'

QUESTION 6
Ace, Squeeze, Mike & The Mechanics

QUESTION 7
Living in a Box, Talk Talk, Jilted John

QUESTION 8
Kim Carnes, Suzanne Vega, Elton John

QUESTION 9
Beats International, Freakpower, The Housemartins

QUESTION 10
Eurythmics, The Police, Sheena Easton

A answers

QUIZ 254

Q1 *'All by Myself'*

Q2 *Johann Pachelbel*

Q3 *'It's Now or Never'*

Q4 *'Night of Fear'*

Q5 *Modest Mussorgsky*

Q6 *'Madam Butterfly'*

Q7 *'Joybringer'*

Q8 *J.S. Bach*

Q9 *'Minuetto Allegretto'*

Q10 *'Someone to Call My Lover'*

QUIZ 255

Q1 *All have recorded songs with actors in the title (Michael Caine, Robert De Niro and Clint Eastwood)*

Q2 *All feature Stevie Wonder harmonica solos*

Q3 *They have all name-checked themselves in one of their own songs*

Q4 *They all have songs that name-check other acts in the lyrics*

Q5 *The lead singer is uncredited on each of the singles (Randy Crawford, Seal, Rod Stewart)*

Q6 *The titles of the songs are not in the lyrics*

Q7 *The singer isn't the group's usual lead singer (Björn Ulvaeus, Noel Gallagher, Randy Meisner)*

Q8 *All have exclamation marks after the band name (left off the question so as not to give it away!)*

Q9 *Debut hits for backing vocalists recording in their own right (Barry White, Wham!, various)*

Q10 *All three songs originally had French lyrics*

QUIZ 257 POPMASTER

DAYS OF THE WEEK

QUESTION 1
Topping the UK chart for three weeks in 1979, what was the title of Blondie's second No 1 hit?

QUESTION 2
Which group achieved a UK Top 5 hit in the year 2000 with 'Sunday Morning Call', taken from their album Standing on the Shoulder of Giants?

QUESTION 3
From 1966, can you name the first UK Top 10 hit and American No 1 for The Mamas and The Papas?

QUESTION 4
Can you name the group who in 1992 achieved their first UK top twenty hit in nearly six years with 'Tuesday Morning'?

QUESTION 5
With which group did Feargal Sharkey enjoy the 1980 UK top twenty hit 'Wednesday Week'?

QUESTION 6
Originally written for the computer game Omikron: The Nomad Soul, who had a top twenty hit with the song 'Thursday's Child', taken from his 1999 album Hours?

QUESTION 7
Can you name the singer and blues guitarist who scored a top forty hit in 1987 with the revival of The Easybeats' 1966 Top 10 chart entry 'Friday on My Mind'?

QUESTION 8
In 2006, which boy band achieved a UK Top 3 hit with their double 'A'-sided single 'Sorry's Not Good Enough' and 'Friday Night'?

QUESTION 9
What hit song title is shared by Whigfield in 1994, Suede in 1997 and UD Project in 2004?

QUESTION 10
Released at the end of 1985, which soul singer joined Cherrelle on 'Saturday Love', her UK Top 10 hit in early 1986?

POPMASTER QUIZ 258

FEELING CRAZY

QUESTION 1
Which Welsh classical singer turned pop star enjoyed a Top 3 hit in 2005 with 'Crazy Chick'?

QUESTION 2
Can you name the rock band that made the UK Top 5 in 1987 with 'Crazy Crazy Nights'?

QUESTION 3
What was the title of the debut hit and No 1 from The Temperance Seven in 1961?

QUESTION 4
Can you name the American female singer who achieved her biggest UK hit in 1989 with 'Miss You Like Crazy'?

QUESTION 5
In 1979, which legendary rock band topped the American chart for four weeks and reached No 2 in the UK with 'Crazy Little Thing Called Love'?

QUESTION 6
What is the common song title shared on hits by Patsy Cline, Mud, Gnarls Barkley and Seal, to name but four?

QUESTION 7
Two hit songs by Madonna were featured in the 1985 movie *Vision Quest,* in which she played a club singer. One was 'Gambler' – what was the other?

QUESTION 8
In 1981, which singer achieved his second Top 10 hit with the song 'You Drive Me Crazy'?

QUESTION 9
Which American family group earned their first UK Top 3 hit in 1972 with 'Crazy Horses'?

QUESTION 10
Can you name the female singer who made her 2003 UK chart debut with 'The Closest Thing to Crazy'?

A answers

QUIZ 256

Q1 *Lead singers are all known by single names (Suggs, Bono, Sting)*

Q2 *Covers of songs not released as UK singles by the song's writers (Costello, Bowie, Prince)*

Q3 *Uncredited female voices on hit duets ('Dead Ringer for Love', 'Lucky Stars', 'U Got the Look')*

Q4 *Have all acted in Coronation Street*

Q5 *No 1 songs whose title isn't in the lyrics*

Q6 *Paul Carrack has played in all three groups*

Q7 *Have all had hits with eponymously titled songs*

Q8 *Songs about actresses ('Bette Davis Eyes', 'Marlene on the Wall', 'Candle in the Wind')*

Q9 *All featured Norman Cook before he recorded as Fatboy Slim*

Q10 *Their second Top 40 hit was a re-release, having been a Top 75 hit before their Top 40 debut!*

QUIZ 257

Q1
'Sunday Girl'

Q2
Oasis

Q3
'Monday Monday'

Q4
The Pogues

Q5
The Undertones

Q6
David Bowie

Q7
Gary Moore

Q8
McFly

Q9
'Saturday Night'

Q10
Alexander O'Neal

QUIZ 259 POPMASTER

FEET

QUESTION 1
Which group followed their 1967 No 1 hit 'Baby Now that I've Found You' with 'Back on My Feet Again'?

QUESTION 2
The song 'Head over Feet' became the first UK Top 10 hit for which Canadian female singer in 1996?

QUESTION 3
Can you name the singer who released a 2015 single, 'Fire Under My Feet', from her first album in nearly two years, I Am?

QUESTION 4
Who sang the title song to the 1984 movie and had a Top 10 hit with the song 'Footloose'?

QUESTION 5
Which child actor turned singing star had a 1952 Top 3 UK hit with 'Feet Up! (Pat Her on the Po-Po)'?

QUESTION 6
In 1974, what was the title of the first No 1 hit for glam-rock band Mud?

QUESTION 7
What was the title of the song that gave both Steve Lawrence and Ronnie Carroll a hit in 1960 and was successfully revived in 1981 by Showaddywaddy?

QUESTION 8
What was the title of the hit single by rock band Embrace that became the official song of the England World Cup Squad during their 2006 FIFA World Cup campaign?

QUESTION 9
Can you name the instrumental group that topped the UK singles chart in 1963 with 'Foot Tapper'?

QUESTION 10
What was the collective name of the Danish duo consisting of Jesper Mortensen and Jeppe Laursen who achieved a UK Top 3 hit in 2003 with 'Move Your Feet'?

POPMASTER QUIZ 260

FESTIVAL FEVER

QUIZ 258

Q1 *Charlotte Church*

Q2 *KISS*

Q3 *'You're Driving Me Crazy'*

Q4 *Natalie Cole*

Q5 *Queen*

Q6 *'Crazy'*

Q7 *'Crazy for You'*

Q8 *Shakin' Stevens*

Q9 *The Osmonds*

Q10 *Katie Melua*

QUESTION 1
Who reached No 1 in 1970 with the song 'Woodstock'?

QUESTION 2
...and which singer-songwriter and guitarist was the opening act at that 1969 festival?

QUESTION 3
Which band had to pull out of a headlining slot at the 2015 Glastonbury festival due to the drummer breaking his leg?

QUESTION 4
Founded in 1971, in which country is the Roskilde Festival held?

QUESTION 5
The songs 'Ooh Stick You!', 'Ugly' and 'School's Out' were all hits in 2000 for a female duo who were bottled off the main stage at Reading Festival after just two songs in that same year. Name the duo.

QUESTION 6
Having been revived in 2002, which festival takes place at Seaclose Park?

QUESTION 7
Lilith Fair was a concert tour and travelling music festival of the late Nineties founded by which Canadian singer and songwriter?

QUESTION 8
Who was brought on stage in a wheelchair at the 1992 Reading Festival?

QUESTION 9
Which UK festival is held in both Hylands Park, Chelmsford, and Weston Park, Staffordshire?

QUESTION 10
Which American festival was founded in the early Nineties by Perry Farrell of Jane's Addiction?

QUIZ 259

Q1
The Foundations

Q2
Alanis Morissette

Q3
Leona Lewis

Q4
Kenny Loggins

Q5
Guy Mitchell

Q6
'Tiger Feet'

Q7
'Footsteps'

Q8
'World at Your Feet'

Q9
The Shadows

Q10
Junior Senior

QUIZ 261 POPMASTER

FILM MUSIC (1)

QUESTION 1
'The Power of Love' by Huey Lewis & The News features in which Michael J. Fox film of the mid-Eighties?

QUESTION 2
What is the title of Seal's hit song that appears over the closing credits of the film *Batman Forever*?

QUESTION 3
What was the title of the 1995 No 1 by Coolio featuring LV that featured in the film *Dangerous Minds*, starring Michelle Pfeiffer?

QUESTION 4
For what film did the Pet Shop Boys write the Dusty Springfield hit 'Nothing has Been Proved'?

QUESTION 5
Which American singer has acted in the films *The Social Network, Friends with Benefits and Trouble with the Curve*?

QUESTION 6
Name one of the three original hit singles from the soundtrack to the 1988 film *Buster*.

QUESTION 7
Purple Rain was the title of Prince's first film. What was his second, released in 1986?

QUESTION 8
'(Best That You Can Do)' is the subtitle to the theme song from a film starring Dudley Moore that became the only UK Top 40 hit for Christopher Cross – what is the full title of the song?

QUESTION 9
Released in America in 1960, what was the name of the first film Elvis Presley made after he left the army?

QUESTION 10
The song 'Raindrops Keep Falling on My Head', made famous by both BJ Thomas and Sacha Distel, featured in which 1969 film?

POPMASTER QUIZ 262

FILM MUSIC (2)

QUESTION 1
Who appeared in the films *The Hunger, Merry Christmas, Mr Lawrence* and *Absolute Beginners* in the Eighties?

QUESTION 2
Which group sang 'Disco Inferno' on the *Saturday Night Fever* soundtrack?

QUESTION 3
Released in 1996, what is the title of Celine Dion's UK Top 5 and US No.1 single subtitled '(Theme from *Up Close and Personal*)?

QUESTION 4
In which 1970 film did Mick Jagger star as the lead character in a story about a 19th-century Australian bushranger?

QUESTION 5
What was the title of Lionel Richie's hit song from the film *White Nights*, starring Mikhail Baryshnikov and Gregory Hines?

QUESTION 6
Who recorded the soundtrack to the film *When Harry Met Sally* and starred himself in the films *Memphis Belle, Copycat* and *Little Man Tate*?

QUESTION 7
Duran Duran got their name from a character in which fantasy film starring Jane Fonda?

QUESTION 8
In which film did Eminem appear as the character Jimmy "B-Rabbit" Smith Jr?

QUESTION 9
Actor Will Smith's 2002 Top 3 hit 'Black Suits Comin (Nod Ya Head)' featured vocals from Tra-Knox and was featured on the soundtrack to which of his hit movies?

QUESTION 10
Which American singer won a 'Best Supporting Actress' Academy award for her role in the film *Dreamgirls*?

QUIZ 260

Q1
Matthews' Southern Comfort

Q2
Richie Havens

Q3
Foo Fighters

Q4
Denmark

Q5
Daphne & Celeste

Q6
Isle of Wight Festival

Q7
Sarah McLachlan

Q8
Kurt Cobain of Nirvana

Q9
V Festival

Q10
Lollapalooza

QUIZ 261

Q1
Back to the Future

Q2
'Kiss from a Rose'

Q3
'Gangsta's Paradise'

Q4
Scandal

Q5
Justin Timberlake

Q6 *'A Groovy Kind of Love', 'Two Hearts' (both Phil Collins), 'Loco in Acapulco' (The Four Tops)*

Q7
Under the Cherry Moon

Q8
'Arthur's Theme (Best that You Can Do)'

Q9
G.I. Blues

Q10
Butch Cassidy and the Sundance Kid

QUIZ 263 POPMASTER

GUEST STARRING (1)

Guest appearances by chart artists on other hit records

QUESTION 1
Billed as 'special guest star', Gene Pitney appeared on which Marc Almond single that spent a month at No 1 in 1989?

QUESTION 2
Which female vocal group appeared alongside Earth Wind & Fire on their hit 'Boogie Wonderland'?

QUESTION 3
Miles Davis played trumpet on which hit single by Scritti Politti?

QUESTION 4
Which female singer featured alongside Maroon 5 on their international hit 'Moves Like Jagger'?

QUESTION 5
Neil Hannon of The Divine Comedy and Neil Tennant of the Pet Shop Boys both featured on backing vocals on which 1998 Robbie Williams single?

QUESTION 6
Which two of Michael Jackson's siblings are amongst the backing vocalists on his 1984 hit 'P.Y.T. (Pretty Young Thing)'?

QUESTION 7
Daft Punk's international No 1 'Get Lucky' both featured and was co-written by Pharrell Williams and which guitarist?

QUESTION 8
Carl Wilson and Bruce Johnston of The Beach Boys sang backing vocals on which hit single from Elton John's 1974 album Caribou?

QUESTION 9
Which female R&B/hip-hop singer featured on Puff Daddy's 1997 worldwide No 1 'I'll be Missing You'?

QUESTION 10
Which Donna Summer single features a backing choir that includes Lionel Richie, Dionne Warwick, Michael McDonald, Brenda Russell and Stevie Wonder?

POPMASTER QUIZ 264

GUEST STARRING (2)

Guest appearances by chart artists on other hit records... and beyond!

QUESTION 1
Who popped into the studio to add his backing vocals to Carly Simon's debut hit 'You're So Vain'?

QUESTION 2
What is the title of Sam Smith's 2015 No 1 that features American singer John Legend?

QUESTION 3
In which Australian TV programme did Chris Lowe of the Pet Shop Boys make a guest appearance in 1995?

QUESTION 4
Who was the guest guitarist on the 1986 No 1 remake of 'Living Doll' by Cliff Richard & The Young Ones?

QUESTION 5
Which actress, model and singer provided guest vocals on the Thompson Twins' 1983 hit 'Watching'?

QUESTION 6
Red Hot Chili Peppers, Paul McCartney, The White Stripes and the Ramones have all made guest appearances on which animated TV series?

QUESTION 7
Who was the guest lead guitarist on 'While My Guitar Gently Weeps', from The Beatles' White Album?

QUESTION 8
Lou Reed made a cameo appearance on a 1989 Top 20 single by Simple Minds. What was it called?

QUESTION 9
Which of these three singles by Tina Turner features a guest vocal from Sting – is it 'In Your Wildest Dreams', 'It's Only Love' or 'On Silent Wings'?

QUESTION 10
Which British group were guest stars in a 1986 episode of *The A-Team*?

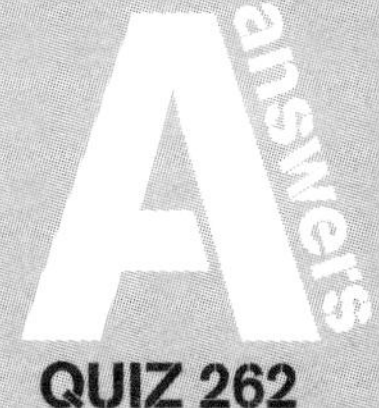

QUIZ 262

Q1 *David Bowie*

Q2 *The Trammps*

Q3 *'Because You Loved Me'*

Q4 *Ned Kelly*

Q5 *'Say You, Say Me'*

Q6 *Harry Connick Jr*

Q7 *Barbarella*

Q8 *8 Mile*

Q9 Men In Black II

Q10 *Jennifer Hudson*

QUIZ 263

Q1
'Something's Gotten Hold of My Heart'

Q2
The Emotions

Q3
'Oh Patti (Don't Feel Sorry for Loverboy)'

Q4
Christina Aguilera

Q5
'No Regrets'

Q6
LaToya and Janet Jackson

Q7
Nile Rodgers

Q8
'Don't Let the Sun Go Down on Me'

Q9
Faith Evans

Q10
'State of Independence'

QUIZ 265 POPMASTER

HANDS

QUESTION 1
From 1957, what was the title of the only hit single achieved by Laurie London?

QUESTION 2
Which Birmingham-based band's second Top 10 hit from 1980 was called 'Hands Off - She's Mine'?

QUESTION 3
Topping the UK chart for five weeks in 1987, what was the title of the only No 1 hit for T'Pau?

QUESTION 4
Which singer enjoyed a No 2 hit in the UK in 1999 with 'If I Could Turn Back the Hands of Time'?

QUESTION 5
In 1972, which female duo made their top forty chart debut with a cover of Martha & The Vandellas' 'Third Finger, Left Hand'?

QUESTION 6
Can you name the first UK Top 10 hit achieved by Nine Inch Nails that made the singles chart in 2005?

QUESTION 7
Elton John achieved his first solo No 1 hit in the UK in 1990 with a double 'A'-sided hit that topped the chart for five weeks. One side was called 'Sacrifice', but what was the other song?

QUESTION 8
What was the name of the disco group that enjoyed a massive holiday hit in 1981 with 'Hands Up (Give Me Your Heart)'?

QUESTION 9
Can you give the title of the only major hit achieved in 1988 by UK act Breathe?

QUESTION 10
What were the names of the two children's TV entertainers who made the UK top twenty in 2000 with 'Hands Up'?

POPMASTER QUIZ 266

HEADS

QUESTION 1
What was the title of the debut hit and only Top 10 single achieved by the rock band Argent?

QUESTION 2
Jamaican reggae artist Clifford Smith achieved a top twenty hit in 1998 called 'Heads High'. Under what name did he release the single?

QUESTION 3
From 1965, what was the title of the only top forty hit achieved by Roy Head?

QUESTION 4
Can you name the female singer who topped the UK singles chart for four weeks in 2001 with 'Can't Get You out of My Head'?

QUESTION 5
Which group won a Grammy in 2003 for 'Best Alternative Album' with their classic release A Rush of Blood to the Head?

QUESTION 6
In 1978, the Electric Light Orchestra achieved a Top 10 hit with their eponymous EP containing a song that gave them their first American Top 10 hit. Can you name it?

QUESTION 7
In what year did the duo Kosheen achieve a UK Top 10 hit with 'All in My Head'?

QUESTION 8
Which group enjoyed the top twenty hit 'Head over Heels' in 1985, taken from their album Songs from the Big Chair?

QUESTION 9
Name the act that topped the chart in 2009 with 'Killing in the Name', who made the top twenty in 1993 with 'Bullet in the Head'?

QUESTION 10
Owing much of their success to an early Eighties 'rowing boat' dance craze, which R&B group made their chart debut in 1980 with 'Oops Up Side Your Head'?

QUIZ 264

Q1 *Mick Jagger*

Q2 *'Lay Me Down'*

Q3 *Neighbours*

Q4 *Hank Marvin*

Q5 *Grace Jones*

Q6 *The Simpsons*

Q7 *Eric Clapton*

Q8 *'This is Your Land'*

Q9 *'On Silent Wings'*

Q10 *Culture Club (the episode was called Cowboy George)*

QUIZ 265

Q1
'He's Got the Whole World in His Hands'

Q2
The Beat

Q3
'China in Your Hand'

Q4
R Kelly

Q5
The Pearls

Q6
'The Hand that Feeds'

Q7
'Healing Hands'

Q8
Ottawan

Q9
'Hands to Heaven'

Q10
Trevor and Simon

QUIZ 267 POPMASTER

HEALTH CARE

QUESTION 1
Which group featured Yazz & The Plastic Population on their debut hit single 'Doctorin' the House'?

QUESTION 2
Can you name the rock band that topped the American chart for two weeks in 1988 and made the UK top twenty with 'Bad Medicine'?

QUESTION 3
What was the title of the 1997 top twenty hit by Sly & Robbie that also featured Simply Red?

QUESTION 4
Which singer released a top twenty hit in 1983 called 'Pills and Soap' as Imposter?

QUESTION 5
In 1998, Danish group Aqua topped the UK chart for the second time with their follow-up record to 'Barbie Girl'. What was its title?

QUESTION 6
Which group included a song called 'Auto Surgery' on their 1993 Top 10 hit EP 'Shortsharpshock'?

QUESTION 7
Can you name the comedy star and actress whose record made the UK Top 5 in 1960 inspired by, but not included in their movie *The Millionairess*? The single was titled 'Goodness Gracious Me'.

QUESTION 8
Which rock band released their third album in 1974 called Sheer Heart Attack?

QUESTION 9
Although they achieved several big hits in the Seventies and Eighties, Dr Hook only topped the UK singles chart on one occasion. Can you name the song?

QUESTION 10
What was the collective name of Paul Glancey and Duncan Glasson, who topped the UK chart in 1998 with 'Gym and Tonic'?

POPMASTER QUIZ 268

HERE COMES THE RAIN

QUESTION 1
In 1984, which duo made the UK Top 10 with their hit single 'Here Comes the Rain Again'?

QUESTION 2
Which successful Australian singer achieved a UK Top 10 hit in 1990 with a revival of The Cascades' 1963 hit 'Rhythm of the Rain'?

QUESTION 3
Following in the footsteps of 'Pearl's a Singer', whose second UK Top 10 hit in 1977 was called 'Sunshine After the Rain'?

QUESTION 4
Can you name the singer-songwriter whose 1966 recording of 'Rainy Day Women Nos. 12 & 35' made the UK Top 10?

QUESTION 5
In 2008, which female singer embraced the UK chart with her top twenty hit 'Rain on Your Parade'?

QUESTION 6
With which American vocal group did Frankie Laine enjoy a UK Top 10 hit in 1954 with 'Rain, Rain, Rain'?

QUESTION 7
Which American singer-songwriter topped the American chart and scored a UK top twenty hit in 1974 with 'Laughter in the Rain'?

QUESTION 8
A year-and-a-half after their first Top 10 hit, which group achieved their second with 'Raincloud'?

QUESTION 9
Although not a major hit in the UK, which German act topped the American chart in 1989 with 'Blame it on the Rain'?

QUESTION 10
Which American female singer enjoyed a UK top twenty hit in 1981 with her hit single 'Rainy Night in Georgia'?

QUIZ 266

Q1
'Hold Your Head Up'

Q2
Mr Vegas

Q3
'Treat Her Right'

Q4
Kylie Minogue

Q5
Coldplay

Q6
'Can't Get it out of My Head'

Q7
2003

Q8
Tears for Fears

Q9
Rage Against the Machine

Q10
The Gap Band

QUIZ 267

Q1
Coldcut

Q2
Bon Jovi

Q3
'Night Nurse'

Q4
Elvis Costello

Q5
'Doctor Jones'

Q6
Therapy?

Q7
Peter Sellers and Sophia Loren

Q8
Queen

Q9
'When You're in Love with a Beautiful Woman'

Q10
Spacedust

QUIZ 269 POPMASTER

HERE COMES THE SUN

QUESTION 1
Name the singer who achieved his first solo UK Top 10 hit in 1973 with Bob Dylan's song 'A Hard Rain's Gonna Fall'.

QUESTION 2
Which band reached No 1 early in 1986 with 'The Sun Always Shines on TV'?

QUESTION 3
Can you name the male duo who achieved a UK top twenty hit in 2004 with 'The Sun has Come Your Way'?

QUESTION 4
Which group took George Harrison's song 'Here Comes the Sun' into the UK Top 10 in 1976?

QUESTION 5
What hit song title is shared on chart records by Gabrielle in 1999, Gareth Gates in 2003 and Twista in 2004?

QUESTION 6
Which group topped the UK chart for four weeks in 1966 with 'The Sun Ain't Gonna Shine Anymore'?

QUESTION 7
Can you name the male singer who achieved his first and only major UK hit in 2008 with 'Sun Goes Down'?

QUESTION 8
Which group first made the UK top twenty in 1968 with 'I Live for the Sun'?

QUESTION 9
What was the title of the 1999 Top 3 UK hit by Bob Marley vs. Funkstar De Luxe?

QUESTION 10
Which legendary pop vocal duo achieved a 1962 UK top twenty hit with 'No One Can Make My Sunshine Smile'?

POPMASTER QUIZ 270

HOW GREEN IS YOUR GRASS?

QUESTION 1
Which legendary singer topped the singles charts for seven weeks in 1966 with 'The Green Green Grass Of Home'?

QUESTION 2
Can you name the group that have never achieved UK chart success but made the American Top 10 with their hits 'Let's Live For Today, 'Midnight Confessions' and 'Sooner Or Later'?

QUESTION 3
The Move's 1967 debut Top 10 hit was 'Night Of Fear,' what was the second?

QUESTION 4
Which classic Ink Spots hit gave Windsor Davies and Don Estelle a three week run at the top of the charts in 1975?

QUESTION 5
In 1967, which female singer made the top twenty with Tony Hatch's song, 'The Other Man's Grass (Is Always Greener)'?

QUESTION 6
Which group made the top forty for the thirteenth and final time in 1969 with 'Snake In The Grass'?

QUESTION 7
Friends Of Distinction achieved two Top 10 hits in America, one was 'Love Or Let Me Be Lonely' in 1970, what was the title of the first from 1969?

QUESTION 8
In 1957 Johnny Duncan reached No 2 in the charts with 'Last Train To San Fernando,' what was the name of his backing group?

QUESTION 9
Which group sang about the 'Night Of The Long Grass' on their 1967 top twenty hit?

QUESTION 10
Can you give the title of the only top forty hit achieved in 1969 by vocal group, Harmony Grass?

A answers

QUIZ 268

Q1
Eurythmics

Q2
Jason Donovan

Q3
Elkie Brooks

Q4
Bob Dylan

Q5
Duffy

Q6
The Four Lads

Q7
Neil Sedaka

Q8
The Lighthouse Family

Q9
Milli Vanilli

Q10
Randy Crawford

QUIZ 269

Q1
Bryan Ferry

Q2
A-ha

Q3
Sam & Mark

Q4
Steve Harley & Cockney Rebel

Q5
'Sunshine'

Q6
The Walker Brothers

Q7
David Jordan

Q8
Vanity Fare

Q9
'Sun is Shining'

Q10
The Everly Brothers

QUIZ 271 POPMASTER

I LOVE MY CAR

QUESTION 1
Which group achieved a Top 5 hit in 1984 and again in 1985 with their song 'Drive'?

QUESTION 2
After his No 1 hit 'Are 'Friends' Electric?' with Tubeway Army, what was the title of Gary Numan's only other chart-topper?

QUESTION 3
What was the title of the album by The Beatles that first included their song 'Drive My Car' as the opening track?

QUESTION 4
Can you name the singer who topped the American chart for two weeks and made the UK Top 3 with 'Get outta My Dreams Get into My Car'?

QUESTION 5
What was the title of the only top forty hit credited to Paul & Linda McCartney?

QUESTION 6
Acccording to their Top 10 hit from 2006 and 2007, which group were 'Chasing Cars'?

QUESTION 7
Which American singer won a Grammy in 1988 for her only UK Top 5 hit, 'Fast Car'?

QUESTION 8
In 2005, which legendary singer recorded the UK top twenty hit 'What Car'?

QUESTION 9
Which group achieved their 11th UK Top 10 hit with 'Driving in My Car'?

QUESTION 10
Under what name did performer Paul Phillips release his only UK Top 10 hit, 'Car 67', in 1978?

POPMASTER QUIZ 272

I SEE THE LIGHT

QUESTION 1
Which successful drummer, composer and singer achieved his final Top 10 hit of the Nineties with 'Dance into the Light'?

QUESTION 2
What hit song has been successfully recorded by The Doors, Jose Feliciano and Will Young?

QUESTION 3
Who wrote Manfred Mann's Earth Band's 1976 American No 1 and UK Top 10 hit 'Blinded by the Light'?

QUESTION 4
Which legendary rock 'n' roll performer scored a UK top twenty hit in 1959 with 'By the Light of the Silvery Moon'?

QUESTION 5
In 2005, which American female rapper achieved a UK top twenty hit with her hit record 'Lighters Up'?

QUESTION 6
Can you name the Romanian panpipe player who scored a 1976 UK Top 5 hit with the instrumental theme music to the TV series The Light of Experience called '(Light of Experience) Doina de Jale'?

QUESTION 7
After the success of her 1970 Eurovision Song Contest and No 1 hit 'All Kinds of Everything', Dana had to wait nearly a year for her next top twenty hit. Can you name it?

QUESTION 8
Which one-time member of the group Eternal achieved her first solo hit in 1995 with 'Light of My Life'?

QUESTION 9
Scott Walker achieved two solo top twenty hits in the Sixties - the first was 'Joanna', what was the second?

QUESTION 10
The daughter of Elvis Presley, Lisa Marie Presley, achieved a UK top twenty hit in 2003. What was the title?

QUIZ 270

Q1 *Tom Jones*

Q2 *The Grass Roots*

Q3 *'I Can Hear the Grass Grow'*

Q4 *'Whispering Grass'*

Q5 *Petula Clark*

Q6 *Dave Dee, Dozy, Beaky, Mick & Tich*

Q7 *'Grazing in the Grass'*

Q8 *The Blue Grass Boys*

Q9 *The Troggs*

Q10 *'Move in a Little Closer Baby'*

QUIZ 271

Q1
The Cars

Q2
'Cars'

Q3
Rubber Soul

Q4
Billy Ocean

Q5
'Back Seat of My Car'

Q6
Snow Patrol

Q7
Tracy Chapman

Q8
Cliff Richard

Q9
Madness

Q10
Driver 67

QUIZ 273 POPMASTER

I WRITE THE SONGS

QUESTION 1
What are the names of the two-man songwriting team behind the biggest hits for The Sweet, Mud and Suzi Quatro?

QUESTION 2
Which superstar has written songs under the names Alexander Nevermind, Joey Coco and 'Symbol'?

QUESTION 3
Which successful singer bucked the trend by choosing to sing an original song when she first auditioned for *The X Factor* in 2012?

QUESTION 4
The singer-songwriter who won the BBC's *Fame Academy* and reached No 1 with 'Stop Living the Lie' has written for Matt Cardle, Hurts, Lana Del Rey, Morten Harket and Newton Faulkner. Who is he?

QUESTION 5
One of America's most successful female songwriters penned 'How Do I Live' for LeAnn Rimes, 'I Don't Want to Miss a Thing' for Aerosmith and 'Because You Loved Me' for Celine Dion. Who is she?

QUESTION 6
Who is Chris Difford's songwriting partner on the Squeeze hit singles?

QUESTION 7
What is the name of the legendary New York building that was the songwriting 'office' to Carole King, Neil Sedaka, Gerry Goffin and Johnny Mercer, amongst others?

QUESTION 8
The 1998 album Painted from Memory was a collaboration between two hugely successful songwriters. Who are they?

QUESTION 9
What are the first names of the successful Motown writing partnership of Ashford and Simpson?

QUESTION 10
Who actually wrote the Barry Manilow signature song 'I Write the Songs' – was it Stephen Sondheim, Bruce Johnston of The Beach Boys, David Cassidy or Dewey Bunnell of America?

POPMASTER QUIZ 274

IFS AND BUTS

QUESTION 1
Which legendary American country singer achieved a top twenty hit in 1969 with 'But You Love Me Daddy'?

QUESTION 2
Can you name the husband and wife duo who achieved a UK top twenty hit in 1965 with 'But You're Mine'?

QUESTION 3
Can you name the female singer who made her UK chart debut in 1971 with Bob Dylan's song 'If Not for You'?

QUESTION 4
Which successful American group achieved a UK Top 10 hit in 1976 with 'If Not You'?

QUESTION 5
Can you name the successful vocal duo who achieved a top twenty hit in 1999 with 'I Don't Know What You Want but I Can't Give it Anymore'?

QUESTION 6
Which American country singer scored a UK top twenty hit in 2002 with 'But I Do Love You'?

QUESTION 7
What was the title of Clarence 'Frogman' Henry's first UK hit from 1961?

QUESTION 8
Can you name the Irish singer who sadly passed away in 2015, who after changing record labels from Decca to Pye in 1967 scored a Top 3 hit with 'If the Whole World Stopped Lovin''?

QUESTION 9
Daniel Bedingfield topped the singles chart in late 2001 and again in early 2002 with 'Gotta Get Thru This', but what was the title of his next No 1 single?

QUESTION 10
Which British actor and singer achieved a Top 5 hit in 1960 with his hit recording of 'If She Should Come to You?

QUIZ 272

Q1 *Phil Collins*

Q2 *'Light My Fire'*

Q3 *Bruce Springsteen*

Q4 *Little Richard*

Q5 *Lil' Kim*

Q6 *Gheorghe Zamfir*

Q7 *'Who Put the Lights Out'*

Q8 *Louise*

Q9 *'Lights of Cincinnati'*

Q10 *'Lights Out'*

QUIZ 273

Q1
Nicky Chinn and Mike Chapman

Q2
Prince

Q3
Ella Henderson

Q4
David Sneddon

Q5
Diane Warren

Q6
Glenn Tilbrook

Q7
Brill Building

Q8
Elvis Costello and Burt Bacharach

Q9
Nickolas and Valerie

Q10
Bruce Johnston

QUIZ 275 POPMASTER

IN ORDER (1)

In each case, and beginning with the earliest, put these three songs by each group or artist in the order they were originally UK Top 40 hits

QUESTION 1
Billy Joel - 'The River of Dreams', 'The Longest Time', 'My Life'

QUESTION 2
Elvis Presley - 'Suspicious Minds', 'Wooden Heart', 'Suspicion'

QUESTION 3
Texas - 'Getaway', 'Black Eyed Boy', 'I Don't Want a Lover'

QUESTION 4
Take That - 'Rule the World', 'These Days', 'Back for Good'

QUESTION 5
Rod Stewart - 'Young Turks', 'Downtown Train', 'Oh! No Not My Baby'

QUESTION 6
Kim Wilde - 'Chequered Love', 'Love is Holy', 'You Came'

QUESTION 7
Blur - 'Tender', 'Girls and Boys', 'Under the Westway'

QUESTION 8
Madonna - 'Jump', 'Rain', 'Angel'

QUESTION 9
George Michael - 'Spinning the Wheel', 'One More Try', 'Amazing'

QUESTION 10
Status Quo - 'Rollin' Home', 'Whatever You Want', 'Paper Plane'

POPMASTER QUIZ 276

IN ORDER (2)

In each case, beginning with the earliest, put these three songs by each group or artist in the order they were originally UK Top 40 hits

QUESTION 1
Duran Duran - '(Reach Up for the) Sunrise', 'Ordinary World', 'Notorious'

QUESTION 2
Janet Jackson - 'All for You', 'Runaway','Let's Wait Awhile'

QUESTION 3
Paul McCartney - 'Young Boy', 'Once Upon a Long Ago', 'Coming Up'

QUESTION 4
Will Young - 'Jealousy', 'Don't Let Me Down', 'All Time Love'

QUESTION 5
The Rolling Stones - 'Mixed Emotions', 'Miss You', 'Let's Spend the Night Together'

QUESTION 6
Simply Red - 'Sunrise', 'Fairground', 'The Right Thing'

QUESTION 7
Diana Ross - 'One Shining Moment', 'All of My Life', 'Work that Body'

QUESTION 8
Oasis - 'Go Let it Out', 'Some Might Say', 'The Importance of Being Idle'

QUESTION 9
Lady Gaga - 'Applause', 'Just Dance', 'The Edge of Glory'

QUESTION 10
David Bowie - 'Jump They Say', 'Blue Jean', 'Heroes'

QUIZ 274

Q1 *Jim Reeves*

Q2 *Sonny & Cher*

Q3 *Olivia Newton-John*

Q4 *Dr Hook*

Q5 *Pet Shop Boys*

Q6 *LeAnn Rimes*

Q7 *'But I Do'*

Q8 *Val Doonican*

Q9 *'If You're Not the One'*

Q10 *Anthony Newley*

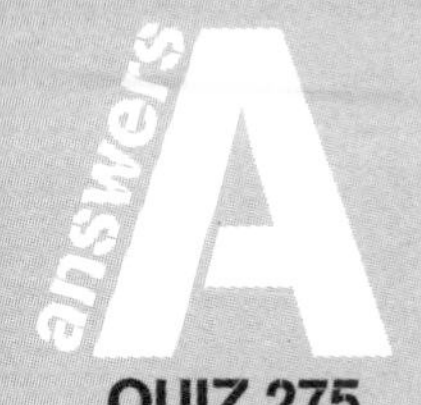

QUIZ 275

Q1
'My Life' ('78), 'The Longest Time' ('84), 'The River of Dreams' ('93)

Q2
'Wooden Heart' ('61), 'Suspicious Minds' ('69), 'Suspicion' ('76)

Q3
'I Don't Want a Lover' ('89), 'Black Eyed Boy' ('97), 'Getaway' ('05)

Q4
'Back for Good' ('95), 'Rule the World' ('07), 'These Days' ('14)

Q5
'Oh! No Not My Baby' ('73), 'Young Turks' ('81), 'Downtown Train' ('90)

Q6
'Chequered Love' ('81), 'You Came' ('88), 'Love is Holy' ('92)

Q7
'Girls and Boys' ('94), 'Tender' ('99), 'Under the Westway' ('12)

Q8
'Angel' ('85), 'Rain' ('93), 'Jump' ('06)

Q9
'One More Try' ('88), 'Spinning the Wheel' ('96), 'Amazing' ('04)

Q10
'Paper Plane' ('73), 'Whatever You Want' ('79), 'Rollin' Home' ('86)

QUIZ 277 POPMASTER

INSTRUMENTAL HITS

Simply name the chart acts that had these hits all classed as instrumentals

QUESTION 1
'Frankenstein' (1973)

QUESTION 2
'The Groove' (1980)

QUESTION 3
'The Man in Black' (1974)

QUESTION 4
'Side Saddle' (1959)

QUESTION 5
'Footsee' (1975)

QUESTION 6
'Tired of Getting Pushed Around' (1988)

QUESTION 7
'Oxygene Part IV' (1977)

QUESTION 8
'Infinity' (1990)/'Infinity 2008' (2008)

QUESTION 9
'Toccata' (1980)

QUESTION 10
'Keep Your Eye on Me' (1987)

POPMASTER QUIZ 278

IT'S A SIGN

QUESTION 1
Released in 1967, whose only Top 10 hit was 'Gimme Little Sign'?

QUESTION 2
Which of his hit songs did Stevie Wonder revive in 2003 when he was featured with Angie Stone on the top twenty hit by Blue?

QUESTION 3
Can you name the only Top 10 hit achieved by girl group The Belle Stars in 1983?

QUESTION 4
Terence Trent D'Arby achieved three Top 10 hits in the Eighties with 'If You Let Me Stay', 'Wishing Well' and which other single?

QUESTION 5
Which long-running music radio show features a piece of music called 'At the Sign of the Swinging Cymbal' as its signature tune?

QUESTION 6
Also the title track of his first solo album following the departure of his backing band, who achieved a Top 10 hit in 1987 with 'Sign o' the Times'?

QUESTION 7
Can you name the legendary female Tamla Motown group who achieved a top forty hit in 1969 with 'No Matter What Sign You Are'?

QUESTION 8
From 2003, can you name the only top twenty hit by studio group Kontakt?

QUESTION 9
Following 'All that She Wants', which Swedish group achieved their second Top 3 hit in 1994 with 'The Sign'?

QUESTION 10
Which male rapper reached No 2 in 2005 with his hit 'Signs', featuring Charlie Wilson and Justin Timberlake?

QUIZ 276

Q1 *'Notorious' ('86), 'Ordinary World' ('93), '(Reach Up for the) Sunrise' ('04)*

Q2 *'Let's Wait Awhile' ('87), 'Runaway' ('95), 'All for You' ('01)*

Q3 *'Coming Up' ('80), 'Once Upon a Long Ago' ('87), 'Young Boy' ('97)*

Q4 *'Don't Let Me Down' ('02), 'All Time Love' ('06), 'Jealousy' ('11)*

Q5 *'Let's Spend the Night Together' ('67), 'Miss You' ('78), 'Mixed Emotions' ('89)*

Q6 *'The Right Thing' ('87), 'Fairground' ('95), 'Sunrise' ('03)*

Q7 *'All of My Life' ('74), 'Work that Body' ('82), 'One Shining Moment' ('92)*

Q8 *'Some Might Say' ('95), 'Go Let it Out' ('00), 'The Importance of Being Idle' ('05)*

Q9 *'Just Dance' ('09), 'The Edge of Glory' ('11), 'Applause' ('13)*

Q10 *'Heroes' ('77), 'Blue Jean' ('84), 'Jump They Say' ('93)*

QUIZ 277

QUIZ 279 POPMASTER

IT'S BED TIME

Q1
Edgar Winter Group

Q2
Rodney Franklin

Q3
Cozy Powell

Q4
Russ Conway

Q5
Wigan's Chosen Few

Q6
Two Men, a Drum Machine and a Trumpet

Q7
Jean-Michel Jarre

Q8
Guru Josh (Guru Josh Project for 2008 version)

Q9
Sky

Q10
Herb Alpert

QUESTION 1
What was the title of the UK Top 5 novelty hit of the Eighties by Morris Minor & The Majors?

QUESTION 2
Which successful vocal group achieved an American Top 10 hit in 1972 with Tony Macaulay's song '(Last Night) I Didn't Get to Sleep at All'?

QUESTION 3
Can you name the Australian band that achieved their only UK Top 10 hit in 1989 with 'Beds are Burning'?

QUESTION 4
Ray Parker Jr achieved two UK top twenty hits in the Eighties - the first was 'Ghostbusters', but what was the title of the other?

QUESTION 5
Which trio consisting of Tom Chaplin, Richard Hughes and Tim Rice-Oxley achieved a 2004 Top 10 hit with 'Bedshaped'?

QUESTION 6
Can you name the successful group that achieved a top twenty hit in the UK in 1968 with 'Sleepy Joe'?

QUESTION 7
What was the title of Madonna's 1995 Top 10 hit written by Björk, Nellee Hooper and Marius de Vries?

QUESTION 8
Name the instrumental duo that topped the American chart and made the UK top forty in 1959 with 'Sleep Walk'.

QUESTION 9
In 1967, which successful female artist said 'Don't Sleep in the Subway'?

QUESTION 10
Which 1993 top twenty hit by Bon Jovi begins with the lines "Sitting here wasted and wounded at this old piano, trying hard to capture the moment this morning I don't know."

POPMASTER QUIZ 280

IT'S TEA TIME

QUESTION 1
Can you name the American pop group that made the top twenty in 1964 with 'Bread and Butter'?

QUESTION 2
Released in 1980, what was the title of the only top forty hit achieved by R&B group Coffee?

QUESTION 3
Which group made the top twenty for the first of many times in 1977 with their hit 'All Around the World'?

QUESTION 4
Can you name the band that won a 1999 MTV award for 'Best Video' for their hit song 'Coffee + TV'?

QUESTION 5
From 1978, which group featuring Paul Young on vocals achieved their only hit with their double 'A'-sided hit 'Toast' and 'Hold On'?

QUESTION 6
What was the title of the 1958 Top 3 hit by Tommy Dorsey & His Orchestra starring Warren Covington?

QUESTION 7
In 2002, which legendary rock band was back in the top twenty with their recording of 'Jam Side Down'?

QUESTION 8
Can you name the group that topped the chart for a total of three weeks at the beginning of 1969 with Lennon and McCartney's 'Ob-La-Di, Ob-La-Da'?

QUESTION 9
In 1970, which singer-songwriter released his successful album Tea for the Tillerman?

QUESTION 10
Which American band made their chart debut in 1997 with 'The Distance'?

QUIZ 278

Q1
Brenton Wood

Q2
'Signed, Sealed, Delivered, I'm Yours'

Q3
'Sign of the Times'

Q4
'Sign Your Name'

Q5
Pick of the Pops

Q6
Prince

Q7
Diana Ross & The Supremes

Q8
'Show Me a Sign'

Q9
Ace of Base

Q10
Snoop Dogg

QUIZ 279

Q1
'Stutter Rap (No Sleep 'Til Bedtime)'

Q2
The 5th Dimension

Q3
Midnight Oil

Q4
'I Don't Think that Man Should Sleep Alone'

Q5
Keane

Q6
Herman's Hermits

Q7
'Bedtime Story'

Q8
Santo and Johnny

Q9
Petula Clark

Q10
'Bed of Roses'

QUIZ 281 POPMASTER

JOE MEEK PRODUCTIONS

QUESTION 1
The Honeycombs achieved two UK top twenty hits in the Sixties, the first being their No 1 'Have I the Right'. What was the title of the other?

QUESTION 2
What was the name of the short-lived but successful label formed by Joe Meek in the early Sixties?

QUESTION 3
The biggest hit on the label Joe Meek formed was the 1960 UK Top 10 hit by Michael Cox - what was the title?

QUESTION 4
An international hit for Joe Meek was the 1962 UK and American No 1 'Telstar', recorded by which successful instrumental group?

QUESTION 5
Which one-time member of the group that recorded 'Telstar' achieved his only Top 10 hit in 1963 with his tribute to Eddie Cochran, titled 'Just Like Eddie'?

QUESTION 6
In 1961, which male vocalist made the UK top forty with his debut hit produced by Joe Meek, 'Tribute to Buddy Holly'?

QUESTION 7
A much sought-after and requested record today is the 1966 top forty hit by The Cryin' Shames. Can you name it?

QUESTION 8
Can you name the singer who appeared with Lulu in the 1965 movie Gonks Go Beat and achieved a UK top forty hit in 1962 with 'Can't You Hear the Beat of a Broken Heart'?

QUESTION 9
Can you name the group who made the UK top forty in 1960 with their instrumental hit 'Green Jeans', based on the traditional folk song 'Greensleeves'?

QUESTION 10
Which actor achieved a No 1 hit in 1961 with a song that was featured in the TV series *Harpers West One*, 'Johnny Remember Me'?

POPMASTER QUIZ 282

KEEP ON DREAMING

QUESTION 1
Which group enjoyed a week at the top of the American chart and a first major UK hit in 1983 with 'Sweet Dreams (Are Made of This)'?

QUESTION 2
Can you name the American group that topped the UK chart for three weeks in 1956 with 'It's Almost Tomorrow'?

QUESTION 3
In 1979, which hugely successful male and female group had a Christmas Top 3 hit in the UK with 'I Have a Dream'?

QUESTION 4
'Dream On' was the first Top 10 hit of the Noughties for which successful Essex group?

QUESTION 5
What is the common name of the group that made the Top 10 in 1974 with 'Honey Honey' and the act that performed the 1983 UK entry into the Eurovision Song Contest, 'I'm Never Giving Up'?

QUESTION 6
What was the collective name of the UK male production trio Paul Spencer, Scott Rosser and Stephen Spencer, who made the Top 10 in 2001 with 'Dream to Me'?

QUESTION 7
In 1961, which legendary pop star made the UK Top 3 with his hit single 'Theme for a Dream'?

QUESTION 8
Can you name the trio who achieved their only UK top twenty hit in 1985 with 'Life in a Northern Town'?

QUESTION 9
Which American singer topped the UK singles chart for four weeks in 1959 with 'Dream Lover'?

QUESTION 10
What was the title of the debut UK Top 10 hit in 2007 by vocalist and guitarist Newton Faulkner?

QUIZ 280

Q1 *The Newbeats*

Q2 *'Casanova'*

Q3 *The Jam*

Q4 *Blur*

Q5 *Streetband*

Q6 *'Tea for Two Cha-Cha'*

Q7 *Status Quo*

Q8 *Marmalade*

Q9 *Cat Stevens*

Q10 *Cake*

QUIZ 281

Q1
'That's the Way'

Q2
Triumph

Q3
'Angela Jones'

Q4
The Tornados

Q5
Heinz

Q6
Mike Berry (billed as Mike Berry with The Outlaws)

Q7
'Please Stay'

Q8
Iain Gregory

Q9
The Flee-Rekkers

Q10
John Leyton

QUIZ 283 POPMASTER

LEFT AND RIGHT

QUESTION 1
Which legendary singer achieved a UK top forty hit in 1958 with 'I'm Left, You're Right, She's Gone'?

QUESTION 2
Can you name the duo who achieved their 11th consecutive top twenty hit in 1988 with 'Left to My Own Devices'?

QUESTION 3
Can you name the hit song title that was shared between The Creatures in 1983, Atomic Kitten in 1999 and Akon in 2008?

QUESTION 4
From 1999, can you name the performer who was once a member of The Housemartins, formed Beats International, and reached No 2 in the UK with 'Right Here, Right Now'?

QUESTION 5
Which male vocalist was featured playing piano on Suzanne Vega's 1986 top forty hit 'Left of Center'?

QUESTION 6
By what collective name are Frankee Connolly and Britt Love - who made the UK Top 10 in 2009 with 'I Left My Heart in Tokyo' - better known?

QUESTION 7
What was the title of Sinitta's 1989 Top 10 hit that was a revival of Maxine Nightingale's 1975 original?

QUESTION 8
Can you name the American rapper who achieved his first UK No 1 in 2009 with 'Right Round'?

QUESTION 9
In 1989, Richard Marx achieved his biggest UK hit, reaching No 2 with a song that topped the American chart for three weeks. What was the title?

QUESTION 10
Which group achieved a top twenty hit in 1998 with 'She Left Me on Friday'?

POPMASTER QUIZ 284

LISTEN TO THE BANNED

These are questions about records that have been refused play by one organization or another, for whatever reasons they felt necessary.

QUESTION 1
Whilst presenting BBC Radio 1's breakfast show in the Eighties, which Frankie Goes to Hollywood record did Mike Read refuse to play on the grounds of its references to carnal knowledge?

QUESTION 2
Many football grounds refused to play 'Glad all Over' by The Dave Clark Five. Can you offer a reason why?

QUESTION 3
Which group had a 1997 Top 10 hit that many radio stations refused to play for obvious reasons - the song was called 'Smack My Bitch Up'?

QUESTION 4
Which 1970 No 2 hit by The Kinks required a line about Coca-Cola being changed to cherry-cola to avoid advertising?

QUESTION 5
In 2007, Radio 1 refused to play a re-issued single by The Pogues featuring the late Kirsty MacColl unless certain words were edited out. After many complaints, the ban was revoked. What was the song?

QUESTION 6
In 1967, DJ Simon Dee was told not to play Scott Walker's first solo hit because of the lyrics. He ignored the instruction and was suspended from the programme. What was the title of the offending song?

QUESTION 7
'Johnny Remember Me' by John Leyton, 'Moody River' by Pat Boone and 'Terry' by Twinkle were just three records that caused the BBC concern for the same reason - what was it?

QUESTION 8
A record by Lil Louis caused an outcry from radio stations in 1989 because of its sexual overtones, but despite many not playing it the record reached No 2 in the UK. What was the title?

QUESTION 9
The Stranglers' first Top 10 hit from 1977 was a double 'A' side. One of the songs was 'Go Buddy Go'. What was the title of the other side, which failed to receive plays because of the lyrical content?

QUESTION 10
Why were the BBC reluctant to play the Sixties instrumental hits 'Nut Rocker' by B Bumble & The Stingers, 'Saturday Night at the Duck Pond' by The Cougars and 'Can Can '62' by Peter Jay & The Jaywalkers?

QUIZ 282

Q1 *Eurythmics*

Q2 *The Dreamweavers*

Q3 *ABBA*

Q4 *Depeche Mode*

Q5 *Sweet Dreams*

Q6 *Dario G*

Q7 *Cliff Richard*

Q8 *Dream Academy*

Q9 *Bobby Darin*

Q10 *'Dream Catch Me'*

QUIZ 283

Q1
Elvis Presley

Q2
Pet Shop Boys

Q3
'Right Now'

Q4
Fatboy Slim

Q5
Joe Jackson

Q6
Mini Viva

Q7
'Right Back Where We Started From'

Q8
Flo Rida

Q9
'Right Here Waiting'

Q10
Shed Seven

QUIZ 285 POPMASTER

LITERARY POP

QUESTION 1
The 1995 Top 10 song 'Wake Up Boo!' was the biggest hit for The Boo Radleys, who took their name from which book?

QUESTION 2
Named after the fictional band in *A Clockwork Orange* by Anthony Burgess, Heaven 17 had their biggest hit in 1983 with which Top 3 song?

QUESTION 3
Who was the mastermind songwriter and producer behind the musical version of *The War of the Worlds* in the late Seventies?

QUESTION 4
Ian Dury recorded the song 'Profoundly in Love with Pandora' as the theme song to a 1985 TV adaptation of which Sue Townsend book?

QUESTION 5
Which duo provided the musical soundtrack to the film version of George Orwell's *1984*, starring John Hurt?

QUESTION 6
Which Neil Diamond song, recorded by Urge Overkill, was a Top 40 hit having been featured in Quentin Tarantino's film *Pulp Fiction*?

QUESTION 7
Though not a hit single, which famous song by Jefferson Airplane references the work of Lewis Carroll?

QUESTION 8
Which musical by Andrew Lloyd Webber is closely linked to the work of T.S. Eliot?

QUESTION 9
'Lovefool' by The Cardigans, 'Talk Show Host' by Radiohead and Kym Mazelle's version of 'Young Hearts Run Free' all featured on the soundtrack album to which Baz Luhrmann-directed film?

QUESTION 10
Which British rock band that had a run of chart albums in the Seventies and early Eighties takes its name from a character in Charles Dickens' *David Copperfield*?

POPMASTER QUIZ 286

LIVE AID

Live Aid happened 30 years ago this year. How good is your memory?

QUESTION 1
Which group opened the 1985 Live Aid concert?

QUESTION 2
Madonna and Nile Rodgers joined the Thompson Twins on stage in Philadelphia for a version of which Beatles song?

QUESTION 3
Thomas Dolby played keyboards at Wembley for which superstar's set?

QUESTION 4
Who performed on both the London and Philadelphia stages?

QUESTION 5
Who was the only female act to play a full set on the Wembley stage?

QUESTION 6
Former Temptations members Eddie Kendricks and David Ruffin joined one of America's most successful duos on stage in Philadelphia. Name the duo.

QUESTION 7
While most of Live Aid's London acts performed well-known hits, who came on stage and performed his upcoming single 'Vive le Rock'?

QUESTION 8
Who performed a medley of 'Amazing Grace' and 'We Are the World' in Philadelphia?

QUESTION 9
Elton John had both a female and male guest singer during his set. Name both of them.

QUESTION 10
Which one-time Radio 1 DJ made the famous opening PA announcement at Live Aid?

QUIZ 284

Q1 *'Relax'*

Q2 *Fans stomped their feet to the beat, causing concern that the stands might collapse*

Q3 *The Prodigy*

Q4 *'Lola'*

Q5 *'Fairytale of New York'*

Q6 *'Jackie'*

Q7 *They are all about death*

Q8 *'French Kiss'*

Q9 *'Peaches'*

Q10 *They were offended by tunes based on classical themes given a pop treatment*

QUIZ 285

Q1
To Kill a Mockingbird by *Harper Lee*

Q2
'Temptation'

Q3
Jeff Wayne

Q4
The Secret Diary of Adrian Mole Aged 13 3/4

Q5
Eurythmics

Q6
'Girl, You'll be a Woman Soon'

Q7
'White Rabbit'

Q8
Cats

Q9
Romeo and Juliet

Q10
Uriah Heep

QUIZ 287 POPMASTER

LONG PLAYERS

Questions relating to songs that have spent at least six weeks as the UK's No 1 single

QUESTION 1
Which film featured Wet Wet Wet's 15-week No 1 'Love is All Around'?

QUESTION 2
Which of Frankie Goes to Hollywood's singles spent the longest at No 1?

QUESTION 3
Released in 1962 and with eight weeks at No 1, name both the group and the title of the UK's most successful instrumental chart-topper.

QUESTION 4
Which rapper featured as a guest on Rihanna's 2007 10-week No 1 'Umbrella'?

QUESTION 5
One of the co-writers of The Archies' eight-week No 1 'Sugar, Sugar' is Andy Kim, who went on to have his own Top 3 single in 1974. What was that called?

QUESTION 6
Who is the frontman of the group Mungo Jerry, who wrote the band's 1970 No 1 'In the Summertime'?

QUESTION 7
In 1956, 'Just Walking in the Rain' spent seven weeks at No 1 for a singer who is name-checked in the lyrics of 'Come on Eileen' by Dexy's Midnight Runners. Who is he?

QUESTION 8
Stevie Wonder's six-week No 1 'I Just Called to Say I Love You' featured in a 1984 romantic comedy starring Gene Wilder and Kelly LeBrock. What was it called?

QUESTION 9
Who is the vocalist on Gnarls Barkley's 'Crazy', which spent nine weeks at No 1 in 2006?

QUESTION 10
Queen's 'Bohemian Rhapsody' spent nine weeks at No 1 in 1975-1976. It was knocked off the top by an ABBA single whose title is contained within 'Bohemian Rhapsody's lyrics. Name it.

POPMASTER QUIZ 288

MAGNETIC MUSIC

Questions about the hit record label Magnet Records

QUESTION 1
The label's co-founder wrote the majority of Alvin Stardust's hits on the label and reached the chart himself with 'Gee Baby' and 'Love Me Love My Dog'. Who is he?

QUESTION 2
...and in 1974, Alvin Stardust had his only UK No 1 with his second hit single on the label. What was it called?

QUESTION 3
The 1983 Top 20 single 'Last Film' was the only chart hit for the group Kissing the… what?

QUESTION 4
Which vocal group released the hit singles 'There's a Whole Lot of Loving' and 'You Don't Have to Say You Love Me' on the label in the mid-Seventies?

QUESTION 5
The ska-flavoured band Bad Manners had a run of hits on Magnet in the early Eighties. What is the name of their lead singer?

QUESTION 6
Darts had three consecutive No 2 hits on Magnet in 1978 – 'The Boy from New York City' was the middle of these three, but can you name one of the other two?

QUESTION 7
Which group had Top 10 hits on the label in the mid-Nineties called 'U R the Best Thing' (remix) and 'Shoot Me with Your Love'?

QUESTION 8
The singles 'Rockabilly Rebel' and a medley of 'Over the Rainbow – You Belong to Me' were the first and last of five Top 40 hits on the label for the group Matchbox. Name one of the other three.

QUESTION 9
MAG 111 was the record number of Chris Rea's chart debut in 1978. What was the title of this first hit single for him?

QUESTION 10
'Cry Boy Cry' was a hit for the label in 1982. Which group recorded it?

QUIZ 286

Q1 *Status Quo (though the Coldstream Guards had performed the National Anthem before this)*

Q2 *'Revolution'*

Q3 *David Bowie*

Q4 *Phil Collins*

Q5 *Sade*

Q6 *Daryl Hall and John Oates*

Q7 *Adam Ant*

Q8 *Joan Baez*

Q9 *Kiki Dee ('Don't Go Breaking My Heart'), George Michael ('Don't Let the Sun Go Down on Me')*

Q10 *Richard Skinner*

QUIZ 287

Q1
Four Weddings and a Funeral

Q2
'Two Tribes' (nine consecutive weeksin 1984)

Q3
The Shadows – 'Wonderful Land'

Q4
Jay Z

Q5
'Rock Me Gently'

Q6
Ray Dorset

Q7
Johnnie Ray

Q8
The Woman in Red

Q9
CeeLo Green

Q10
'Mamma Mia'

QUIZ 289 POPMASTER

MICKIE MOST PRODUCTIONS

QUESTION 1
What was the title of the 1970 Top 3 UK hit that was placed second in the Eurovision Song Contest that year, performed by Mary Hopkin and produced by Mickie Most?

QUESTION 2
What was the title of the 1969 Top 3 UK hit that was placed joint winner with three other countries in the Eurovision Song Contest that year, performed by Lulu and produced by Mickie Most?

QUESTION 3
Who was the singer who formed the group C.C.S. and achieved their first hit in 1970 with a cover of Led Zeppelin's 'Whole Lotta Love'?

QUESTION 4
What was the title of the only No 1 hit by The Animals that topped both the UK and American charts in 1964?

QUESTION 5
Which group featured on Donovan's 1969 UK top twenty hit 'Goo Goo Barabajagal (Love is Hot)'?

QUESTION 6
Which British group scored American No 1 hits in America in 1965 with 'Mrs Brown You've Got a Lovely Daughter' and 'I'm Henry VIII, I Am', neither of which were released as singles in the UK?

QUESTION 7
Written by Kenny Young, who had a top forty hit with the Mickie Most production of 'The Highway Song'?

QUESTION 8
Mickie Most produced a top twenty hit for Brenda Lee in the Sixties whilst she was visiting the UK. Was it 'Losing You', 'Is it True' or 'It Started all Over Again'?

QUESTION 9
Which well-established folk singer achieved her only UK top twenty hit in 1970 with a cover of Paul Simon's 'If I Could (El Condor Pasa)'?

QUESTION 10
Can you name the group that achieved two Top 10 hits in 1964 with 'Tobacco Road' and 'Google Eye', both written by John D Loudermilk?

POPMASTER QUIZ 290

MONTHS OF THE YEAR

QUESTION 1
'December Will be Magic Again' was a Christmas hit in 1980 for whom?

QUESTION 2
What type of '...Rain' featured in the title of a 1992 Top 5 single by Guns N' Roses?

QUESTION 3
Which month of the year did Earth Wind & Fire sing about in 1978?

QUESTION 4
Which member of Queen reached the Top 10 in 1992 with 'Too Much Love Will Kill You'?

QUESTION 5
The 1991 single 'Winter in July' was the fourth and final Top 10 hit for UK producer Tim Simenon, recording under what name?

QUESTION 6
Which singer-songwriter released a live double album in the early Seventies called Hot August Night?

QUESTION 7
Which month of the year provided the title of the only No 1 single by Pilot?

QUESTION 8
Released in 1987, the song 'April Skies' was the first Top 10 hit by the band formed by brothers Jim and William Reid. What are they called?

QUESTION 9
The U2 singles 'Fire' and 'Gloria' featured on the second studio album by U2. What was it called?

QUESTION 10
In 1977, the Trinidad Oil Company had its only chart hit with a song subtitled '(January, February, March, April, May)'. What was it called?

QUIZ 288

Q1 *Peter Shelley*

Q2 *'Jealous Mind'*

Q3 *Pink*

Q4 *Guys 'N' Dolls*

Q5 *Buster Bloodvessel*

Q6 *'Come Back My Love', 'It's Raining'*

Q7 *D:Ream*

Q8 *'Buzz Buzz a Diddle It', 'Midnite Dynamos', 'When You Ask About Love'*

Q9 *'Fool (If You Think it's Over)'*

Q10 *Blue Zoo*

QUIZ 289

Q1
'Knock Knock Who's There'

Q2
'Boom Bang-A-Bang'

Q3
Alexis Korner

Q4
'The House of the Rising Sun'

Q5
The Jeff Beck Group

Q6
Herman's Hermits

Q7
Nancy Sinatra

Q8
'Is it True'

Q9
Julie Felix

Q10
The Nashville Teens

QUIZ 291 POPMASTER

NAME THE ALBUM

For each question, name the artist and the studio album that contains the songs. An extra point if you also know the year of the album's release!

QUESTION 1
'Another Part of Me', 'Liberian Girl', 'Smooth Criminal'

QUESTION 2
'I Predict a Riot', 'Modern Way', 'Oh My God'

QUESTION 3
'Satellite of Love', 'Perfect Day', 'Walk on the Wild Side'

QUESTION 4
'Eleanor Rigby', 'And Your Bird Can Sing', 'Good Day Sunshine'

QUESTION 5
'Country House', 'Charmless Man', 'The Universal'

QUESTION 6
'Private Investigations', 'Telegraph Road', 'Industrial Disease'

QUESTION 7
'Shake it Off', 'Blank Space', 'Welcome to New York'

QUESTION 8
'Walking on the Moon', 'Bed's Too Big Without You', 'Bring on the Night'

QUESTION 9
'Baba O'Reilly', 'Behind Blue Eyes', 'Won't Get Fooled Again'

QUESTION 10
'Warwick Avenue', 'Stepping Stone', 'Mercy'

POPMASTER QUIZ 292

NOT ON THIS ALBUM

Ten No 1 albums and their artists are listed along with three songs, one of which was not on the album. Can you spot the bogus track?

QUESTION 1
Thriller – Michael Jackson
'Billie Jean', 'Rock with You', 'The Girl is Mine'

QUESTION 2
Can't Slow Down – Lionel Richie
'Say You, Say Me', 'Running with the Night', 'Stuck on You'

QUESTION 3
Talk that Talk – Rihanna
'Rude Boy', 'Where Have You Been', 'Birthday Cake'

QUESTION 4
A Date with Elvis – Elvis Presley
'Blue Moon of Kentucky', 'Baby Let's Play House', 'Such a Night'

QUESTION 5
Popped in Souled Out – Wet Wet Wet
'Sweet Little Mystery', 'Sweet Surrender', 'Wishing I was Lucky'

QUESTION 6
Help! – The Beatles
'Drive My Car', 'You've Got to Hide Your Love Away', 'Ticket to Ride'

QUESTION 7
Performance and Cocktails – Stereophonics
'The Bartender and the Thief', 'Local Boy in the Photograph', 'I Wouldn't Believe Your Radio'

QUESTION 8
A Night on the Town – Rod Stewart
'I Don't Want to Talk About It', 'The First Cut is the Deepest', 'Pretty Flamingo'

QUESTION 9
Demon Days – Gorillaz
'Rock the House', 'Dirty Harry', 'Kids with Guns'

QUESTION 10
Sticky Fingers – The Rolling Stones
'Brown Sugar', 'I Got the Blues', 'Tumbling Dice'

Answers

QUIZ 290

Q1 *Kate Bush*

Q2 *'November Rain'*

Q3 *'September'*

Q4 *Brian May*

Q5 *Bomb the Bass*

Q6 *Neil Diamond*

Q7 *'January'*

Q8 *Jesus and Mary Chain*

Q9 *October*

Q10 *'The Calendar Song'*

QUIZ 291

Q1
Bad – Michael Jackson (1987)

Q2
Employment – Kaiser Chiefs (2005)

Q3
Transformer – Lou Reed (1972; did not chart in UK until 1973)

Q4
Revolver – The Beatles (1966)

Q5
The Great Escape – Blur (1995)

Q6
Love Over Gold – Dire Straits (1982)

Q7
1989 – Taylor Swift (2014)

Q8
Regatta de Blanc – The Police (1979)

Q9
Who's Next – The Who (1971)

Q10
Rockferry – Duffy (2008)

QUIZ 293 POPMASTER

NOT ON TV

QUESTION 1
What was the title of the 2002 debut hit and No 1 single by the ten-piece vocal group Blazin' Squad?

QUESTION 2
Can you name the Jamaican duo who achieved a top forty hit in 1994 with 'Murder She Wrote'?

QUESTION 3
Which Swedish group made our top twenty in 1993 with a song called 'Wheel of Fortune'?

QUESTION 4
In which 1956 movie did Frank Sinatra and Celeste Holm sing the Cole Porter song 'Who Wants to be a Millionaire'?

QUESTION 5
Which Canadian rock band achieved a top forty hit in 1983 with the double 'A'-sided single 'Countdown' and 'New World Man'?

QUESTION 6
In 1967, which legendary Tamla Motown star achieved his second UK top twenty hit with 'A Place in the Sun'?

QUESTION 7
Which group included a song called 'Match of the Day' on their 1977 hit EP 'Spot the Pigeon'?

QUESTION 8
Can you name the duo who topped the UK chart in 1992 with their recording of 'Would I Lie to You'?

QUESTION 9
In 1978, the Scottish band The Rezillos achieved their one and only UK top forty hit. Can you remember the title?

QUESTION 10
Which group, who scored a No 3 hit in 1980 with 'Turning Japanese', just missed out on making the top forty with another release later in the same year called 'News at Ten'?

POPMASTER QUIZ 294

NO 1S (1)

In each case, simply name the year these three songs all reached No 1

QUESTION 1
'Tiger Feet' by Mud, 'Kung Fu Fighting' by Carl Douglas and 'Gonna Make You a Star' by David Essex

QUESTION 2
'Goodnight Girl' by Wet Wet Wet, 'Deeply Dippy' by Right Said Fred and 'Sleeping Satellite' by Tasmin Archer

QUESTION 3
'Happy' by Pharrell Williams, 'Stay with Me' by Sam Smith and 'Sing' by Ed Sheeran

QUESTION 4
'Heart' by Pet Shop Boys, 'I Owe You Nothing' by Bros and 'He Ain't Heavy, He's My Brother' by The Hollies

QUESTION 5
'King of the Road' by Roger Miller, 'Mr Tambourine Man' by The Byrds and 'Get Off of My Cloud' by The Rolling Stones

QUESTION 6
'Radio' by Robbie Williams, 'Everytime' by Britney Spears and 'Vertigo' by U2

QUESTION 7
'Frozen' by Madonna, 'Deeper Underground' by Jamiroquai and 'It's Like That' by Run-DMC vs Jason Nevins

QUESTION 8
'Return of the Mack' by Mark Morrison, '2 Become 1' by Spice Girls and 'Fastlove' by George Michael

QUESTION 9
'Ghost Town' by The Specials, 'Prince Charming' by Adam & The Ants and 'Being with You' by Smokey Robinson

QUESTION 10
'Space Oddity' by David Bowie, 'Oh Boy' by Mud and 'January' by Pilot

A answers

QUIZ 292

Q1 *'Rock with You'*

Q2 *'Say You, Say Me'*

Q3 *'Rude Boy'*

Q4 *'Such a Night'*

Q5 *'Sweet Surrender'*

Q6 *'Drive My Car'*

Q7 *'Local Boy in the Photograph'*

Q8 *'I Don't Want to Talk About It'*

Q9 *'Rock the House'*

Q10 *'Tumbling Dice'*

QUIZ 293

Q1 *'Crossroads'*

Q2 *Chaka Demus & Pliers*

Q3 *Ace of Base*

Q4 High Society

Q5 *Rush*

Q6 *Stevie Wonder*

Q7 *Genesis*

Q8 *Charles & Eddie*

Q9 *'Top of the Pops'*

Q10 *The Vapors*

QUIZ 295 POPMASTER

NO 1S (2)

In each case, simply name the year these three songs all reached No 1

QUESTION 1
'The House of the Rising Sun' by The Animals, 'Baby Love' by The Supremes and 'A Hard Day's Night' by The Beatles

QUESTION 2
'Innuendo' by Queen, 'Should I Stay or Should I Go' by The Clash and 'The One and Only' by Chesney Hawkes

QUESTION 3
'No Tomorrow' by Orson, 'America' by Razorlight and 'Patience' by Take That

QUESTION 4
'Everything I Own' by Boy George, 'You Win Again' by the Bee Gees and 'La Bamba' by Los Lobos

QUESTION 5
'Dream Lover' by Bobby Darin, 'Here Comes Summer' by Jerry Keller and 'Roulette' by Russ Conway

QUESTION 6
'So You Win Again' by Hot Chocolate, 'Knowing Me, Knowing You' by ABBA and 'I Feel Love' by Donna Summer

QUESTION 7
'The Power' by Snap!, 'A Little Time' by The Beautiful South and 'World in Motion...' by Englandneworder

QUESTION 8
'Jailhouse Rock' by Elvis Presley, 'Axel F' by Crazy Frog and 'Dakota' by Stereophonics

QUESTION 9
'Sealed with a Kiss' by Jason Donovan, 'Eternal Flame' by The Bangles and 'Swing the Mood' by Jive Bunny and the Mastermixers

QUESTION 10
'Mighty Quinn' by Manfred Mann, 'With a Little Help from My Friends' by Joe Cocker and 'Do it Again' by The Beach Boys

POPMASTER QUIZ 296

NO 1S (3)

In each case simply name the year these three songs all reached No 1?

QUESTION 1
'Save Your Kisses for Me' by Brotherhood of Man, 'Don't Go Breaking My Heart' by Elton John & Kiki Dee and 'Under the Moon of Love' by Showaddywaddy

QUESTION 2
'House of Fun' by Madness, 'Beat Surrender' by The Jam and 'Ebony and Ivory' by Paul McCartney with Stevie Wonder

QUESTION 3
'Don't Speak' by No Doubt, 'Beetlebum' by Blur and 'Barbie Girl' by Aqua

QUESTION 4
'Don't Stop Movin'' by S Club 7, 'Can't Get You out of My Head' by Kylie Minogue and 'Uptown Girl' by Westlife

QUESTION 5
'Every Loser Wins' by Nick Berry, 'The Final Countdown' by Europe and 'Don't Leave Me this Way' by The Communards

QUESTION 6
'Someone Like You' by Adele, 'Cannonball' by Little Mix and 'What Makes You Beautiful' by One Direction

QUESTION 7
'Fairground' by Simply Red, 'Some Might Say' by Oasis and 'Earth Song' by Michael Jackson

QUESTION 8
'See My Baby Jive' by Wizzard, 'Rubber Bullets' by 10cc and 'Skweeze Me Pleeze Me' by Slade

QUESTION 9
'Puppet on a String' by Sandie Shaw, 'Silence is Golden' by The Tremeloes and 'Baby Now that I've Found You' by The Foundations

QUESTION 10
'Cars' by Gary Numan, 'Sunday Girl' by Blondie and 'Walking on the Moon' by The Police

Answers

QUIZ 294

Q1 *1974*

Q2 *1992*

Q3 *2014*

Q4 *1988*

Q5 *1965*

Q6 *2004*

Q7 *1998*

Q8 *1996*

Q9 *1981*

Q10 *1975*

QUIZ 295

QUIZ 297 POPMASTER

OFF THE RAK

Questions about the hit record label and its artists

Answers	Questions
Q1 *1964*	**QUESTION 1** Which record producer formed RAK Records in 1969?
Q2 *1991*	**QUESTION 2** Name the guitarist with RAK favourites Mud who went on to write No 1 hits for both Spiller and Kylie Minogue.
Q3 *2006*	**QUESTION 3** The singer Clark Datchler released the singles 'I Don't Want You' and 'Things Can't Get Any Worse' on RAK in 1984. They failed to chart, but three years later he hit the Top 10 as singer with which group?
Q4 *1987*	**QUESTION 4** 'Whole Lotta Love' was the first of five Top 40 hits on the label for the band C.C.S. Name one of the other four.
Q5 *1959*	**QUESTION 5** What is the first name of Kim Wilde's brother, who both co-wrote her debut hit 'Kids in America' with their father Marty and also produced the song?
Q6 *1977*	**QUESTION 6** Having made appearances on *Top of the Pops* dressed as a Womble(!), which guitarist appeared on the show as himself, performing his 1975 hit single 'Motor Bikin''?
Q7 *1990*	**QUESTION 7** The American group Exile had its only UK Top 40 hit with which 1978 Top 10 song?
Q8 *2005*	**QUESTION 8** Racey's final hit for the label was a 1980 cover version of which early Sixties hit for both Dion and Doug Sheldon?
Q9 *1989*	**QUESTION 9** Hot Chocolate had a hit in 1978 with a song that featured in the Don Black/Geoff Stephens musical *Dear Anyone*, which was about the tribulations of being an agony aunt. What was this Top 20 hit called?
Q10 *1968*	**QUESTION 10** Which three-piece group had two hits on the label in the mid-Seventies with the songs 'A Touch Too Much' and 'My Last Night with You'?

POPMASTER QUIZ 298

ON AND OFF

QUIZ 296

QUESTION 1
Which female singer enjoyed a UK top twenty hit in 2004 with her song 'Call off the Search'?

QUESTION 2
Can you name the soul singer who made the UK top twenty in 1984 with his hit single 'On the Wings of Love'?

QUESTION 3
Which member of The Beatles scored a solo No 2 hit in 1972 with 'Back off Boogaloo'?

QUESTION 4
What is the title of the 2015 Top 3 hit by Major Lazer and French producer DJ Snake, with vocals by Danish singer MØ?

QUESTION 5
Who achieved a Top 5 album and a Top 10 single in the Seventies called 'Off the Wall'?

QUESTION 6
Which Sixties UK No 1 hit by The Rolling Stones featured the song 'Off the Hook' on the 'B' side?

QUESTION 7
Can you name the duo who in 1992 reached No 2 in the UK with 'On a Ragga trip' and returned to the top forty in 1997 with a re-mixed version?

QUESTION 8
What was the title of the 1997 UK Top 10 hit single by Propellerheads and David Arnold that shares its title with a James Bond movie?

QUESTION 9
Which member of Madness achieved a solo UK Top 10 hit in 1995 with the double 'A'-sided hit 'I'm Only Sleeping' and 'Off on Holiday'?

QUESTION 10
In 2014, which recording artist topped the UK chart with his second single, 'Money on My Mind', from his debut album In the Lonely Hour?

Q1 *1976*

Q2 *1982*

Q3 *1997*

Q4 *2001*

Q5 *1986*

Q6 *2011*

Q7 *1995*

Q8 *1973*

Q9 *1967*

Q10 *1979*

QUIZ 299 POPMASTER

PEACE AND QUIET

QUESTION 1
Which female Icelandic singer achieved a Top 5 hit in 1995 with 'It's Oh So Quiet'?

QUESTION 2
Can you name the Irish trio who achieved a 1966 Top 3 hit in the UK with their cover of Simon & Garfunkel's 'The Sound of Silence'?

QUESTION 3
What was the name of the group whose only UK hit was their 1971 recording of 'Softly Whispering I Love You'?

QUESTION 4
In 1982, what was the title of the hit duet medley between Bing Crosby and David Bowie?

QUESTION 5
What was the name of the group with which John Lennon recorded his 1969 Top 3 hit 'Give Peace a Chance'?

QUESTION 6
What was the title of the hit song that Canadian female singer Sarah McLachlan took into the UK chart in 2000 and again in 2004 with the production duo Delerium?

QUESTION 7
Can you name the group that first made the UK top twenty in 1981 with 'Quiet Life'?

QUESTION 8
After the departure of Brian Poole, what was the title of The Tremeloes' only UK No 1 hit?

QUESTION 9
What was the title of the 1991 debut Top 10 hit for Sabrina Johnston?

QUESTION 10
In 1968, New Zealand-born singer John Rowles achieved two UK top twenty hits. The first was 'If I Only Had Time', but what was the title of the second?

QUIZ 297

Q1 *Mickie Most*

Q2 *Rob Davis*

Q3 *Johnny Hates Jazz*

Q4 *'Walkin'', 'Tap Turns on the Water', 'Brother', 'The Band Played the Boogie'*

Q5 *Ricky*

Q6 *Chris Spedding*

Q7 *'Kiss You All Over'*

Q8 *'Runaround Sue'*

Q9 *'I'll Put You Together Again'*

Q10 *The Arrows*

POPMASTER QUIZ 300

PICTURE THIS

QUESTION 1
Which Beatle had a Top 10 solo hit in 1973 called 'Photograph'?

QUESTION 2
'Centerfold' was one of two Top 40 UK chart hits by America's J Geils Band. The other was also the title track of their hit album that contained both singles – what is its title?

QUESTION 3
The songs 'Angels', 'Old Before I Die' and 'Let Me Entertain You' all featured on which Robbie Williams album?

QUESTION 4
In 1967, The Who reached the Top 5 singing about 'Pictures of…' who?

QUESTION 5
Which British group released an album and single in 1980 called 'Gentlemen Take Polaroids'?

QUESTION 6
'Kodachrome' is the opening track to which of these solo albums by Paul Simon – Still Crazy After All These Years, There Goes Rhymin' Simon or Paul Simon?

QUESTION 7
Which boy band had a Top 3 hit in 1997 with 'Picture of You'?

QUESTION 8
What type of '...Games' did Lana Del Rey sing about on her 2011 Top 10 debut hit?

QUESTION 9
A song called 'Photograph' was a Top 20 hit in the summer of 2015 for one of the UK's most successful singer-songwriters of recent years. Who is he?

QUESTION 10
The 1982 single 'Wishing (If I Had a Photograph of You)' was the only Top 10 single by A Flock of Seagulls, but the group had three other Top 40 songs. Name one of them.

QUIZ 298

Q1 *Katie Melua*

Q2 *Jeffrey Osborne*

Q3 *Ringo Starr*

Q4 *'Lean On'*

Q5 *Michael Jackson*

Q6 *'Little Red Rooster'*

Q7 *SL2*

Q8 *'On Her Majesty's Secret Service'*

Q9 *Suggs*

Q10 *Sam Smith*

QUIZ 299

Q1
Björk

Q2
The Bachelors

Q3
The Congregation

Q4
'Peace on Earth - Little Drummer Boy'

Q5
The Plastic Ono Band

Q6
'Silence'

Q7
Japan

Q8
'Silence is Golden'

Q9
'Peace'

Q10
'Hush... Not a Word to Mary'

QUIZ 301 POPMASTER

PROG ROCK

Bands and artists who have been associated with prog rock over the years

QUESTION 1
What are the first names of the trio Emerson, Lake & Palmer?

QUESTION 2
The band East of Eden had its only hit single in 1971 with which Top 10 song?

QUESTION 3
Often considered the UK's first 'concept' album, which group released the 1967 album Days of Future Passed?

QUESTION 4
Despite a run of hit albums, Yes didn't have their first hit single until 1977 with which Top 10 song?

QUESTION 5
Over the course of their chart career, Marillion have had two main lead singers. Name both of them.

QUESTION 6
In 1974, Rick Wakeman had a No 1 album and won an Ivor Novello award for his live album based on a work by Jules Verne. What was it called?

QUESTION 7
Sonja Kristina is best known as the lead singer with which prog rock group formed in 1970?

QUESTION 8
Which Genesis album includes the songs 'Firth of Fifth', 'The Battle of Epping Forest' and 'I Know What I Like (In Your Wardrobe)'?

QUESTION 9
Over the course of the band's career, which group has released albums called Lizard, Larks' Tongues in Aspic and In the Wake of Poseidon?

QUESTION 10
Featuring vocals by Annie Haslam, the group Renaissance is best remembered for a Top 10 single in 1978 - the band's only hit. What is it called?

POPMASTER QUIZ 302

PSEUDONYMS

These are famous acts who have released records under alternative names.

QUESTION 1
Under what name did Ant & Dec achieve a Top 10 hit in 1994 with 'Let's Get Ready to Rhumble', which went to No 1 in 2013 when re-released?

QUESTION 2
What was the name of the group who made the Top 3 in 1972 with 'In a Broken Dream', on which Rod Stewart sang the uncredited lead vocals?

QUESTION 3
Under what group name was Eric Clapton featured on the hit single 'Layla?'

QUESTION 4
Prior to achieving hits as Sonny & Cher, under what name did the duo release a couple of singles?

QUESTION 5
The 1968 Top 10 hit by The Bonzo Dog Doo-Dah Band, 'I'm the Urban Spaceman', was produced by Apollo C Vermouth - a pseudonym for whom?

QUESTION 6
Which member of Queen released a 1973 single version of 'I Can Hear Music' under the name of Larry Lurex?

QUESTION 7
The 1986 debut UK hit by The Bangles, 'Manic Monday', had the composer credit as 'Christopher'. This was a pseudonym for whom?

QUESTION 8
Which American singer and songwriter composed Bobby Vee's 1961 hit 'Rubber Ball' with Aaron Schroeder under his mother's name, Ann Orlowski?

QUESTION 9
Can you name the radio presenter who achieved a northern soul hit in 1978 with his version of Doris Troy's 'I'll do Anything'?

QUESTION 10
Which member of The Beatles wrote the hit 'Badge' for Cream under the name of L'Angelo Misterioso?

QUIZ 300

Q1 *Ringo Starr*

Q2 *'Freeze-Frame'*

Q3 *Life Thru a Lens*

Q4 *Lily*

Q5 *Japan*

Q6 *There Goes Rhymin' Simon*

Q7 *Boyzone*

Q8 *'Video Games'*

Q9 *Ed Sheeran*

Q10 *'Space Age Love Song', 'Transfer Affection', 'The More You Live, the More You Love'*

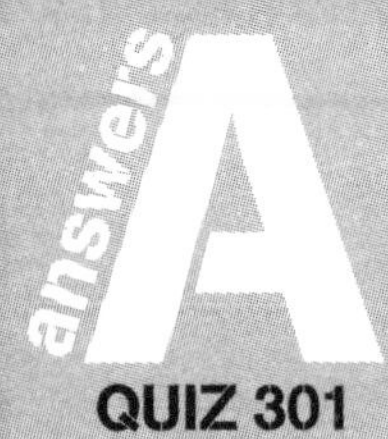

QUIZ 301

Q1
Keith Emerson, Greg Lake, Carl Palmer

Q2
'Jig-a-Jig'

Q3
The Moody Blues

Q4
'Wondrous Stories'

Q5
Fish (1981-1988), Steve Hogarth (1989-present)

Q6
Journey to the Centre of the Earth

Q7
Curved Air

Q8
Selling England by the Pound

Q9
King Crimson

Q10
'Northern Lights'

QUIZ 303 POPMASTER

REAL NAMES (1)

Here are the real names of ten successful pop, rap and rockstars – how are they best known?

QUESTION 1
Stefani Joanne Angelina Germanotta

QUESTION 2
David Evans (a guitarist)

QUESTION 3
Stevland Hardaway Judkins

QUESTION 4
Elizabeth Woolridge Grant

QUESTION 5
Gary Webb

QUESTION 6
Ella Marija Lani Yelich-O'Connor

QUESTION 7
Eilleen Regina Edwards

QUESTION 8
Georgios Kyriacos Panayiotou

QUESTION 9
Sean Combs

QUESTION 10
Rita Sahatçiu

POPMASTER QUIZ 304

REAL NAMES (2)

Here are the real names of ten successful pop, rap and rockstars – how are they best known?

QUESTION 1
Katheryn Elizabeth Hudson

QUESTION 2
Farrokh Bulsara

QUESTION 3
Tim Bergling

QUESTION 4
Onika Maraj

QUESTION 5
John Simon Ritchie (punk bassist)

QUESTION 6
Tramar Dillard

QUESTION 7
Brian Hugh Warner

QUESTION 8
Anna Mae Bullock

QUESTION 9
John Anthony Gillis

QUESTION 10
Peter Gene Hernandez

Answers

QUIZ 302

Q1
PJ & Duncan

Q2
Python Lee Jackson

Q3
Derek & The Dominoes

Q4
Caesar & Cleo

Q5
Paul McCartney

Q6
Freddie Mercury

Q7
Prince

Q8
Gene Pitney

Q9
Tony Blackburn

Q10
George Harrison

QUIZ 305 POPMASTER

REFLECTIONS

QUESTION 1
Which Motown group achieved a Top 5 hit in 1967 with a song called 'Reflections'?

QUESTION 2
Name the duo consisting of David Van Day and Thereze Bazar who achieved a Top 5 hit in 1981 with 'Mirror Mirror (Mon Amour)'.

QUESTION 3
Can you name the famous rock star who made the top forty in 1994 with 'Objects in the Rear View Mirror May Appear Closer than they Are'?

QUESTION 4
Which successful Motown act achieved a Top 10 hit in 1972 with 'Lookin' Through the Windows'?

QUESTION 5
Who achieved his debut solo hit in 1978 with the song 'I Love the Sound of Breaking Glass'?

QUESTION 6
After a number of hits with CBS, which Scottish group signed to Decca in 1969, achieving their first hit for the label with 'Reflections of My Life'?

QUESTION 7
Can you name the British group who had their first top forty hit in America and their seventh Top 10 hit in the UK with 'Look Through Any Window'?

QUESTION 8
Which group reached No 2 in the UK in 1982 with their hit single 'Mirror Man'?

QUESTION 9
Who topped the American chart and made the UK Top 5 in 1972 with 'I Can See Clearly Now'?

QUESTION 10
Who had a Top 5 hit in 1980 with 'We are Glass'?

QUIZ 303

Q1 *Lady Gaga*

Q2 *The Edge*

Q3 *Stevie Wonder*

Q4 *Lana Del Rey*

Q5 *Gary Numan*

Q6 *Lorde*

Q7 *Shania Twain*

Q8 *George Michael*

Q9 *Puff Daddy/P. Diddy/Diddy*

Q10 *Rita Ora*

POPMASTER QUIZ 306

ROCK AND ROLL

QUIZ 304

QUESTION 1
Can you name the Austrian singer who topped the American chart for three weeks and was No 1 in the UK for one week with 'Rock Me Amadeus'?

QUESTION 2
Which American group found themselves in the singles chart in 1956 with 'Rockin' Through the Rye'?

QUESTION 3
In 1995, which group scored a major hit with their single 'Roll with It'?

QUESTION 4
'I'm Just a Singer (In a Rock 'n' Roll Band)' was a 1973 top forty hit for which legendary band?

QUESTION 5
Which classic Chuck Berry song became a Top 10 hit in 1973 for the Electric Light Orchestra?

QUESTION 6
With contributions from the uncredited rappers DMX, Redman and Method Man, which American rock band topped the UK chart for two weeks in 2001 with 'Rollin''?

QUESTION 7
What was the title of the only UK Top 10 hit for Joan Jett & The Blackhearts that also topped the American chart for seven weeks in 1982?

QUESTION 8
Can you name the group who had their third and final UK Top 10 hit with 'Roll Away the Stone' in 1973?

QUESTION 9
Which John Fogerty song gave Status Quo a Top 3 hit in 1977?

QUESTION 10
First released in 1973, what was the title of the only hit by Australian-born Kevin Johnson that made the UK chart when re-released in 1975?

Q1 *Katy Perry*

Q2 *Freddie Mercury*

Q3 *Avicii*

Q4 *Nicki Minaj*

Q5 *Sid Vicious*

Q6 *Flo Rida*

Q7 *Marilyn Manson*

Q8 *Tina Turner*

Q9 *Jack White*

Q10 *Bruno Mars*

QUIZ 305

Q1
Diana Ross & The Supremes

Q2
Dollar

Q3
Meat Loaf

Q4
The Jackson Five

Q5
Nick Lowe

Q6
Marmalade

Q7
The Hollies

Q8
Human League

Q9
Johnny Nash

Q10
Gary Numan

QUIZ 307 POPMASTER

ROUGH TRADE

Questions about the influential record label and its artists

QUESTION 1
Name the lead singer with Pulp, who released both his 2006 self-titled debut solo album and its 2009 follow-up, Further Complications, on the Rough Trade label?

QUESTION 2
Written by Elvis Costello and Clive Langer, what was the title of Robert Wyatt's 1983 hit single?

QUESTION 3
Which group released the hit albums Meat is Murder and The Queen is Dead on the label in the Eighties?

QUESTION 4
Signed to Fontana Records, the group James first reached the Top 10 in 1991 with a song whose original version was released on Rough Trade in 1989. What is the song?

QUESTION 5
Which band that had hits on Rough Trade in the Noughties with 'Step into My Office Baby' and 'I'm a Cuckoo' took its name from a French TV series of the 1960s?

QUESTION 6
...and what TV series 'appears' to be referenced in the title of The Libertines' 2004 Top 10 hit on the label?

QUESTION 7
Before a run of Top 40 hits on WEA Records, the band formed by singer/songwriter Roddy Frame was signed to Rough Trade for the singles 'Oblivious' and 'Walk out to Winter'. Name the band.

QUESTION 8
In 1986, Madness had a hit with a song that had originally been recorded and released on Rough Trade in 1981 by Scritti Politti. What is the song?

QUESTION 9
Rough Trade artists The Sundays wrote and recorded the original version of a song that would become a 1998 Top 10 cover version for Tin Tin Out featuring Shelley Nelson. What is the song?

QUESTION 10
The early UK hits by Canadian band Arcade Fire were all released on Rough Trade. Who is the group's lead singer?

POPMASTER QUIZ 308

ROUND AND AROUND

QUESTION 1
Which female singer scored Top 10 hits in the Eighties with 'Set Me Free' and 'Round and Round'?

QUESTION 2
Bing Crosby, Gracie Fields and Ronnie Hilton each released Top 10 singles in 1957 with their recordings of which song?

QUESTION 3
What was the hit title shared in different songs by East 17 in 1994, Daft Punk in 1997 and ATC in 2002?

QUESTION 4
Can you name the Tamla Motown act that scored a top twenty hit in 1971 with '(Come Round Here) I'm the One You Need' that had first been released in 1966?

QUESTION 5
What was the title of the 1987 Top 10 hit by Carly Simon that was featured in the movie *Heartburn*?

QUESTION 6
Which American crooner achieved a Top 10 hit in 1958 with 'Love Makes the World Go Round'?

QUESTION 7
Which group had a Top 10 hit in 1967 with the title song to the movie *Here We Go Round the Mulberry Bush?*

QUESTION 8
In 2002, which band formed in Newport, Wales, scored a top twenty hit with 'Come Back Around'?

QUESTION 9
Which folk group achieved their only Top 10 hit in 1975 with 'All Around My Hat'?

QUESTION 10
Can you name the rock band that made their last appearance in the Top 10 in 1970 with 'Up Around the Bend'?

QUIZ 306

Q1
Falco

Q2
Bill Haley & His Comets

Q3
Oasis

Q4
The Moody Blues

Q5
'Roll over Beethoven'

Q6
Limp Bizkit

Q7
'I Love Rock 'n' Roll'

Q8
Mott the Hoople

Q9
'Rockin' All Over the World'

Q10
'Rock 'n' Roll (I Gave You the Best Years of My Life)'

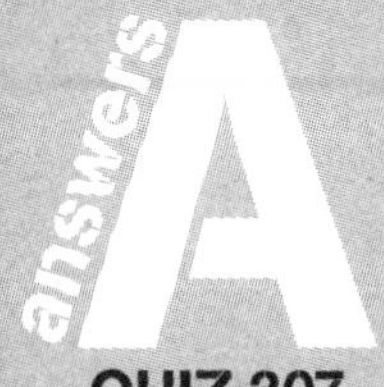

QUIZ 307

Q1 *Jarvis Cocker (his debut was titled Jarvis)*

Q2 *'Shipbuilding'*

Q3 *The Smiths*

Q4 *'Sit Down'*

Q5 *Belle and Sebastian*

Q6 *The Likely Lads (though 'What Became of the Likely Lads' has nothing to do with TV)*

Q7 *Aztec Camera*

Q8 *'The Sweetest Girl'*

Q9 *'Here's Where the Story Ends'*

Q10 *Win Butler*

QUIZ 309 POPMASTER

SECOND TIME AROUND

These are questions about records that were reissued after their initial outing and became bigger hits second time around.

QUESTION 1
Which group first released their single 'Kings of the Wild Frontier' in 1980 to little success, but ended up reaching No 2 when re-issued a year later?

QUESTION 2
Can you name the American female singer who achieved a minor hit in 1993 with 'Another Sad Love Song' but made the top twenty with it a year later?

QUESTION 3
Which group of brothers who released 'This Ole Heart of Mine' on the Tamla Motown label in 1966 found themselves riding high with the song in 1968?

QUESTION 4
In the year 2000, which group made the top twenty with 'Dancing in the Moonlight', only to find the record climbing into the Top 10 later the same year when it was re-promoted?

QUESTION 5
What was the title of the Andy Williams hit that first made the top forty in 1967 but found its way into the Top 10 in 1999 after being featured in a TV commercial for cars?

QUESTION 6
Can you name the group that achieved a top forty hit in 1999 and then a No 1 in 2000 when their record, 'Don't Call Me Baby', was re-issued?

QUESTION 7
What was the title of the hit record by Freddie Mercury and Montserrat Caballé that first made the Top 10 in 1987 and then became an even bigger hit in 1992?

QUESTION 8
Which group had a top forty hit in 1993 with 'Things Can Only Get Better' and went to No 1 when it was re-issued in 1994 and into the Top 20 in 1997 following its use in Labour's election campaign?

QUESTION 9
What was the title of the first hit by The Beatles that reached the top twenty in 1962 but climbed into the Top 5 when it was re-issued twenty years later, in 1982?

QUESTION 10
In 1984, The Bluebells reached the Top 10 with the biggest hit of their career to date, but then went on to top the chart in 1993 when it was re-issued. What was the title of the song?

POPMASTER QUIZ 310

SEE-SAW

QUESTION 1
Which legendary rock band achieved a minor hit in the Sixties with 'Ride My See-Saw'?

QUESTION 2
Can you name the American female singer who made her chart debut in 1972 with the classic song 'The First Time Ever I Saw Your Face'?

QUESTION 3
What was the title of the 1985 Top 5 hit by Dee C Lee that was successfully covered in 2005 by Girls Aloud?

QUESTION 4
Which rock and roll group scored a Top 10 hit in 1956 with 'See You Later, Alligator'?

QUESTION 5
Can you name the song that John Lennon sang with Elton John on the 1981 live top forty hit duet?

QUESTION 6
Which female singer had a top twenty hit in America and a top forty UK chart entry in 1974 with 'Last Time I Saw Him'?

QUESTION 7
In 1966, which American male and female vocal group made the top twenty with 'I Saw Her Again'?

QUESTION 8
Which larger-than-life American soul singer reached No 2 in 1976 with 'You See the Trouble with Me'?

QUESTION 9
What was the title of the only Top 10 hit single of the Sixties by Pink Floyd?

QUESTION 10
Which successful pop group recorded the 1965 Top 10 hit 'See My Friend'?

QUIZ 308

Q1
Jaki Graham

Q2
'Around the World'

Q3
'Around the World'

Q4
The Miracles

Q5
'Coming Around Again'

Q6
Perry Como

Q7
Traffic

Q8
Feeder

Q9
Steeleye Span

Q10
Creedence Clearwater Revival

QUIZ 309

Q1
Adam & The Ants

Q2
Toni Braxton

Q3
The Isley Brothers

Q4
Toploader

Q5
'Music to Watch Girls By'

Q6
Madison Avenue

Q7
'Barcelona'

Q8
D:Ream

Q9
'Love Me Do'

Q10
'Young at Heart'

QUIZ 311 POPMASTER

SHAPES OF THINGS

QUESTION 1
Can you name the vocal group that achieved a Top 5 hit in 1972 with a song called 'Circles'?

QUESTION 2
Which successful American singer and songwriter considered changing his name to Noah Kaminsky early in his career?

QUESTION 3
In 1982, which UK rock band achieved a minor hit with a song titled 'Market Square Heroes'?

QUESTION 4
Can you name the successful American singer who reached our top twenty in 1981 with 'Bermuda Triangle'?

QUESTION 5
On which Coldplay album did the group originally feature the song 'Square One'?

QUESTION 6
Which group reached the UK Top 5 in 2001 with their hit single 'Pyramid Song'?

QUESTION 7
In 2007, which group achieved their 13th Top 10 hit in the UK with 'The Heart Never Lies'?

QUESTION 8
The song 'Cross My Heart and Hope to Die' appeared in the 1965 movie *Girl Happy*, starring which legendary performer?

QUESTION 9
Which Scottish female singer-songwriter released her fourth album in 2013 with Invisible Empire//Crescent Moon?

QUESTION 10
Can you name the group who achieved their first Top 10 hit in 1982 with 'Poison Arrow'?

POPMASTER QUIZ 312

SINGING COMEDIANS

QUIZ 310

QUESTION 1
Which Welsh funnyman achieved a top forty hit in 1961 with 'Don't Jump off the Roof Dad'?

QUESTION 2
In 1975, Jasper Carrott achieved a Top 5 hit with a double 'A'-sided single. One of the tracks was called 'Magic Roundabout', but what was the other?

QUESTION 3
Which American comedian made the UK top twenty in 1954 with his parody of The Crew Cuts' hit 'Sh-Boom'?

QUESTION 4
Apart from topping the UK chart in 1971 with 'Ernie (The Fastest Milkman in the West)', Benny Hill achieved two top twenty hits in the Sixties. Can you name either of them?

QUESTION 5
In 1984, Nigel Planer won a BRIT award for 'Best Comedy Record', the only time that category had been included. Under what name did he record his version of Traffic's 'Hole in My Shoe'?

QUESTION 6
None of comedian Des O'Connor's hit records have been intentionally humorous and all of them have made the top thirty, but only one managed to top the UK chart. Can you name it?

QUESTION 7
Which comedy team achieved hits in the Seventies with 'Funky Gibbon', 'Black Pudding Bertha (The Queen of Northern Soul)' and 'Father Christmas Do Not Touch Me'?

QUESTION 8
Recorded live at the Apollo Theatre in Glasgow, which comedian topped the UK chart in 1975 with his parody of Tammy Wynette's hit 'D.I.V.O.R.C.E'?

QUESTION 9
In 1965, Ken Dodd achieved his only UK No 1, topping the singles chart for five weeks. What was the title?

QUESTION 10
Which comedian and one-time host of Sunday Night at the London Palladium had a minor hit in 1962 with 'Swinging in the Rain'?

Answers – Quiz 310

Q1 *The Moody Blues*

Q2 *Roberta Flack*

Q3 *'See the Day'*

Q4 *Bill Haley & His Comets*

Q5 *'I Saw Her Standing There'*

Q6 *Diana Ross*

Q7 *The Mamas and The Papas*

Q8 *Barry White*

Q9 *'See Emily Play'*

Q10 *The Kinks*

QUIZ 311

Q1 *The New Seekers*

Q2 *Neil Diamond*

Q3 *Marillion*

Q4 *Barry Manilow*

Q5 *X & Y*

Q6 *Radiohead*

Q7 *McFly*

Q8 *Elvis Presley*

Q9 *KT Tunstall*

Q10 *ABC*

QUIZ 313 POPMASTER

SMOKE GETS IN YOUR EYES

QUESTION 1
Can you name the group whose only UK Top 5 hit, 'Underwater Love', was featured in a 1997 TV ad for a famous brand of jeans?

QUESTION 2
What was the title of the only UK top forty hit from 1974 by the American rock band Brownsville Station?

QUESTION 3
What hit song has been shared by The Platters in 1959, Blue Haze in 1972, Bryan Ferry in 1974 and John Alford in 1996?

QUESTION 4
What was the title of the UK 1997 top twenty hit by Warren G that also featured Ron Isley?

QUESTION 5
Can you name the Australian female singer who made the UK Top 10 in 1998 with her hit single 'Smoke'?

QUESTION 6
From 1962, which singer achieved his second top forty UK hit with 'Puff (Up in Smoke)'?

QUESTION 7
Can you name the group who successfully revived The Searchers' 1964 No 1 hit 'Needles and Pins' in 1977?

QUESTION 8
What was the title of the 2000 top twenty UK hit by DJ Dee Kline that contained a sample of Harry Hill's 'Barking' dialogue from his Channel 4 TV series?

QUESTION 9
First released in 1995, what was the title of the only UK top twenty hit by The Smokin' Mojo Filters?

QUESTION 10
Can you name the group that achieved a UK Top 10 hit in 2007 with 'Smokers Outside the Hospital Doors'?

POPMASTER QUIZ 314

SOMETHING BEGINNING WITH 'BE'

QUESTION 1
Can you name the actor and singer who reached No 2 in 1957 with 'Be My Girl'?

QUESTION 2
In 1993, Faith No More achieved a Top 3 hit with a double 'A'-sided single, with one song being 'I'm Easy'. What was the title of the other?

QUESTION 3
What was the title of the 2003 No 1 hit by Fatman Scoop featuring The Crooklyn Clan?

QUESTION 4
Can you name the female group produced by Phil Spector who scored their only UK Top 10 hit in 1963 with 'Be My Baby'?

QUESTION 5
What hit song title was shared by Lance Fortune in 1960, David Gray in 2003 and Robyn in 2008?

QUESTION 6
Which legendary singer from New Orleans scored a top twenty hit in 1959 with 'Be My Guest'?

QUESTION 7
In the late Eighties, Brother Beyond scored three top twenty hits, the first two being 'The Harder I Try' and 'Ain't No Competition'. What was the title of the third?

QUESTION 8
Can you name the heavy metal band that scored a Top 3 hit in 1992 with 'Be Quick or be Dead'?

QUESTION 9
From 1999, what was the title of the first Top 10 hit by boy band A1?

QUESTION 10
Under what collective name did the German duo Gottfried Engels and Ramon Zenker release their 2002 Top 10 hit 'Be Cool'?

Answers

QUIZ 312

Q1
Tommy Cooper

Q2
'Funky Moped'

Q3
Stan Freberg

Q4
'Gather in the Mushrooms', 'Harvest of Love'

Q5
Neil

Q6
'I Pretend'

Q7
The Goodies

Q8
Billy Connolly

Q9
'Tears'

Q10
Norman Vaughan

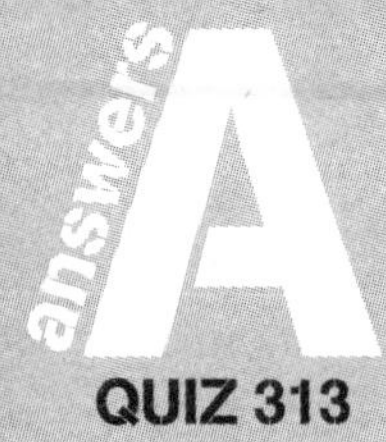

QUIZ 313

Q1
Smoke City

Q2
'Smokin' in the Boys' Room'

Q3
'Smoke Gets in Your Eyes'

Q4
'Smokin' Me Out'

Q5
Natalie Imbruglia

Q6
Kenny Lynch

Q7
Smokie

Q8
'I Don't Smoke'

Q9
'Come Together (War Child)'

Q10
Editors

QUIZ 315 POPMASTER

STOP AND GO

QUESTION 1
Name the group that achieved a UK Top 3 hit in 1966 with 'Stop Stop Stop'.

QUESTION 2
Can you name the group that returned to the chart for the first time in 2000 after a two-year absence with their No 1 hit 'Go Let it Out'?

QUESTION 3
'Go on Move' was a 1994 Top 10 UK hit for which act that also featured The Mad Stuntman?

QUESTION 4
Which group made their UK chart debut in 1964 with their No 1 hit 'Go Now'?

QUESTION 5
What was the title of the 2007 No 2 hit by Mark Ronson that also featured Daniel Merriweather?

QUESTION 6
In 1997, which female singer successfully revived the Average White Band's 1980 original 'Let's Go Round Again'?

QUESTION 7
Which soul singer first made the chart in 1966 with 'Stop Her on Sight (SOS)' that became a bigger hit when re-issued in 1968?

QUESTION 8
What was the title of the song that topped the UK chart in 2015 by Tinie Tempah, featuring vocals from Jess Glynne?

QUESTION 9
Can you name the group who achieved their only UK Top 10 hit in 1967 with 'Let's Go to San Francisco'?

QUESTION 10
Which Eighties duo achieved their only major UK hit with their debut chart entry, 'Don't Stop the Music'?

POPMASTER QUIZ 316

STUCK IN THE MIDDLE

QUESTION 1
Can you name the female group who achieved a Top 10 hit in 2004 with 'In the Middle'?

QUESTION 2
Which group made their final top forty appearance in 1966 with 'Trouble is My Middle Name'?

QUESTION 3
Which vocal duo made their last top forty appearance in 1963 with 'Trouble is My Middle Name'?

QUESTION 4
In 2001, which female singer made the Top 5 with the revival of Stealers Wheel's 1973 hit 'Stuck in the Middle with You'?

QUESTION 5
Can you name the group that topped the EP chart in 1965 with their four-track release 'The One in the Middle'?

QUESTION 6
What was the name of the group that topped the chart for five weeks in 1971 with 'Chirpy Chirpy Cheep Cheep'?

QUESTION 7
Which duo made the Top 10 in 2001 with their single 'Up Middle Finger'?

QUESTION 8
Alma Cogan, The Johnston Brothers and Jimmy Parkinson each released hit versions in 1956 of which song?

QUESTION 9
Which boy band achieved a No 2 hit in 2002 with 'Caught in the Middle'?

QUESTION 10
In 1965, which female singer found herself 'In the Middle of Nowhere'?

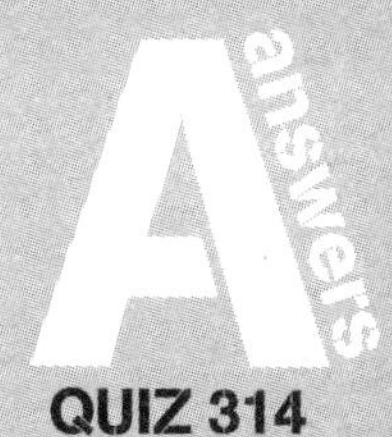

QUIZ 314

Q1 *Jim Dale*

Q2 *'Be Aggressive'*

Q3 *'Be Faithful'*

Q4 *The Ronettes*

Q5 *'Be Mine'*

Q6 *Fats Domino*

Q7 *'Be My Twin'*

Q8 *Iron Maiden*

Q9 *'Be the First to Believe'*

Q10 *Paffendorf*

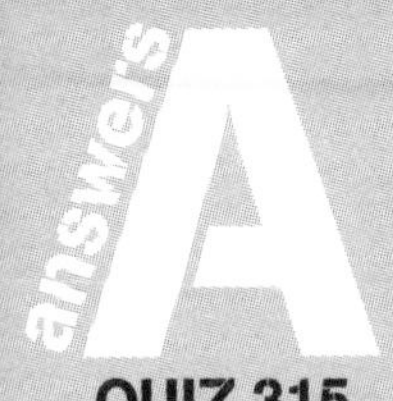

QUIZ 315

Q1 *The Hollies*

Q2 *Oasis*

Q3 *Reel 2 Real*

Q4 *The Moody Blues*

Q5 *'Stop Me'*

Q6 *Louise*

Q7 *Edwin Starr*

Q8 *'Not Letting Go'*

Q9 *The Flowerpot Men*

Q10 *Yarbrough & Peoples*

QUIZ 317 POPMASTER

STUCK ON TWO

This is a round of questions about records that peaked at No 2 on the UK charts.

QUESTION 1
In 1995, Pulp's first record to make the UK Top 10 was held off the top spot by Robson & Jerome's 'Unchained Melody'/'(There'll be Bluebirds Over) the White Cliffs of Dover'. What was the title?

QUESTION 2
Robson & Jerome's 'I Believe'/'Up on the Roof', also from 1995, managed to keep at bay what many believe was the most iconic single release by Oasis. Can you name it?

QUESTION 3
In 1981 Joe Dolce Music Theatre's 'Shaddup You Face' kept which classic Ultravox record off the top spot for three weeks?

QUESTION 4
Bryan Adams' 16-week run at No 1 with '(Everything I Do) I Do it for You' in 1991 blocked the biggest hit achieved by rock band Extreme from hitting the top spot. Can you name it?

QUESTION 5
Natalie and Nicole were regular visitors to the top with All Saints but had to settle for No 2 as Appleton. Which Appleton song did Atomic Kitten trump in 2002 with 'The Tide is High (Get the Feeling)'?

QUESTION 6
For two weeks in 1980, Diana Ross sat at No 2 with 'Upside Down' whilst which ABBA record refused to give way to this legendary American diva?

QUESTION 7
Status Quo must have thought they were about to have their first No 1 since 1975 with 'What You're Proposing' in 1980, but which Barbra Streisand hit stood in their way for two weeks?

QUESTION 8
Which 1970 single by Free sat at No 2 for five weeks whilst Mungo Jerry's 'In the Summertime' held fast for four weeks, before Elvis Presley jumped over them with 'The Wonder of You'?

QUESTION 9
Motown Records re-issued 'My Girl' by The Temptations in 1992 due to its appearance in the film of the same name, but it was stuck at No 2 for two weeks, blocked by which single by Shakespear's Sister?

QUESTION 10
Re-issued from 1969, which iconic David Bowie hit held Roxy Music's 1975 No 2 'Love is the Drug' from No 1?

POPMASTER QUIZ 318

SUBTITLES

QUIZ 316

QUESTION 1
The T.Rex single 'Get it On' was reduced to being a subtitle on its American release as it was deemed as being too risqué – what was its American title?

QUESTION 2
Tori Amos reached No 1 in 1997 with a song that has the subtitle '(It's Got to be Big)' – what is it called?

QUESTION 3
What is the subtitle of the Carpenters 1977 hit 'Calling Occupants of Interplanetary Craft'?

QUESTION 4
The Spice Girls re-formed briefly in 2007 and released a Top 20 single called 'Headlines', which had a subtitle that was a lyric from their debut hit 'Wannabe' – what is that subtitle?

QUESTION 5
Which part of Steve Harley and Cockney Rebel's No 1 'Make Me Smile Come Up and See Me' is the bit that is officially in brackets?

QUESTION 6
Which David Bowie album contains the hit singles 'Ashes to Ashes', 'Fashion' and 'Up the Hill Backwards'?

QUESTION 7
Bruno Mars reached No 1 in 2010 with a song that has the subtitle '(Amazing)' – what is it called?

QUESTION 8
Which 1974 single by The Faces has one of the longest ever subtitles of any single release?

QUESTION 9
Human League's first Top 10 hit has the subtitle '(I Believe in Love)' – what is it called?

QUESTION 10
Featured on Abbey Road, what is the subtitle of the Beatles song 'I Want You'?

Q1 *Sugababes*

Q2 *The Four Pennies*

Q3 *The Brook Brothers*

Q4 *Louise*

Q5 *Manfred Mann*

Q6 *Middle of the Road*

Q7 *Oxide & Neutrino*

Q8 *'In the Middle of the House'*

Q9 *A1*

Q10 *Dusty Springfield*

QUIZ 317

Q1
'Common People'

Q2
'Wonderwall'

Q3
'Vienna'

Q4
'More than Words'

Q5
'Fantasy'

Q6
'The Winner Takes it All'

Q7
'Woman in Love'

Q8
'All Right Now'

Q9
'Stay'

Q10
'Space Oddity'

QUIZ 319 POPMASTER

THAT'S LIFE

QUESTION 1
From 1998, who made the Top 3 with the hit single 'If You Buy this Record Your Life will be Better'?

QUESTION 2
Can you name the Austrian group whose only major success was the 1985 Top 10 hit 'Live is Life'?

QUESTION 3
In 2003, which female singer took the song 'Life for Rent' into the Top 10?

QUESTION 4
According to their 1971 top twenty hit, which group claimed that 'Life is a Long Song'?

QUESTION 5
Who topped the singles chart for one week in the year 2000 with 'Life is a Rollercoaster'?

QUESTION 6
Can you name the movie that featured the Top 10 hit duet from the Eighties by Bill Medley and Jennifer Warnes, '(I've Had) the Time of My Life'?

QUESTION 7
Who made their top forty chart debut in 1961 with '(I Wanna) Love My Life Away'?

QUESTION 8
From 1976, can you name the only Top 10 hit achieved by Sheer Elegance?

QUESTION 9
Which female group made the Top 3 for the third time in 2003 with their third hit, 'Life Got Cold'?

QUESTION 10
From which musical did Nina Simone's 1968 No 2 hit 'Ain't Got No... I Got Life' originate?

POPMASTER QUIZ 320

THEY'RE ONLY NUMBERS

QUESTION 1
Which one-time milkman from the Isle of Wright made the UK Top 10 in 1961 with a cover of Gene McDaniels' American hit 'A Hundred Pounds of Clay'?

QUESTION 2
Can you name the successful group that made the UK Top 10 in 1992 with 'A Million Love Songs'?

QUESTION 3
Which German act topped the UK chart for three weeks with the hit single '99 Red Balloons'?

QUESTION 4
In 1976, which American singer-songwriter found '50 Ways to Leave Your Lover', topping the US chart for three weeks?

QUESTION 5
Can you name the American rap and vocal band that achieved their only UK Top 10 hit in 1991 with 'Wiggle It'?

QUESTION 6
American actress and singer Connie Stevens achieved a solo hit in 1960. What was the title?

QUESTION 7
'57 Channels (And Nothin' On)' was the claim made in song by which American superstar?

QUESTION 8
Which group topped the American chart for two weeks and enjoyed a Top 3 UK hit in 1970 with 'Mama Told Me Not to Come'?

QUESTION 9
Can you name the psychedelic folk band that released a successful album in 1967 called The 5000 Spirits or the Layers of the Onion?

QUESTION 10
Released in 1988, which female singer achieved the last of eight UK Top 10 hits with 'Four Letter Word'?

QUIZ 318

Q1 *Bang A Gong*

Q2 *Professional Widow*

Q3 *(The Recognised Anthem Of World Contact Day)*

Q4 *(Friendship Never Ends)*

Q5 *(Come Up And See Me)*

Q6 *Scary Monsters (And Super Creeps)*

Q7 *Just The Way You Are*

Q8 *'You Can Make Me Dance, Sing or Anything' (Even Take the Dog for a Walk, Mend a Fuse, Fold Away the Ironing Board...)*

Q9 *Love Action*

Q10 *(She's So Heavy)*

QUIZ 319

Q1 *The Tamperer featuring Maya*

Q2 *Opus*

Q3 *Dido*

Q4 *Jethro Tull*

Q5 *Ronan Keating*

Q6 *Dirty Dancing*

Q7 *Gene Pitney*

Q8 *'Life is Too Short Girl'*

Q9 *Girls Aloud*

Q10 *Hair*

QUIZ 321 POPMASTER

THIS IS NOT MY SONG

Each question lists four songs: one of these songs is not credited to the composer(s) at the start of each question. Do you know which one?

QUESTION 1
Cat Stevens
a) 'Matthew and Son' b) 'The First Cut is the Deepest' c) 'Another Saturday Night' d) 'Lady D'Arbanville'

QUESTION 2
Burt Bacharach & Hal David
a) 'Raindrops Keep Fallin' on My Head' b) 'Make it Easy on Yourself' c) 'What's New Pussycat' d) 'All the Love in the World'

QUESTION 3
John Lennon & Paul McCartney
a) 'Ticket to Ride' b) 'Something' c) 'Hey Jude' d) 'With a Little Help from My Friends'

QUESTION 4
Mick Jagger & Keith Richards
a) 'Jumpin' Jack Flash' b) 'It's All Over Now' c) 'As Tears Go By' d) 'Out of Time'

QUESTION 5
Diane Warren
a) 'Love Don't Cost a Thing' b) 'Only Love Can Hurt Like This' c) 'I Don't Want to Miss a Thing' d) 'How Do I Live'

QUESTION 6
David Bowie
a) 'All the Young Dudes' b) 'The Man Who Sold the World' c) 'Under Pressure' d) 'Sorrow'

QUESTION 7
Prince
a) 'Love... Thy Will be Done' b) 'Nothing Compares 2 U' c) 'Alphabet Street' d) 'Modern Girl'

QUESTION 8
Brian Holland, Lamont Dozier & Eddie Holland
a) 'Reach Out - I'll be There' b) 'You Can't Hurry Love' c) 'The Tears of a Clown' d) 'Heaven Must Have Sent You'

QUESTION 9
Mark Ronson
a) 'Uptown Funk!' b) 'Love is a Losing Game' c) 'Bang Bang Bang' d) 'Slow Down Baby'

QUESTION 10
Jackie De Shannon
a) 'When You Walk in the Room' b) 'Bette Davis Eyes' c) 'Needles and Pins' d) 'Come and Stay with Me'

POPMASTER QUIZ 322

TIME TO PRAY

QUESTION 1
Which American rock band achieved their first UK top twenty hit in 1991 with 'Losing My Religion'?

QUESTION 2
Can you name the legendary American soul singer who achieved UK Top 5 status with her 1968 hit 'I Say a Little Prayer'?

QUESTION 3
Who topped our chart over the first three weeks of December 1999 with his hit single 'The Millennium Prayer'?

QUESTION 4
Which hugely successful vocal group scored their first UK No 1 in 1993 with a song called 'Pray'?

QUESTION 5
Can you name the singer who topped the singles chart in 1996 with 'Jesus to a Child'?

QUESTION 6
Which Beach Boys UK No 2 hit single was held off the No 1 position for two weeks in 1966 by 'Yellow Submarine' and 'Eleanor Rigby' by The Beatles?

QUESTION 7
Which American duo topped the UK chart for four weeks in 1990 with the re-issue of their 1965 top twenty hit 'Unchained Melody'?

QUESTION 8
Which group had two Top 10 hits in the Nineties with 'International Bright Young Thing' in 1991 and 'The Devil You Know' two years later?

QUESTION 9
In 1983, which successful band sang about the 'Church of the Poison Mind'?

QUESTION 10
Can you name the group that successfully revived The Isley Brothers' 1976 Top 10 hit 'Harvest for the World' in 1988?

QUIZ 320

Q1
Craig Douglas

Q2
Take That

Q3
Nena

Q4
Paul Simon

Q5
2 in a Room

Q6
'Sixteen Reasons'

Q7
Bruce Springsteen

Q8
Three Dog Night

Q9
The Incredible String Band

Q10
Kim Wilde

QUIZ 321

Q1 'Another Saturday Night'

Q2 'All The Love in the World'

Q3 'Something'

Q4 'It's All Over Now'

Q5 'Love Don't Cost a Thing'

Q6 'Sorrow'

Q7 'Modern Girl'

Q8 'The Tears of a Clown'

Q9 'Love is a Losing Game'

Q10 'Needles and Pins'

QUIZ 323 POPMASTER

TONY VISCONTI

QUESTION 1
The very first No 1 by T.Rex was a Tony Visconti-produced hit in 1971. What was it called?

QUESTION 2
Tony produced the 1980 album by Hazel O'Connor which was the soundtrack to the film in which she starred. What was the title of both the album and the film?

QUESTION 3
Do it Yourself was the Visconti-produced album by The Seahorses - a group formed by the guitarist from The Stone Roses. Who is he?

QUESTION 4
Adam Ant's final Top 40 hit of the Eighties was a Visconti production with an astronautical theme. What was it called?

QUESTION 5
Often called one of the greatest live albums of the Seventies, which group released the double album Live and Dangerous in 1978?

QUESTION 6
Tony produced the 1975 album by Sparks called Indiscreet, which contained two Top 40 singles. Name either of them.

QUESTION 7
Ringleader of the Tormentors was a 2006 album produced by Tony and recorded by which singer?

QUESTION 8
Who was married to Visconti in the Seventies and sang backing vocals on David Bowie's 'Sound and Vision'?

QUESTION 9
Five of the eight Eighties chart hits by Modern Romance were Visconti productions - 'Cherry Pink and Apple Blossom White' and 'Don't Stop that Crazy Rhythm' were two of them. Name one of the other three.

QUESTION 10
Visconti was part of a supergroup that includes Heaven 17's Glenn Gregory, Mick Woodmansey from The Spiders from Mars and Blondie's Clem Burke amongst its members and special guests. What is it called?

POPMASTER QUIZ 324

TOP RANK RECORDS

Top Rank was one of the most successful independent labels of the late fifties and early sixties.

QUESTION 1
Which guitarist achieved a 1959 Top 10 UK hit with 'Guitar Boogie Shuffle'?

QUESTION 2
The Shirelles' first UK Top 5 hit and American No 1 from 1961 was released on Top Rank. What was the title?

QUESTION 3
A UK Top 10 hit for The Hollies in 1963, the original version of 'Stay' topped the American chart in 1961 and reached the UK top twenty, as recorded by which group?

QUESTION 4
Dion's first two UK top twenty hits were released by Top Rank in the early Sixties, the first being 'Runaround Sue'. What was the second?

QUESTION 5
In 1960, Gary Mills made the UK Top 10 with a song written by Tony Hatch and featured in the movie *Circus of Horrors*. What was the title?

QUESTION 6
The Ventures' debut UK Top 10 hit was released on Top Rank in 1960. Can you name it?

QUESTION 7
From 1959, can you name the only No 1 achieved by Craig Douglas - a cover of Sam Cooke's American hit that topped the UK chart for four weeks?

QUESTION 8
Which American rock and roller achieved his only UK Top 10 hit in 1960 with 'Way Down Yonder in New Orleans'?

QUESTION 9
Which Canadian singer scored his only top twenty UK hit on Top Rank in 1960 with 'What in the World's Come Over You'?

QUESTION 10
Which letters were used as the prefix to Top Rank singles before the actual number: was it CAR, JAR or BAR?

QUIZ 322

Q1
R.E.M.

Q2
Aretha Franklin

Q3
Cliff Richard

Q4
Take That

Q5
George Michael

Q6
'God Only Knows'

Q7
The Righteous Brothers

Q8
Jesus Jones

Q9
Culture Club

Q10
The Christians

QUIZ 323

Q1
'Hot Love'

Q2
Breaking Glass

Q3
John Squire

Q4
'Apollo 9'

Q5
Thin Lizzy

Q6
'Get in the Swing', 'Looks, Looks, Looks'

Q7
Morrissey

Q8
Mary Hopkin

Q9
'Best Years of our Lives', 'High Life', 'Walking in the Rain'

Q10
Holy Holy

QUIZ 325 POPMASTER

TREVOR HORN

Questions about the innovative record producer and his productions

QUESTION 1
For whom did Horn produce the album Slave to the Rhythm?

QUESTION 2
Trevor Horn was a member of The Buggles, who reached No 1 with 'Video Killed the Radio Star', but they had two other Top 40 hits. Name either of these.

QUESTION 3
Following the demise of The Buggles, Horn became a member of which progressive rock band?

QUESTION 4
What is the title of ABC's No 1 album that includes the hits 'Poison Arrow', 'The Look of Love' and 'All of My Heart'?

QUESTION 5
What record label was co-founded by Trevor Horn in 1983?

QUESTION 6
What was the first Horn-produced Top 40 hit for the duo Dollar in the Eighties?

QUESTION 7
The 1994 hit 'If I Only Knew' was produced by Horn for which veteran singer?

QUESTION 8
What was the title of Robbie Williams' 2009 album, produced by Horn?

QUESTION 9
Trevor produced Rod Stewart's hit cover versions of both 'Tom Traubert's Blues' and 'Downtown Train'. Who wrote these two songs?

QUESTION 10
What nationality are the duo t.A.T.u., who reached No 1 in 2003 with 'All the Things She Said'?

POPMASTER QUIZ 326

TROJAN RECORDS

The Trojan organization, famous for reggae, ran several different labels; this quiz concentrates exclusively on releases on the actual imprint.

QUESTION 1
Although he achieved a Top 10 hit in 1972 on the Rhino label with 'Mad About You', what was the title of the only hit by Bruce Ruffin on Trojan from the previous year?

QUESTION 2
From 1974, what was the title of the only hit single released by John Holt?

QUESTION 3
Jamaican reggae group Greyhound achieved three top 20 hits on Trojan but only one made the Top 10. Can you name it?

QUESTION 4
Jimmy Cliff achieved a Top 10 hit on the Island label in 1970 with 'Wild World', but what was the title of his only record to do likewise for Trojan the previous year?

QUESTION 5
'Young, Gifted and Black' by Bob and Marcia was released on the Harry J label and was the first of their two top twenty hits, the second being on Trojan. What was the title?

QUESTION 6
The co-compiler of this quiz book co-produced a 1970 top twenty hit for Trojan titled 'Black Pearl'. Can you name the performer?

QUESTION 7
In 1974, which reggae singer topped the UK chart for three weeks with his revival of the David Gates song 'Everything I Own'?

QUESTION 8
Can you name the group who consisted of members of The Pyramids, who achieved a minor hit in 1980 with 'Skinhead Moonstomp'?

QUESTION 9
What was the title of the only hit by Jamaican singer Nicky Thomas, who made the UK Top 10 in 1970?

QUESTION 10
From 1971, can you name the only UK Top 10 hit achieved by The Pioneers?

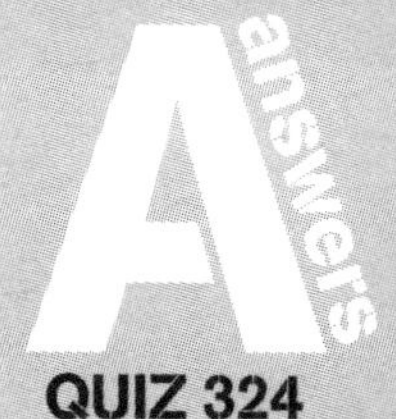

QUIZ 324

Q1 *Bert Weedon*

Q2 *'Will You Love Me Tomorrow'*

Q3 *Maurice Williams & The Zodiacs*

Q4 *'The Wanderer'*

Q5 *'Look for a Star'*

Q6 *'Walk Don't Run'*

Q7 *'Only Sixteen'*

Q8 *Freddy Cannon*

Q9 *Jack Scott*

Q10 *JAR*

QUIZ 325

Q1
Grace Jones

Q2
'The Plastic Age', 'Clean, Clean'

Q3
Yes

Q4
The Lexicon of Love

Q5
ZTT

Q6
'Hand Held in Black and White'

Q7
Tom Jones

Q8
Reality Killed the Video Star

Q9
Tom Waits

Q10
Russian

QUIZ 327 POPMASTER

TWO HIT WONDERS (1)

These groups or artists had just two Top 40 hits, both of them in the Seventies. Their first was the better known. Can you name the second?

QUESTION 1
Crystal Gayle
'Don't It Make My Brown Eyes Blue' (Top 5 hit in 1977)

QUESTION 2
The Motors
'Airport' (Top 5 hit in 1978)

QUESTION 3
Bachman-Turner Overdrive
'You Ain't Seen Nothing Yet' (Top 3 hit in 1974)

QUESTION 4
Slik
'Forever and Ever' (number 1 in 1976)

QUESTION 5
Plastic Bertrand
'Ça Plane Pour Moi' (Top 10 hit in 1978)

QUESTION 6
Hues Corporation
'Rock the Boat' (Top 10 hit in 1974)

QUESTION 7
Marshall Hain
'Dancing in the City' (Top 3 hit in 1978)

QUESTION 8
Baccara
'Yes Sir I Can Boogie' (number 1 hit in 1977)

QUESTION 9
Dandy Livingstone
'Suzanne Beware of the Devil' (Top 20 hit in 1972)

QUESTION 10
Osibisa
'Sunshine Day' (Top 20 hit in 1976)

POPMASTER QUIZ 328

TWO HIT WONDERS (2)

These groups or artists had just two Top 40 hits, both of them in the Eighties. Their first was the better known. Can you name the second?

QUESTION 1
Falco
'Rock Me Amadeus' (number 1 in 1986)

QUESTION 2
Landscape
'Einstein a Go-Go' (Top 5 hit in 1981)

QUESTION 3
Sydney Youngblood
'If Only I Could' (Top 3 in 1989)

QUESTION 4
Jim Diamond
'I Should Have Known Better' (number 1 in 1984)

QUESTION 5
Fat Boys
'Wipeout (with the Beach Boys)' (Top 3 hit in 1987)
Their other hit also featured guest artists...

QUESTION 6
Bob Geldof
'This is the World Calling' (Top 30 hit in 1986)

QUESTION 7
Steve Arrington
'Feel So Real' (Top 5 hit in 1985)

QUESTION 8
H20
'Dream to Sleep' (Top 20 hit in 1983)

QUESTION 9
Robbie Nevil
'C'est la Vie' (Top 3 hit in 1986)

QUESTION 10
Pigbag
'Papa's Got a Brand New Pigbag' (Top 3 hit in 1982)

A answers

QUIZ 326

Q1
'Rain'

Q2
'Help Me Make it Through the Night'

Q3
'Black and White'

Q4
'Wonderful World, Beautiful People'

Q5
'Pied Piper'

Q6
Horace Faith

Q7
Ken Boothe

Q8
Symarip

Q9
'Love of the Common People'

Q10
'Let Your Yeah be Yeah'

QUIZ 327

Q1
'Talking in Your Sleep' (No 11 in '78)

Q2
'Forget About You' (No 13 in '78)

Q3
'Roll on Down the Highway' (No 22 in '75)

Q4
'Requiem' (No 24, also in '76)

Q5
'Sha La La La Lee' (No 39, also in '78)

Q6
'Rockin' Soul' (No 24 in '74)

Q7
'Coming Home' (No 39 in '78)

Q8
'Sorry I'm a Lady' (No 8 in '78)

Q9
'Big City/Think About That' (No 26 in '73)

Q10
'Dance the Body Music' (No 31 in '76)

QUIZ 329 POPMASTER

TWO HIT WONDERS (3)

These groups or artists had just two Top 40 hits in the Nineties and Noughties. Their first was the better known. Can you name the second?

QUESTION 1
Chesney Hawkes
'The One and Only' (No 1 in 1991)

QUESTION 2
One True Voice
'Sacred Trust'/'After You're Gone' (Top 3 hit in 2002)

QUESTION 3
Maria McKee
'Show Me Heaven' (No 1 in 1990)

QUESTION 4
Tony Rich Project
'Nobody Knows' (Top 5 hit in 1996)

QUESTION 5
Modjo
'Lady (Hear Me Tonight)' (No 1 in 2000)

QUESTION 6
Zucchero
'Senza Una Donna (with Paul Young)' (Top 5 hit in 1991)
His other hit was also a duet with another artist...

QUESTION 7
Leon Jackson
'When You Believe' (number 1 in 2007)

QUESTION 8
Adventures of Stevie V
'Dirty Cash' (Top 3 hit in 1990)

QUESTION 9
Sinead Quinn
'I Can't Break Down' (Top 3 hit in 2003)

QUESTION 10
The Mavericks
'Dance the Night Away' (Top 5 hit in 1998)

POPMASTER QUIZ 330

TWO HIT WONDERS (4)

These groups or artists have had just two Top 40 hits in their careers. Their first was the better known. Can you name the second?

QUESTION 1
Danny Wilson
'Mary's Prayer' (Top 3 hit in 1988)

QUESTION 2
The Toys
'A Lover's Concerto' (Top 5 hit in 1965)

QUESTION 3
Will to Power
'Baby I Love Your Way – Freebird' (Top 10 hit in 1989)

QUESTION 4
Sixpence None the Richer
'Kiss Me' (Top 5 hit in 1999)

QUESTION 5
Doctor & The Medics
'Spirit in the Sky' (No 1 in 1986)

QUESTION 6
The 5th Dimension
'Aquarius'/'Let the Sunshine In' (Top 20 hit in 1969)

QUESTION 7
Peter Skellern
'You're a Lady' (Top 3 hit in 1972)

QUESTION 8
Patrice Rushen
'Forget Me Nots' (Top 10 hit in 1982)

QUESTION 9
Marti Pellow
'Close to You' (Top 10 in 2001)

QUESTION 10
OC Smith
'The Son of Hickory Holler's Tramp' (Top 3 hit in 1968)

QUIZ 328

Q1 *'Vienna Calling' (No 10, also in '86)*

Q2 *'Norman Bates' (No 40, also in '81)*

Q3 *'Sit and Wait' (No 16, also in '89)*

Q4 *'Hi Ho Silver' (No 5 in '86)*

Q5 *'The Twist (Yo, Twist)' (with Chubby Checker) ('88 – both songs reached No 2)*

Q6 *'The Great Song of Indifference' (actually charted higher – No 15 in '90)*

Q7 *'Dancin' in the Key of Life' (No 21, also in '85)*

Q8 *'Just Outside of Heaven' (No 38 also in '83)*

Q9 *'Dominoes' (No 26 in '87)*

Q10 *'The Big Bean' (No 40, also in '82)*

QUIZ 329

Q1
'I'm a Man Not a Boy' (No. 27 also in '91)

Q2
'Shakespeare's Way with Words' (No. 10 in '03)

Q3
'I'm Gonna Soothe You' (No. 35 in '93)

Q4
'Like a Woman' (No. 27 also in '96)

Q5
'Chillin'' (No. 12 in '01)

Q6
'Miserere' (with Luciano Pavarotti) (No. 15 in '92)

Q7
'Don't Call This Love' (No. 3 in 2008)

Q8
'Body Language' (No. 29 also in '90)

Q9
'What You Need Is...' (No. 19 in 2003)

Q10
'I've Got this Feeling' (No. 27 also in '98)

QUIZ 331 POPMASTER

UK TOUR (1)

QUESTION 1
Which group had both a hit single and album in 1979 called 'London Calling'?

QUESTION 2
Mick Jones of The Clash and Big Audio Dynamite guested on a 1990 Top 20 single by Aztec Camera. What was it called?

QUESTION 3
Which group sang about 'Winchester Cathedral' on their 1966 Top 5 debut hit?

QUESTION 4
The roots of the groups Heaven 17, Human League, Arctic Monkeys, ABC and Pulp are all in which South Yorkshire city?

QUESTION 5
The singles 'Sour Times' and 'Glory Box' both feature on the 1994 double-platinum album Dummy, recorded by a band who take their name from a town on the Severn Estuary. What is their name?

QUESTION 6
Where were Fiddler's Dram heading on their 'Daytrip', according to the title of their 1979 Top 3 single?

QUESTION 7
Which footballer was billed alongside Lindisfarne on the 1990 Top 3 hit 'Fog on the Tyne (Revisited)'?

QUESTION 8
What is the location of the 'Airport' Cats U.K. sang about on their only Top 40 hit in the late Seventies?

QUESTION 9
'Sunshine on Leith' was the title of a 1988 single by which duo?

QUESTION 10
What was the title of the sixth and final Top 10 hit for Gerry & The Pacemakers in the Sixties?

POPMASTER QUIZ 332

UK TOUR (2)

QUESTION 1
The 1966 Simon & Garfunkel album Parsley, Sage, Rosemary & Thyme opens with the duo's version of which traditional English ballad?

QUESTION 2
Which group sang 'Come to Milton Keynes' in 1985?

QUESTION 3
What type of 'Dagger' did The Fratellis sing about on their 2006 Top 5 hit?

QUESTION 4
The 1991 Top 10 single 'It's Grim Up North' was the only hit for a duo that also recorded as The KLF and The Timelords, but how were they billed on this hit?

QUESTION 5
Although it missed out on being a Top 40 hit, which Kent seaside town was the destination for a Chas and Dave single in 1982?

QUESTION 6
Which American group released the 1986 single 'Going Down to Liverpool'?

QUESTION 7
Where did the 'Cowboy' come from that Mike Harding sang about on his 1975 hit?

QUESTION 8
Which group released their Top 3 debut album London 0 Hull 4 in 1986?

QUESTION 9
The Wings No 1 'Mull of Kintyre' was a double 'A' side with which other song?

QUESTION 10
Which easy listening singer and whistler was going to leave 'Durham Town' in 1969?

A answers

QUIZ 330

Q1
'The Second Summer of Love' (No 23, also in '88)

Q2
'Attack' (No 36 in '66)

Q3
'I'm Not in Love' (10cc cover) (No 29 in '90)

Q4
'There She Goes' (La's cover) (No 14 in '99)

Q5
'Burn' (No 29, also in '86)

Q6
'Wedding Bell Blues' (No 16 in '70)

Q7
'Hold on to Love' (No 14 in '75)

Q8
'I was Tired of Being Alone' (No 39 ,also in '82)

Q9
I've Been Around the World (No 28, also in '01)

Q10
Together (No 25 in '77)

QUIZ 331

Q1
The Clash

Q2
'Good Morning Britain'

Q3
The New Vaudeville Band

Q4
Sheffield

Q5
Portishead

Q6
Bangor - 'Daytrip to Bangor (Didn't We Have a Lovely Time)'

Q7
Paul Gascoigne (billed as Gazza and Lindisfarne)

Q8
'Luton Airport'

Q9
The Proclaimers (just missed Top 40 - it stalled at No.41)

Q10
'Ferry 'Cross the Mersey'

QUIZ 333 POPMASTER

UPS AND DOWNS

QUESTION 1
What hit song title was shared by Matt Willis in 2006 and Take That in 2009?

QUESTION 2
Can you name the act in which Jim Diamond was a member and achieved just one UK hit in 1982 with 'I Won't Let You Down'?

QUESTION 3
Which legendary soul group scored a UK Top 10 hit in 1974 with 'Down on the Beach Tonight'?

QUESTION 4
Can you name the male trio who scored a 2009 Top 10 hit in the UK with 'Uprising'?

QUESTION 5
In 1970, which female Tamla Motown act scored a Top 10 hit with 'Up the Ladder to the Roof'?

QUESTION 6
'Uptown Funk!' was a 2015 UK No 1 hit for Mark Ronson that featured which other successful performer?

QUESTION 7
What was the title of the 1999 UK Top 10 hit by Tom Jones and The Cardigans?

QUESTION 8
Which one-time lead singer of the group Pickettywitch achieved an American top twenty hit in 1975 with 'Up in a Puff of Smoke', co-written and produced by the co-author of this quiz book, Phil Swern?

QUESTION 9
Which successful group topped the UK chart in 2015 with 'Drag Me Down'?

QUESTION 10
Can you name the group whose only UK hit was with the 1978 Top 10 hit 'Breaking Up Again'?

POPMASTER QUIZ 334

WAS IT SOMETHING I SAID?

QUESTION 1
Barry White asks for "One ticket please…" in the introduction to which of his Top 10 hits?

QUESTION 2
What is the name of Beyoncé's husband, who raps on her No 1 hit 'Crazy in Love'?

QUESTION 3
On which Rolling Stones single does Mick Jagger say he'll be your "knight in shining armour"?

QUESTION 4
Who asks if we all "wanna go down the Devil Gate Drive" at the beginning of her 1974 No 1?

QUESTION 5
On which Frankie Goes to Hollywood No 1 does Holly Johnson want to "protect you from the hooded claw"?

QUESTION 6
The song 'Have You Seen Her' begins with a long spoken section and was a Top 5 hit in both 1972 and 1975 for which American vocal group?

QUESTION 7
Florence + The Machine had a Top 3 hit in 2010 with a live single that featured a rap by Dizzee Rascal. What was it called?

QUESTION 8
At the start of 'Ballroom Blitz' by The Sweet, singer Brian Connolly asks the three other band members if they're ready. What are their names?

QUESTION 9
Which actor recites the verses on the song 'Parklife', by Blur?

QUESTION 10
On which of Blondie's hit singles does Debbie Harry talk about "Fab Five Freddie", "eatin' cars" and a "man from Mars"?

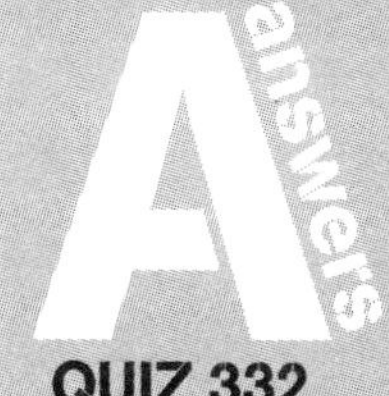

QUIZ 332

Q1 *'Scarborough Fair' (full listing is 'Scarborough Fair/ Canticle')*

Q2 *The Style Council*

Q3 *'Chelsea Dagger'*

Q4 *Justified Ancients of Mu Mu*

Q5 *'Margate' (it reached No.46)*

Q6 *The Bangles (it reached No.56)*

Q7 *Rochdale*

Q8 *The Housemartins*

Q9 *'Girls' School'*

Q10 *Roger Whittaker*

QUIZ 335 POPMASTER

WATER OR WINE

QUIZ 333

Q1 *'Up All Night'*

Q2 *PhD*

Q3 *The Drifters*

Q4 *Muse*

Q5 *The Supremes*

Q6 *Bruno Mars*

Q7 *'Burning Down the House'*

Q8 *Polly Brown*

Q9 *One Direction*

Q10 *Goldie*

QUESTION 1
Which legendary singer and actor achieved an American top forty hit in 1967 with 'Little Ole Wine Drinker Me'?

QUESTION 2
In 1957, Tommy Steele had a Top 5 UK success with the double 'A'-sided single 'A Handful of Songs' and which other song?

QUESTION 3
What title is shared by different hit songs from Paul McCartney in 1980 and TLC in 1995, both of which made the UK Top 10?

QUESTION 4
Under what name is American singer-songwriter Samuel 'Sam' Beam better known?

QUESTION 5
Which American rock band took the song 'Black Water' to the top of the US chart in 1974?

QUESTION 6
Best known for her hit single 'The Clapping Song', which female singer recorded the 1966 novelty song 'Ever See a Diver Kiss His Wife While the Bubbles Bounce About Above the Water'?

QUESTION 7
Originally released in 1966, which act achieved a UK top forty hit in 1972 with the instrumental 'Wade in the Water'?

QUESTION 8
In 1968, which Neil Diamond song gave Jimmy James & The Vagabonds their first top forty hit?

QUESTION 9
Can you name the female singer who took a glass of 'Lilac Wine' into the UK top twenty in 1978?

QUESTION 10
First released in 1985 then re-issued in 1991, what was the title of the only Top 10 hit achieved by The Waterboys?

POPMASTER QUIZ 336

WITH IMMEDIATE EFFECT

These are questions about the short-lived yet very successful Sixties record label Immediate, set up by record producer Andrew Oldham.

QUESTION 1
P.P. Arnold achieved two top forty hits on Immediate. The biggest was 'The First Cut is the Deepest', but what was the title of the second?

QUESTION 2
Who wrote Chris Farlowe's 1966 No 1 hit 'Out of Time'?

QUESTION 3
After leaving Decca in 1966, what was the title of the first top twenty hit for The Small Faces on Immediate the following year?

QUESTION 4
Can you name the group that went on to achieve hits with 'Happy Together' and 'She'd Rather be with Me' who released just one single on Immediate, 'You Baby'?

QUESTION 5
Vocal duo Dave Skinner and Andrew Rose achieved a top forty hit in 1966 with 'Sittin' on a Fence'. Under what collective name did they release their single?

QUESTION 6
In 1969, Fleetwood Mac reached No 2 in the singles chart with their only hit on Immediate. What was the title?

QUESTION 7
Which group topped the chart in 1969 for two weeks with '(If Paradise Is) Half as Nice'?

QUESTION 8
Can you name the American No 1 from 1965 by The McCoys that made the UK Top 5 when released on Immediate?

QUESTION 9
What was the name of the group formed by Steve Marriott and Peter Frampton that made the Top 5 in 1969 with 'Natural Born Bugie'?

QUESTION 10
Which rock band saw their arrangement of 'America' from *West Side Story* make the top forty in 1968?

QUIZ 334

Q1 *'Let the Music Play'*

Q2 *Jay Z*

Q3 *'Emotional Rescue'*

Q4 *Suzi Quatro*

Q5 *'The Power of Love'*

Q6 *The Chi-Lites*

Q7 *'You Got the Dirtee Love' (a version of The Source/Candi Staton hit 'You Got the Love')*

Q8 *Steve (Priest), Andy (Scott) and Mick (Tucker)*

Q9 *Phil Daniels*

Q10 *'Rapture'*

QUIZ 335

Q1
Dean Martin

Q2
'Water Water'

Q3
'Waterfalls'

Q4
Iron & Wine

Q5
The Doobie Brothers

Q6
Shirley Ellis

Q7
The Ramsey Lewis Trio

Q8
'Red Red Wine'

Q9
Elkie Brooks

Q10
'The Whole of the Moon'

QUIZ 337 POPMASTER

CHAMPION OF CHAMPIONS 1

Really tough stuff – have you got what it takes?

QUESTION 1
The band The Members had its only two Top 40 singles in 1979. 'The Sound of the Suburbs' was one, what was the other?

QUESTION 2
Which one-time *Home and Away* actress had hits in 1997 called 'Everything I Wanted' and 'All I Wanna Do'?

QUESTION 3
What is the name of the English art design group that designed album sleeves in the Seventies for 10cc, Pink Floyd, Peter Gabriel and Led Zeppelin, amongst others?

QUESTION 4
'My Boy Lollipop' was a Top 3 hit for Millie in 1964, but she released another single that year which was to be her only other Top 40 hit. What is it called?

QUESTION 5
Which group's only Top 40 hit was in 1994 with the Top 3 song 'Compliments on Your Kiss'?

QUESTION 6
Which two film stars had a hit in 2001 with the song 'Come What May'?

QUESTION 7
The duo Baccara may come from Spain, but which country did they represent at the 1978 Eurovision Song Contest?

QUESTION 8
David Hasselhoff's 2006 Top 10 hit 'Jump in My Car' was a cover of a song originally recorded in 1975 by an Australian-based rock band. What were they called?

QUESTION 9
Which two David Bowie singles in the Nineties either musically or lyrically reference his song 'Space Oddity'?

QUESTION 10
M is often considered a one-hit wonder for the 1979 Top 3 hit 'Pop Muzik', which also reached the Top 20 ten years later as a remix. But M had another Top 40 hit. What was it called?

POPMASTER QUIZ 338

CHAMPION OF CHAMPIONS 2

Really tough stuff – have you got what it takes?

QUESTION 1
Following hits in the Seventies as the Tom Robinson Band, Tom Robinson had two further Top 40 solo hits in the Eighties. Name both of them.

QUESTION 2
Which one-time Coronation Street actor had Top 40 hits in 1998 with the songs 'The Heart's Lone Desire' and 'She's Gone', which featured Destiny's Child as guest artists?

QUESTION 3
The band The Merton Parkas had its only Top 40 hit in 1979. What was it called?

QUESTION 4
Prior to her radio and television career, Lauren Laverne reached the charts in the Nineties as the lead singer with which group?

QUESTION 5
Jess Glynne featured on Clean Bandit's No 1 'Rather Be' in 2014, but she also featured on another No 1 that year – a song called 'My Love'. Who recorded this?

QUESTION 6
Peter Blake designed the cover of Sgt. Pepper's Lonely Hearts Club Band, but who designed the drum skin in the centre of the sleeve?

QUESTION 7
...and which 1995 No 1 album by Paul Weller has a sleeve designed by Peter Blake?

QUESTION 8
What links the Elvis Presley No 1s 'All Shook Up', 'It's Now or Never' and 'The Wonder of You'?

QUESTION 9
Which Jackson brother left and which Jackson joined when The Jackson 5 changed record labels in the mid-Seventies and became The Jacksons?

QUESTION 10
The group Liquid Gold had all three of its Top 40 hits in 1980 – both 'Dance Yourself Dizzy' and 'Substitute' reached the Top 10, but the third languished at No.32. What was it called?

A answers

QUIZ 336

Q1
'Angel of the Morning'

Q2
Mick Jagger and Keith Richards

Q3
'Here Comes the Nice'

Q4
The Turtles

Q5
Twice as Much

Q6
'Man of the World'

Q7
Amen Corner

Q8
'Hang on Sloopy'

Q9
Humble Pie

Q10
The Nice

QUIZ 337

Q1
'Offshore Banking Business'

Q2
Dannii Minogue

Q3
Hipgnosis

Q4
'Sweet William'

Q5
Red Dragon (full title Red Dragon with Brian and Tony Gold)

Q6
Nicole Kidman and Ewan McGregor (from the film Moulin Rouge)

Q7
Luxembourg

Q8 *Ted Mulry Gang (lead singer Mulry wrote it and it spent 6 weeks as Australian No.1 in 1976)*

Q9 *'Hallo Spaceboy', 'Buddha of Suburbia' (a 'Space Oddity' chord sequence)*

Q10
'Moonlight and Muzak' (peaked at No 33 in January '80)

QUIZ 339 POPMASTER

CHAMPION OF CHAMPIONS 3

Really tough stuff – have you got what it takes?

QUESTION 1
Name the British group that had its only chart hits in 1971 with the Top 20 song 'Tomorrow Night' and the Top 5 single 'Devil's Answer'.

QUESTION 2
What comes next in this sequence – Faith, Listen Without Prejudice Volume 1, Older, Songs from the Last Century... ?

QUESTION 3
Released in 1976, what is the title of Twiggy's one and only Top 40 appearance?

QUESTION 4
In which year were these three songs all American No 1s? 'Love is Here and Now You're Gone' by The Supremes, 'Happy Together' by The Turtles and 'Windy' by The Association.

QUESTION 5
When Kym Marsh left the *Popstars* group Hear'Say, she was replaced by a male singer. What was he called?

QUESTION 6
The Britpop-era band Menswear had three Top 20 and two further Top 30 singles in the mid-Nineties. Name one of these five hits.

QUESTION 7
Complete this band line-up: Noddy Holder, Dave Hill, Jim Lea and who?

QUESTION 8
Of the nine songs on the original release of Michael Jackson's album Thriller, six of them were released as singles in the UK – only three were not. Name one of these three songs.

QUESTION 9
Who produced The Special AKA's 1984 single 'Nelson Mandela'?

QUESTION 10
What one-word song title has provided different hits for Earth Wind & Fire, Mariah Carey and Appleton?

POPMASTER QUIZ 340

CHAMPION OF CHAMPIONS 4

Really tough stuff – have you got what it takes?

QUESTION 1
Released in 1978, what is the title of the only hit single by Mike Oldfield's sister, Sally Oldfield?

QUESTION 2
In 1994, which group spent 14 weeks at No 1 in America with 'I'll Make Love to You', then knocked themselves off the top with their follow-up, 'On Bended Knee', which spent six weeks at No 1?

QUESTION 3
What is the title of Meghan Trainor's 2015 No 1 album?

QUESTION 4
Released in 1981, the group whose only Top 40 hit was 'Me and Mr Sanchez' was called Blue... what?

QUESTION 5
Madonna had over 50 chart hits in the 20th century, but only four of these failed to reach the Top 10. name one of these four songs.

QUESTION 6
Although they are not related, what are the first names of the three members of the original hit line-up of Duran Duran with the surname Taylor?

QUESTION 7
Which Carole King song was a hit for the singer Martika in 1989?

QUESTION 8
Which American group reached the singles chart in 1975 with '7-6-5-4-3-2-1 (Blow Your Whistle)'?

QUESTION 9
Which Rolling Stones LP from the Sixties begins with 'Gimme Shelter' on side one and ends side two with 'You Can't Always Get What You Want'?

QUESTION 10
After TV's *Popstars: The Rivals*, four girls who didn't make it into Girls Aloud and five boys who didn't make it into One True Voice both formed groups and both had Top 40 hits. Name both groups.

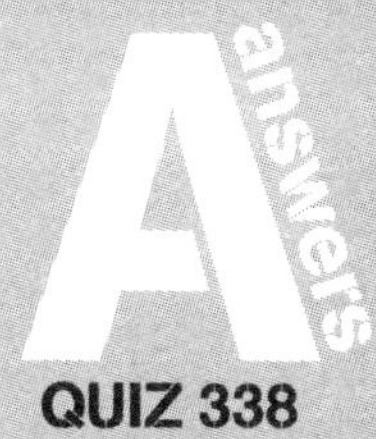

QUIZ 338

Q1 *'War Baby', 'Listen to the Radio: Atmospherics'*

Q2 *Matthew Marsden*

Q3 *'You Need Wheels'*

Q4 *Kenickie*

Q5 *Route 94*

Q6 *Joe Ephgrave*

Q7 *Stanley Road*

Q8 *His first No 1 in the Fifties, Sixties and Seventies*

Q9 *Jermaine left, Randy joined*

Q10 *'The Night, the Wine and the Roses'*

QUIZ 339

Q1
Atomic Rooster

Q2
Patience (studio albums by George Michael)

Q3
'Here I Go Again'

Q4
1967

Q5
Johnny Shentall (married to Lisa Scott-Lee of Steps)

Q6
'Daydreamer', 'Stardust', 'Sleeping In', 'Being Brave', 'We Love You'

Q7
Don Powell (Slade)

Q8 *'Baby be Mine', 'Human Nature', 'The Lady in My Life'*

Q9
Elvis Costello

Q10
'Fantasy'

QUIZ 341 POPMASTER

CHAMPION OF CHAMPIONS 5

Really tough stuff – have you got what it takes?

QUESTION 1
Which Pink Floyd studio album was released after Wish You Were Here but before The Wall?

QUESTION 2
What is the name of the singer who regularly appeared in the TV series *Ally McBeal* and what is the title of her 1998 debut Top 10 single?

QUESTION 3
Who is the drummer in Coldplay?

QUESTION 4
Released in late 1978, what is both the title and subtitle of the only Top 10 hit for the American singer Paul Evans?

QUESTION 5
'Sleepwalk' was the title of the 1980 Top 40 debut by which group?

QUESTION 6
David Bowie's son, once known as Zowie, is now a successful director of the films *Moon* and *Source Code*. What is he called?

QUESTION 7
The 1992 Top 5 single 'Just Another Day' was the biggest hit for the Cuban-born singer Jon Secada, but he had four other Top 40 hits that decade. Name one of them.

QUESTION 8
The song 'I Want an Alien for Christmas' was a Top 40 hit in 1997 for which American group?

QUESTION 9
Bourgeois Tagg had its only chart hit in 1988 – what was it called?

QUESTION 10
Which record label released all the hits in the 1990s by The Beautiful South, as well as several singles by Paul Weller and Billy Bragg?

POPMASTER QUIZ 342

CHAMPION OF CHAMPIONS 6

Really tough stuff – have you got what it takes?

QUESTION 1
What was the title of Dexy's Midnight Runners' 1986 hit theme song to the TV show *Brush Strokes*?

QUESTION 2
Who was the drummer with Joy Division and is the drummer with New Order?

QUESTION 3
Which record label released all the hits in the 1990s by Blur, as well as several singles by Jesus Jones and Shampoo?

QUESTION 4
In 1973, Mud had three hit singles – their debut hit 'Crazy' and their first Top 10 with 'Dyna-mite', but which single was sandwiched between these two?

QUESTION 5
What are the surnames of the original hit five-piece line-up of Boyzone?

QUESTION 6
Who was the lyricist of Elton John's hits 'Blue Eyes', 'Part Time Love' and 'Little Jeannie'?

QUESTION 7
What comes next in this sequence – Generation Terrorists, Gold Against the Soul, The Holy Bible... ?

QUESTION 8
Which singer's only Top 40 hit was in 1984 with the song 'Bird of Paradise'?

QUESTION 9
Released in 1975, which of Showaddywaddy's singles was the group's first hit cover version rather than a self-penned song?

QUESTION 10
Which actress had a Top 10 single in 2001 called 'What If'?

QUIZ 340

Q1 *'Mirrors'*

Q2 *Boyz II Men*

Q3 *Title*

Q4 *Blue Rondo a la Turk*

Q5 *'Lucky Star' (No.14 in '84), 'Take a Bow' (16 in '94), 'Oh Father', 'One More Chance' (16 and 11 in '96)*

Q6 *John, Roger, Andy*

Q7 *'I Feel the Earth Move'*

Q8 *The Rimshots*

Q9 *Let it Bleed*

Q10 *Clea, Phixx*

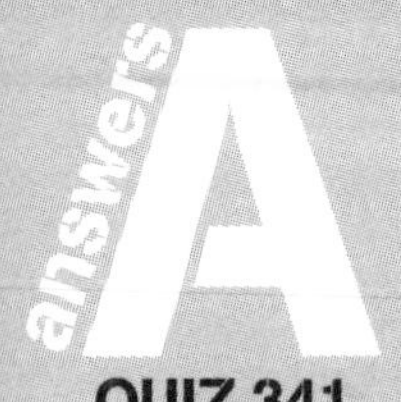

QUIZ 341

Q1
Animals

Q2
Vonda Shepard, 'Searchin' My Soul'

Q3
Will Champion

Q4
'Hello, This is Joannie (The Telephone Answering Machine Song)'

Q5
Ultravox

Q6
Duncan Jones

Q7
'Do You Believe in Us', 'Angel', 'Do You Really Want Me', 'If You Go'

Q8
Fountains of Wayne

Q9
'I Don't Mind at All'

Q10
Go! Discs

QUIZ 343 POPMASTER

CHAMPION OF CHAMPIONS 7

Really tough stuff – have you got what it takes?

QUESTION 1
Which group released albums in the Eighties called Argy Bargy, East Side Story and Cosi Fan Tutti Frutti?

QUESTION 2
The duo Shut Up and Dance, with singer Peter Bouncer, reworked Marc Cohn's 'Walking in Memphis' into a 1992 Top 3 dance track, complete with new lyrics. What was this version called?

QUESTION 3
Which Turkish-born producer worked on the Average White Band's 'Pick Up the Pieces', the Bee Gees' 'Jive Talkin'', Chaka Khan's 'I Feel for You', and 'Against All Odds' by Phil Collins?

QUESTION 4
Taylor Swift made her debut on the albums chart in 2009 with which Top 5 hit?

QUESTION 5
Which UK group featuring singer Roger Chapman made its chart debut in 1969 with 'No Mule's Fool' and had hits in the early Seventies with 'Strange Band', 'Burlesque' and 'In My Own Time'?

QUESTION 6
Tasmin Archer is often considered a one-hit wonder for her 1992 No 1 'Sleeping Satellite', but she had four other Top 40 hits that decade. Name one of them.

QUESTION 7
After he left the band Razorlight, drummer Andy Burrows began playing with an existing American band and also formed his own new group. Name either of these bands.

QUESTION 8
What comes next in this sequence: Sigh No More by Mumford & Sons, 21 by Adele, Our Version of Events by Emeli Sandé, AM by Arctic Monkeys... ?

QUESTION 9
Which British group had all three of its Top 40 hits in 1964 with the songs 'Tell Me When', 'Like Dreamers Do' and 'Three Little Words (I Love You)'?

QUESTION 10
Who is the lyricist of the James Bond theme songs 'The World is Not Enough', 'Diamonds Are Forever' and 'Thunderball'?

POPMASTER QUIZ 344

CHAMPION OF CHAMPIONS 8

Really tough stuff – have you got what it takes?

QUESTION 1
Prior to his solo career, Ricky Martin had been a member of which Puerto Rican boy band?

QUESTION 2
What are the first names of the Motown writing and production team Holland-Dozier-Holland?

QUESTION 3
At the time of publication of this book, what do all 12 of the Pet Shop Boys' studio albums have in common – apart from being written and recorded by the duo?!

QUESTION 4
What is the title of the 1978 Top 30 hit recorded by Paper Lace with the Nottingham Forest football team?

QUESTION 5
Who comes next in this sequence: Jessie J, Jessie J, Kylie Minogue, Rita Ora... ?

QUESTION 6
The singer Alex Parks, who won the second series of *Fame Academy*, went on to have two hit singles. Name either of them.

QUESTION 7
Which two groups combined forces to release the 2015 eponymously titled Top 20 album FFS?

QUESTION 8
What was the title of the 1986 hit by Meat Loaf featuring John Parr?

QUESTION 9
Released in 1975 and 1977, the songs 'Save Me' and 'Everybody's Talkin' 'bout Love' were the first and last Top 40 hits for which female vocal group?

QUESTION 10
Eminem's 1999 Top 3 debut hit 'My Name Is' features a sample from which song written and recorded by Labi Siffre?

QUIZ 342

Q1 *'Because of You'*

Q2 *Stephen Morris*

Q3 *Food Records*

Q4 *'Hypnosis'*

Q5 *Keating, Lynch, Duffy, Graham, Gateley*

Q6 *Gary Osborne*

Q7 *Everything Must Go (studio albums by Manic Street Preachers)*

Q8 *Snowy White (released Dec '83, entered the Top 40 early '84)*

Q9 *'Three Steps to Heaven'*

Q10 *Kate Winslet*

QUIZ 345 POPMASTER

CHAMPION OF CHAMPIONS 9

QUIZ 343

Q1 *Squeeze*

Q2 *'Raving I'm Raving'*

Q3 *Arif Mardin*

Q4 *Fearless*

Q5 *Family*

Q6 *'In Your Care', 'Lords of the New Church', 'Arienne', 'Shipbuilding'*

Q7 *We Are Scientists (US band), I Am Arrows (his new group)*

Q8 *x by Ed Sheeran (winners of 'Album of the Year' at the BRIT Awards from 2011 to 2015)*

Q9 *The Applejacks*

Q10 *Don Black*

QUESTION 1
Russell Thompkins Jr was the lead singer on a run of hits in the Seventies for which American vocal group?

QUESTION 2
The British singer-songwriter Amy Studt had her only two Top 10 hits in 2003 from her album False Smiles. Name either of these songs.

QUESTION 3
Released in 1964, what was the first Bob Dylan studio album not to feature his name in its title?

QUESTION 4
Who was the brains behind the late Eighties/early Nineties dance group S-Express?

QUESTION 5
What is the title of the 1975 compilation album of songs by John Lennon and the Plastic Ono Band?

QUESTION 6
Which group had Top 10 hits in the Nineties with 'Perseverance', 'Bad Actress' and 'Tequila'?

QUESTION 7
The singer Jackie Lee had her only two chart hits in 1968 and 1971. The first was billed as 'Jacky', but both were theme songs to TV programmes. Name both songs.

QUESTION 8
In which year were these three songs all American No 1s: 'You Needed Me' by Anne Murray, 'Shadow Dancing' by Andy Gibb and 'Hot Child in the City' by Nick Gilder?

QUESTION 9
What is the title of the 2013 No 1 album by John Newman that includes the No 1 single 'Love Me Again' and the Top 10 hit 'Cheating'?

QUESTION 10
Having recorded three of the most enduring rock 'n' roll hits of the Fifties, who also had Top 10 hits that decade with 'Rock-a-Beatin' Boogie', 'The Saints Rock 'N Roll' and 'Don't Knock the Rock'?

POPMASTER QUIZ 346

CHAMPION OF CHAMPIONS 10

Really tough stuff – have you got what it takes?

QUESTION 1
What are the full names (first and surname) of the three members of the Thompson Twins?

QUESTION 2
The duo James and Bobby Purify had their only two hit singles in 1976. Name both of them.

QUESTION 3
The 1994 single 'Do You Remember the First Time' was the Top 40 debut by which group?

QUESTION 4
Which 2006 Top 3 single by the Pussycat Dolls featuring will.i.am features a string sample from Electric Light Orchestra's 'Evil Woman'?

QUESTION 5
Who comes next in this sequence: Daz Sampson, Scooch, Andy Abraham, Jade Ewen... ?

QUESTION 6
Which of Level 42's Top 10 hits has the subtitle '(Living it Up)'?

QUESTION 7
Which member of the group Argent wrote Hot Chocolate's 'So You Win Again', 'Since You've Been Gone' by Rainbow, 'New York Groove' by Hello and 'No More the Fool' by Elkie Brooks?

QUESTION 8
Jimmy Somerville's 1989 debut solo hit featured June Miles-Kingston and was the cover of a late Sixties French song written by Serge Gainsbourg and recorded by Françoise Hardy. What is it called?

QUESTION 9
What is the surname of 'Dan' in the Seventies duo England Dan and John Ford Coley?

QUESTION 10
Perfect Symmetry, Hopes and Fears, Under the Iron Sea and Strangeland are Keane's four studio albums to date. All four reached No 1, but in what order were they released?

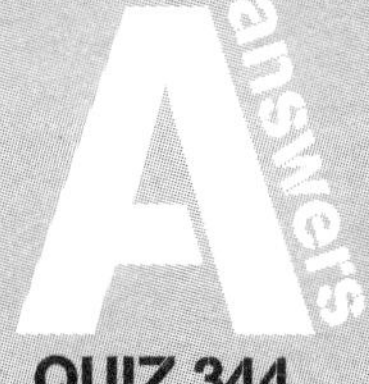

QUIZ 344

Q1 *Menudo*

Q2 *Brian Holland, Lamont Dozier, Eddie Holland*

Q3 *They all have one-word titles*

Q4 *'We Got the Whole World in Our Hands'*

Q5 *Paloma Faith (female coaches on each UK series of The Voice)*

Q6 *'Maybe that's What it Takes' (Top 3), 'Cry' (Top 20)*

Q7 *Franz Ferdinand, Sparks*

Q8 *'Rock 'N' Roll Mercenaries'*

Q9 *Silver Convention*

Q10 *'I Got the...'*

QUIZ

Q1
The Stylistics

Q2
'Misfit', 'Under the Thumb'

Q3
The Times they Are a-Changin'

Q4
Mark Moore

Q5
Shaved Fish

Q6
Terrorvision

Q7
'White Horses', 'Rupert'

Q8
1978

Q9
Tribute

Q10
Bill Haley & His Comets

QUIZ 347 POPMASTER

60s IN THE 70s

Here are ten hits from the sixties that were successfully covered by other artists in the seventies: spot who revived the following songs:

QUESTION 1
'House Of The Rising Sun' was a No 1 hit for The Animals in 1964 but which band successfully revived it in 1970?
Family, Slade, Frijid Pink or Curved Air

QUESTION 2
Again from 1964, 'Baby I Love You' a top twenty hit by The Ronettes made a mighty comeback in 19673, giving which rocker a Top 10 hit? Nick Lowe, Dave Edmunds, Ian Hunter or Pete Wingfield

QUESTION 3
The next song, 'The Pied Piper' dates back to 1966 when Crispian St Peters took it to No 5 but who successfully revived it in 1971? Greyhound, Horace Faith, The Pioneers or Bob & Marcia

QUESTION 4
'Three Steps To Heaven' was a No 1 hit in 1960 for Eddie Cochran but who took it back into the Top 3 in 1975? Mud, Smokie, Showaddywaddy of The Bay City Rollers

QUESTION 5
Dusty Springfield's first solo hit was 'I Only Want To Be With You' from 1963 but which act returned the song to the charts in 1979? The Nolans, Brotherhood Of Man, The Tourists or The Dooleys

QUESTION 6
One of the classic hits of the sixties, 'Concrete And Clay' by Unit 4 + 2 topped our charts in 1965 but who had a top twenty hit with it in 1976? Randy Edelman, Randy Newman, Johnny Cash or Johnny Nash

QUESTION 7
So which of these four singers took The Who's 1969 Top 5 hit 'Pinball Wizard' back into the Top 10 in 1976? Billy Joel, Rod Stewart, Elton John or Paul McCartney

QUESTION 8
'Where Did Our Love Go,' a 1964 Top 3 hit by The Supremes was brough back into the Top 10 in 1972by which male singer? Tony Christie, Donny Osmond, Donnie Elbert or Jimmy Cliff

QUESTION 9
In 1977, which group made a further success with this Searchers 1964 No 1 hit, 'Needles And Pins'? Racey, Smokie, Exile or Arrows

QUESTION 10
Let's end this round by asking about Billy Fury's 1964 top twenty hit, 'I Will' that became a Top 5 hit in 1977 for whom? Gladys Knight, Cher, Melba Moore or Ruby Winters

POPMASTER QUIZ 348

60s IN THE 80s

In this round you'll find another ten hits from the sixties that this time were successfully covered by other artists in the eighties, all you have

QUESTION 1
'More Than I Can Say' was a minor hit for The Crickets in 1960 but who successfully revived it in 1980? Cliff Richard, Paul McCartney, Leo Sayer, George Michael

QUESTION 2
The classic hit 'You Can't Hurry Love' by The Supremes from 1966 made a mighty comeback in 1982 giving which star a No 1? Peter Gabriel, Rod Stewart, Robert Palmer, Phil Collins

QUESTION 3
'Runaround Sue' by Dion was a Top 10 hit in 1962 but which group successfully revived it in 1980? The Sweet, Racey, Mud, Madness

QUESTION 4
The Tokens had a roaring success with 'The Lion Sleeps Tonight' in 1961 but who revived it twenty-one years later? Liquid Gold, Gidea Park, Voice Of The Beehive, Tight Fit

QUESTION 5
In the eighties there were two hit versions of the 1965 Four Seasons hit, 'Let's Hang On,' one was by Darts but who recorded the other? Tom Jones, David Cassidy, Barry Manilow, Billy Ocean

QUESTION 6
'Cryin'' was one of the classic hits of the sixties by Roy Orbison that became a No 1 in 1980 for which singer? Alvin Stardust, Don McLean, Nik Kershaw, Paul Young

QUESTION 7
So which of these four female singers covered Doris Day's 1964 Top 10 hit, 'Move Over Darling' in the eighties? Alison Moyet, Barbara Dickson, Tracey Ullman, Sinitta

QUESTION 8
Smokey Robinson & The Miracles first released 'The Tears Of A Clown' in 1967 but didn't top the charts until 1970 but which band were in the charts with it in 1980? The Beat, The Selecter, The Specials, UB40

QUESTION 9
Can you identify the singer who in 1986 made ? further success of 'Suspicious Minds,' originally a hit for Elvis Presley in 1969? The Communards, Modern Romance, Fine Young Cannibals, Bronski Beat

QUESTION 10
'Days' by The Kinks first became a hit in 1968, then revived in 1989 with both versions reaching number 12 on the charts but who made the successful 80's version? Hazell Dean, Kirsty MacColl, Madonna, Princess

QUIZ

Q1 *Tom Bailey, Alannah Currie, Joe Leeway*

Q2 *'I'm Your Puppet', 'Morning Glory'*

Q3 *Pulp*

Q4 *'Beep'*

Q5 *Josh Dubovie (UK Eurovision Song Contest entries 2006–2010)*

Q6 *'The Sun Goes Down'*

Q7 *Russ Ballard*

Q8 *'Comment te Dire Adieu'*

Q9 *Seals*

Q10 *Hopes and Fears ('04), Under the Iron Sea ('06), Perfect Symmetry ('08), Strangeland ('12)*

QUIZ 347

Q1 *Frijid Pink*

Q2 *Dave Edmunds*

Q3 *Bob & Marcia*

Q4 *Showaddywaddy*

Q5 *The Tourists*

Q6 *Randy Edelman*

Q7 *Elton John*

Q8 *Donnie Elbert*

Q9 *Smokey*

Q10 *Ruby Winters*

QUIZ 349 POPMASTER

FIRSTS AND LASTS

This is a quiz in which all the song titles contain either the word 'first' or 'last,' how good are you at spotting the performers?

QUESTION 1
Which group topped the charts in 1965 with 'The Last Time'? The Pretty Things, The Who, The Rolling Stones, Status Quo

QUESTION 2
Do you know who released the 1988 No 1 hit, 'The First Time'? Robin Beck, Alison Moyet, Dee C Lee, Tracey Ullman

QUESTION 3
Let's try that song title again, 'The First Time' that was a Top 5 hit in 1963 for John Leyton, Mike Sarne, Adam Faith, Jimmy Justice

QUESTION 4
'Our Last Song Together' was the final song which performer composed with one of his co-writers? Neil Sedaka, Paul Anka, Eddie Hodges, Bobby Rydell

QUESTION 5
This song called 'The First Of May' first entered the charts in February 1969 by which group? The Easybeats, The Swinging Blue Jeans, The Bee Gees, The Overlanders

QUESTION 6
Here's hoping you bought a ticket for the 'Last Train To London, a 1979 Top 10 hit for whom? Wizzard, The Move, The Idle Race, The Electric Light Orchestra

QUESTION 7
OK, shall we try another train to a different destination, this time the 'Last train To San Fernando' but who with his Blue Grass Boys took it into the charts back in 1957? Bill Hayes, Jimmy Rodgers, Johnny Duncan, Tennessee Ernie Ford

QUESTION 8
Let's hope you can remember the name of this act from their only top forty hit in 1983 called 'The First Picture Of You'? Men At Work, Icehouse, Flash and The Pan, The Lotus Eaters

QUESTION 9
In 1973, this version of 'Neither One Of Us (Wants To Be The First To Say Goodbye)' won a Grammy for 'Best Pop Vocal performance by which of these acts.'

QUESTION 10
(The Marvelettes, Martha & The Vandellas, Gladys Knight & The Pips, The Shirelles

POPMASTER QUIZ 350

FOLLOW UPS

This is a bit of a tester! The questions involve the follow up hits to the ones given, not for the faint-hearted!

QUESTION 1
Roy Orbison topped our charts in 1964 with 'Oh Pretty Woman' but what was the title of the hit that followed? In Dreams, Pretty Paper, It's Over, Goodnight

QUESTION 2
We hope you won't be kept in the dark over what is OMD's follow up to 'Enola Gay!

QUESTION 3
Souvenir, Joan Of Arc, Maid Of Orleans, Messages

QUESTION 4
'Ain't No Mountain High Enough' was Diana Ross's first major solo hit but what was the follow up? I'm Still Waiting, Surrender, Remember Me, Touch Me In The Morning

QUESTION 5
Rolling Stones fans should have little trouble knowing what was the follow up to '(I Can't Get No) Satisfaction'.

QUESTION 6
Paint It Black, Get Off Of My Cloud, Nineteenth Nervous Breakdown, Jumping Jack Flash

QUESTION 7
'Heaven Must be Missing An Angel' was the first hit by Tavares but what was the second? Mighty Power Of Love, Whodunnit, More Than A Woman, Don't Take Away The Music

QUESTION 8
The Human League made the top twenty for the first time in 1981 with 'The Sound Of The Crowd but what followed?

QUESTION 9
Open Your Heart, Love Action (I Believe In Love), Don't You Want Me, Being Boiled

QUESTION 10
In 1964, Sandie Shaw topped the charts with '(There's) Aways Something There To Remind Me' but what was the follow up? I'll Stop At Nothing, Long Live Love, Girl Don't Come, Message Understood

QUIZ 348

Q1 *Leo Sayer*

Q2 *Phil Collins*

Q3 *Racey*

Q4 *Tight Fit*

Q5 *Barry Manilow*

Q6 *Don McLean*

Q7 *Tracey Allman*

Q8 *The Beat*

Q9 *Fine Young Cannibals*

Q10 *Kirsty McColl*

QUIZ 349

Q1
The Rolling Stones

Q2
Robin Beck

Q3
Adam Faith

Q4
Neil Sedaka

Q5
The Bee Gees

Q6
The Electric Light Orchestra

Q7
Johnny Duncan

Q8
The Lotus Eaters

Q9
Gladys Knight & The Pips

Q10
The Drifters

QUIZ 351 POPMASTER

FOUR GENTLEMAN

From the following ten song titles, can you name which of these four male performers, Ed Sheeran, Calvin Harris, Shawn Mendes or Sam Smith

QUESTION 1
Taken from his album, 'In The Lonely Hour,' who had a Top 3 hit in 2014 with 'I'm Not The Only One'? Ed Sheeran, Calvin Harris, Shawn Mendes, Sam Smith

QUESTION 2
In 2017, who made the Top 10 with his hit, 'There's Nothing Holdin' Me Back'? Ed Sheeran, Calvin Harris, Shawn Mendes, Sam Smith

QUESTION 3
According to his 2014 No 1 hit, who was 'Thinking Out Loud'? Ed Sheeran, Calvin Harris, Shawn Mendes, Sam Smith

QUESTION 4
Who topped the UK singles chart in 2014 with his hit song, 'Summer'? Ed Sheeran, Calvin Harris, Shawn Mendes, Sam Smith

QUESTION 5
From his debut album, 'Handwritten' who topped the UK singles chart in 2016 with 'Stitches'? Ed Sheeran, Calvin Harris, Shawn Mendes, Sam Smith

QUESTION 6
'Writing's On The Wall' was a No 1 hit in 2015 and the title song to the James Bond Movie, 'Spectre,' but who sang it? Ed Sheeran, Calvin Harris, Shawn Mendes, Sam Smith

QUESTION 7
Although not released as an official single, whose 2017 recording of 'How Would You Feel (Paean)' reached No 2 on the UK charts? Ed Sheeran, Calvin Harris, Shawn Mendes, Sam Smith

QUESTION 8
Who reached No 2 on the UK charts in 2011 with his Top 10 hit, 'Feel So Close'? Ed Sheeran, Calvin Harris, Shawn Mendes, Sam Smith

QUESTION 9
On his 2011 Top 5 hit, who sang about his 'Lego House'? Ed Sheeran, Calvin Harris, Shawn Mendes, Sam Smith

QUESTION 10
'You Used To Hold Me' was a 2010 top forty hit for which performer who claimed he would no longer regularly sing on his records? Ed Sheeran, Calvin Harris, Shawn Mendes, Sam Smith

POPMASTER QUIZ 352

FOUR LADIES

From the following ten song titles, in each case can you name which of these four female singers, Lady Gaga, Beyoncé, Pink or Rihanna

QUESTION 1
In 2008, 'If I Were A Boy' was a No 1 hit for one of our four, but which one? recorded the song? Lady Gaga, Beyoncé, Pink, Rihanna

QUESTION 2
Although released at the end of 2010, 'What's My Name' was a No 1 hit in 2011 for which of these singers that also featured Canadian rapper, Drake? Lady Gaga, Beyoncé, Pink, Rihanna

QUESTION 3
Only a minor hit reaching number 38 in 2016, who recorded the song, 'Needed Me'? Lady Gaga, Beyoncé, Pink, Rihanna

QUESTION 4
'Just Give Me a Reason' reached number 2 in the UK in 2013 for which singer that also featured Nate Ruess? Lady Gaga, Beyoncé, Pink, Rihanna

QUESTION 5
A Top 5 recording in 2007, 'Shut Up And Drive' was a hit for which of these singers? Lady Gaga, Beyoncé, Pink, Rihanna

QUESTION 6
Featuring guest vocalist R. Kelly, 'Do What U Want' was a 2013 Top 10 hit for which of these singers? Lady Gaga, Beyoncé, Pink, Rihanna

QUESTION 7
'Best Thing I Never Had' was a 2011 Top 5 hit for which of these famous four? Lady Gaga, Beyoncé, Pink, Rihanna

QUESTION 8
According to her Top 3 hit from 2011, who was 'Born This Way'? Lady Gaga, Beyoncé, Pink, Rihanna

QUESTION 9
Featured in the trailer for the 2003 comedy movie starring Ashton Kutcher, 'Just Married,' the song 'Don't Let Me Get Me' had been a hit the previous year for whom? Lady Gaga, Beyoncé, Pink, Rihanna

QUESTION 10
Who had a No 1 hit duet with Shakira in 2007 with 'Beautiful Liar'? Lady Gaga, Beyoncé, Pink, Rihanna

Answers

QUIZ 350

Q1 *Pretty Paper*

Q2 *Souvenir*

Q3 *Remember Me*

Q4 *Get Off of my Cloud*

Q5 *Don't take away the Music*

Q6 *Love Action (I believe in Love*

Q7 *Girl Don't Come*

Q8 *China Girl*

Q9 *Wake me up*

Q10 *Daniel*

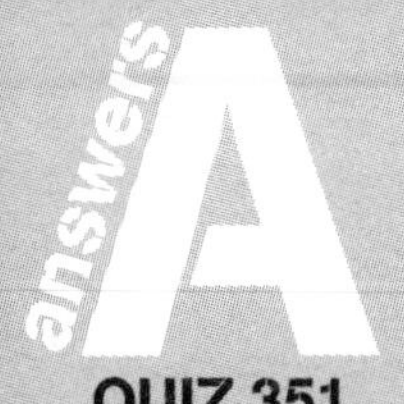

QUIZ 351

Q1
Sam Smith

Q2
Shawn Mendes

Q3
Ed Sheeran

Q4
Calvin Harris

Q5
Shawn Mendes

Q6
Sam Smith

Q7
Ed Sheeran

Q8
Calvin Harris

Q9
Ed Sheeran

Q10
Calvin Harris

QUIZ 353 POPMASTER

GOING SOLO

Time to check out how good you are at spotting one time members of successful bands that left to pursue solo careers.

QUESTION 1
With which successful band was Bryan Ferry once a member? Roxy Music, Soft Cell, 10CC, Cockney Rebel

QUESTION 2
With which boy band do you associate Stephen Gately? Take That, Westlife, Boyzone, McFly

QUESTION 3
Edwyn Collins achieved a Top 5 hit in 1995 with 'A Girl Like You' but with which successful band was he once lead singer? East 17Orange Juice, Lemonheads, Bucks Fizz

QUESTION 4
In 1996, Susanna Hoffs made the top forty with 'All I Want' but prior to that, with which female group was she a member? The Weather Girls, The Emotions, The Bangles, The Three Degrees

QUESTION 5
Now enjoying a successful solo career, with which boy band do you associate Harry Styles? Backstreet Boys, Hanson, Five, One Direction

QUESTION 6
American rapper, Pras Michel was once a member of which successful band? Arrested Development, Public Enemy, The Fugees, House Of Pain

QUESTION 7
'Hit' was in fact a Top 10 hit for a band that included Icelandic singer, Bjork in their line up, so which of the following were they called? Sugababes, Sugar Cane, Sugarcubes, Sugarhill Gang.

QUESTION 8
With which hit making band do you associate Richard Ashcroft? The Verve, The Kaiser Chiefs, Snow Patrol, Razorlight

QUESTION 9
Let's have an easy one, with which group did Diana Ross first come to fame? The Marvelettes, The Elgins, The Velvelettes, The Supremes

QUESTION 10
Beyoncé has had a hugely successful solo career but she also had many big hits with which hit making female group? The Spice Girls, Destiny's Child, Girls Aloud, The Pussycat Dolls

POPMASTER QUIZ 354

HIT DUETS

This round looks at either two males or two females or one of each who either permanently work together as an act or two singers

QUESTION 1
To begin, which pair of Motown artists recorded the 1969 top twenty hit, 'The Onion Song'? Marvin Gaye & Tammi Terrell, Marvin Gaye & Mary Wells, Marvin Gaye & Kim Weston, Marvin Gaye & Diana Ross

QUESTION 2
So can you spot our next pair of singers who came together in 1999 to record 'Written In The Stars' resulting in a Top 10 hit? Elton John & Kiki Dee, LeAnn Rimes & Ronan Keating, Elton John & LeAnn Rimes, Ronan

QUESTION 3
Can you name the two superstars from very different generations who ended up in the Top 10 in 1993 with their version of 'I've Got You Under My Skin'? Frank Sinatra & Robbie Williams, Dean Martin & Justin

QUESTION 4
This song was called 'When You Believe' that made the charts in 1998 and features which two female singers? Whitney Houston & Aretha Franklin, Mariah Carey & Whitney Houston, Mariah Carey & Celine Dion,

QUESTION 5
From 1953, this duet was called 'Full Time Job' and featured which two classic singers? Teresa Brewer & Johnny Ray, Doris Day & Johnny Ray, Doris Day & Frankie Laine, Teresa Brewer & Frankie Laine

QUESTION 6
'The Best Things In Life Are Free' was a Top 10 hit in 1992 and again in 1995 for which two singers that also featured special guests BBD and Ralph Tresvant? Janet Jackson & Luther Vandross, Janet Jackson &

QUESTION 7
In 1967 Frank Sinatra with his daughter Nancy took the song 'Somethin' Stupid' to No 1 in the charts. Which couple repeated that success in 2001? George Michael & Lisa Stansfield, Robbie Williams & Kylie

QUESTION 8
Can you name the two performers who topped the charts in 2008 with '4 Minutes'? Madonna & Kanye West, Madonna & Justin Timberlake, Nelly Furtado & Justin Timberlake, Prince & Madonna

QUESTION 9
The Everly Brothers took it to No 1 in 1958 but which two singers successfully revived 'All I Have To Do Is Dream' in 1969? Dolly Parton & Kenny Rogers, Kenny Rogers & Sheena Easton, Glen Campbell &

QUESTION 10
The final pairing in this quiz is from 1995, the title of the top twenty hit was 'Where The Wild Roses Grow' by which two performers? Kylie Minogue & Jason Donovan, Kylie Minogue & Keith Washington, Kylie Minogue &

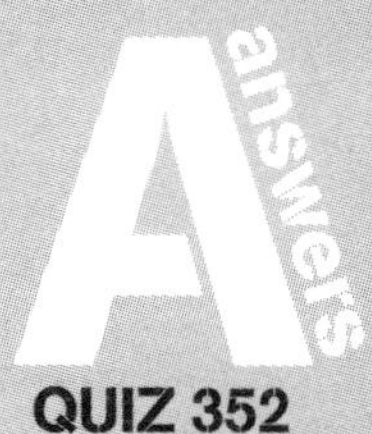

QUIZ 352

Q1 *Beyonce*

Q2 *Rihanna*

Q3 *Rihanna*

Q4 *Pink*

Q5 *Rihanna*

Q6 *Lady Gaga*

Q7 *Beyonce*

Q8 *Lady Gaga*

Q9 *Pink*

Q10 *Beyonce*

QUIZ 353

Q1
Roxy Music

Q2
Boyzone

Q3
Orange Juice

Q4
The Bangles

Q5
One Direction

Q6
The Fugges

Q7
Sugarcubes

Q8
The Verve

Q9
The Supremes

Q10
Destiny's Child

QUIZ 355 POPMASTER

I WRITE THE SONGS

These questions relate to hit songs that have been recorded by the composers either prior or after the hit version.

QUESTION 1
I Write The Songs', a hit for David Cassidy in 1975 was in fact written by a member of The Beach Boys but which one? Brian Wilson, Mike Love, Bruce Johnston, Al Jardine

QUESTION 2
Cliff Richard's first No 1 was 'Living Doll' that was later recorded by the composer, can you name him? Mitch Murray, Les Reed, Lionel Bart, Les Vandyke

QUESTION 3
The composer of both Herman's Hermits' 'No Milk Today' and The Yardbirds' 'For Your Love' recorded versions of both of those songs, who is he? Graham Nash, Graham Gouldman, Graham Lyle,

QUESTION 4
The original version of 'My Toot Toot,' a Top 10 hit in 1985 for Denise LaSalle was originally recorded by its composer, what is his name? Rockin' Sydney, Rockin' RobinRockwell, Rococo

QUESTION 5
In 1995, Boyzone had a Top 5 hit with 'Father And Son' that had first been recorded by its composer, can you name him? Neil Diamond, David Bowie, Cat Stevens, Jim Webb

QUESTION 6
Can you name the singer and song writer who wrote and recorded the original version of The Searchers 1964 Top 5 hit, 'When You Walk In The Room'? Carole King, Carol Bayer-Sager, Jackie

QUESTION 7
Andy Williams made the Top 5 in 1974 with 'Solitaire' but who originally co-wrote and recorded it? Bob Dylan, Bruce Springsteen, Neil Sedaka, Joe South

QUESTION 8
'Manic Monday' was a No 2 hit in 1986 for The Bangles but who wrote the song under the pseudonym of Christopher? Michael Jackson, Stevie WonderBarry Mann, Prince

QUESTION 9
In 1973, Perry Como achieved his last UK Top 10 hit with 'For The Good Times' that had been written and previously recorded by whom? Albert Hammond, Kris Kristofferson, Tom Waits, Don Gibson

QUESTION 10
Both Bobby Darin and The Four Tops had Top 10 hits with 'If I Were A Carpenter' in the sixties but which of these performers wrote and also recorded the song? Tim Hardin, Chip Taylor, Paul Anka, Mickey

POPMASTER QUIZ 356

MISSING WORDS

Here is a list of ten hit song titles but in each instance, there's a word or words missing. All you have to do is fill in the blanks!

QUESTION 1
So what was the full title of this Drifters hit? YOU'RE MORE THAN A ...... IN MY LITTLE RED BOOK Photograph, Memory, Number, Entry

QUESTION 2
What was Meat Loaf going on about in 1996? NOT A DRY.......IN THE HOUSE Eye, Towel, Plate, Wine

QUESTION 3
This was a No 1 in 2006 for Fedde Le Grand PUT YOUR HANDS UP FOR .... New York, San Francisco, Chicago, Detroit

QUESTION 4
So what was Billy Fury's question in 1963? WHEN WILL YOU SAY........... I Want You, I Need You, I Love You, I Miss You

QUESTION 5
In 1993, what was it that The Orb were discussing? LITTLE FLUFFY....... Blanket, Dog, Clouds, Song

QUESTION 6
Can you remember this 1996 top twenty hit by Primal Scream? THE BIG MAN AND ....TEAM MEET THE BARMY ARMY UPTOWN The Family, The Scarecrow, The Scream, The Russian

QUESTION 7
What was Iron Maiden going on about in 1988? CAN I PLAY WITH.. ...... Fire, Water, Evil, Madness

QUESTION 8
This was a top twenty hit for The Thompson Twins in 1985 DON'T ...... WITH DOCTOR DREAM
Visit, Practice, Mess, Live, Ride

QUESTION 9
A vintage track by Tommy Steele that was also a hit for Vic Damone THE ONLY MAN ON THE .... Moon, Toilet, Island, Mountain

QUESTION 10
This was a Top 5 hit in 1991 for C & C Music Factory featuring Freedom Williams THINGS THAT MAKE YOU GO............ Crazy, Yes, Wild, Hmmm

QUIZ 354

Q1 *Marvin Gaye & Tami Terrell*

Q2 *Elton John & LeAnn Rimes*

Q3 *Frank Sinatra & Bono*

Q4 *Mariah Carey & Whitney Houston*

Q5 *Doris Day & Johnny Ray*

Q6 *Janet Jackson & Luther Vandross*

Q7 *Robbie Williams & Nicole Kidman*

Q8 *Madonna & Justin Timberlake*

Q9 *Glen Campbell & Bobbie Gentry*

Q10 *Kylie Minogue & Nick Cave*

QUIZ 355

Q1
Bruce Johnston

Q2
Lionel Bart

Q3
Graham Gouldman

Q4
Rockin' Sydney

Q5
Cat Stevens

Q6
Jackie DeShannon

Q7
Niel Sedaka

Q8
Prince

Q9
Kris Kristofferson

Q10
Tim Hardin

QUIZ 357 POPMASTER

NAME THE YEAR

How good are you in remembering the year in which records were first released? Here are ten for you to test your knowledge

QUESTION 1
BEST YEARS OF OUR LIVES, Modern Romance 1981, 1982, 1983, 1985

QUESTION 2
AUBERGE, Chris Rea 1991, 1992, 1993, 1994

QUESTION 3
IT'S ONLY MAKE BELIEVE, Billy Fury 1963, 1964, 1965, 1966

QUESTION 4
A DESIGN FOR LIFE, The Manic Street Preachers 1994, 1995, 1996, 1997

QUESTION 5
RUDE BOY, Rihanna 2010, 2011, 2012, 2013

QUESTION 6
LOVE TRAIN, The O' Jays 1971, 1972, 1973, 1974 1-2-3 O LEARY, Des O' Connor 1966, 1967, 1968, 1969

QUESTION 7
DON'T STOP MOVIN', S CLUB 7 2001, 2002, 2003, 2004

QUESTION 8
RIP IT UP, Bill Haley & His Comets 1954, 1955, 1956, 1957

QUESTION 9
PRETTY LITTLE ANGEL EYES, Showaddywaddy 1976, 1977, 1978, 1979

QUESTION 10

POPMASTER QUIZ 358

NO 1 HIT ALBUMS

QUIZ 356

QUESTION 1
In 1976, which legendary group topped the album charts with 'Blue For You'? Queen, Status Quo, Supertramp, The Who

QUESTION 2
Which male singer reached No 1 in 1962 with his album, 'Pot Luck'? Cliff Richard, Roy Orbison, Adam Faith, Elvis Presley

QUESTION 3
In 2017, who topped the album charts with 'Divide'? Ed Sheeran, Rag 'N' Bone Man, Harry Styles, Justin Bieber

QUESTION 4
Can you name the heavy rock band who took their 1992 album, 'Fear Of The Dark' to No 1? AC/DC, Saxon, Iron Maiden, Metallica

QUESTION 5
'Back To Front' was a No 1 album in 1973 for which male vocalist? Tom Jones, Engelbert Humperdinck, Gilbert O' Sullivan, Matt Monro

QUESTION 6
Can you name the female singer whose 1986 compilation album 'The Whole Story' topped the album charts in 1987? Kate Bush, Madonna, Cyndi Lauper, Gloria Estefan

QUESTION 7
Which successful band topped the album charts in 2005 with 'Don't Believe The Truth'? Blur, Oasis, Coldplay, Foo Fighters

QUESTION 8
In 1987, which band achieved their only No 1 album with 'Keep Your Distance'? Swing Out Sister, Five Star, Curiosity Killed The Cat, Big Country

QUESTION 9
Which female singer reached No 1 in 1993 with her album, 'Music Box'? Celine Dion, Madonna, Annie Lennox, Mariah Carey

QUESTION 10
1Can you name the boy band that topped the album charts in 1995 with 'Said And Done'? Take That, Boyzone, 911, Let Loose

Q1 *Number*

Q2 *Eye*

Q3 *Detroit*

Q4 *I Love You*

Q5 *Clouds*

Q6 *The Screen*

Q7 *Madness*

Q8 *Mess*

Q9 *Island*

Q10 *Hmmm*

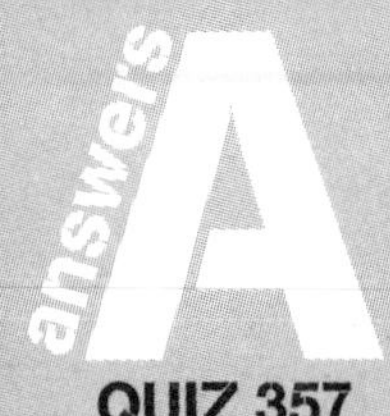

QUIZ 357

Q1
1982

Q2
1991

Q3
1964

Q4
1996

Q5
2010

Q6
1973

Q7
1968

Q8
2001

Q9
1956

Q10
1978

QUIZ 359 POPMASTER

POP STARS REAL NAMES

Here's a chance for you to test your knowledge on the real names of some of the famous

QUESTION 1
Whose real name is Stuart Leslie Goddard? Boy George, Adam Ant, Nik Kershaw, Neil Tennant

QUESTION 2
Which American male rapper has the real name of Armando Perez? Pitbull, Eminem, Snoop Dogg, Drake

QUESTION 3
Can you name the female singer whose real name is Elaine Bookbinder? Sandie Shaw, Dusty Springfield, Elkie Brooks, Nina Simone

QUESTION 4
'Calling Your Name' was the only top twenty hit for Peter Robinson but under what name did he release this 1983 recording? Jackie, Louise, Marilyn, Nora

QUESTION 5
Which member of U2 has the real name of Paul Hewson? The Edge, Adam Clayton, Bono, Larry Mullen

QUESTION 6
Can you name the American female singer whose real name is Natalie McIntyre? Macy Gray, Chaka Khan, Tina Turner, Toni Braxton

QUESTION 7
Which male hit maker might have answered to the name of John Henry Deighton? Joe Cocker, Chris Farlowe, Val Doonican, Cat Stevens

QUESTION 8
Shawn Carter is the real name of which American male rapper? Kanye West, Dr Dre, Q Tip, Jay-Z

QUESTION 9
Which successful drummer had the real name of Colin Flooks? Tony Meehan, Cozy Powell, Keith Moon, John Bonham

QUESTION 10
1Can you name the No 1 hit maker whose real name is David Richard Solberg? David Essex, David Cassidy, David Soul, David Bowie

POPMASTER QUIZ 360

SOMETHING BEGINNING WITH 'E'

QUESTION 1
Which successful act made the Top 10 in 1962 with 'Cryin' In The Rain'? Extreme, The Everly Brothers, The Exciters, The Equals

QUESTION 2
'Every Time You Go Away' was a Top 10 hit in 1985 for which successful singer? Paul Evans, Paul McCartney, Paul Young, Paul Weller

QUESTION 3
Who made her chart debut in 1978 with the song 'Shame?'

QUESTION 4
Evelyn 'Champagne' King, Betty Everett, Missy Elliott, Sheena Easton

QUESTION 5
'Nothing Lasts Forever' was a Top 10 hit in 1997 for which popular group? Echobelly, East 17Echo & The Bunnymen, Elbow

QUESTION 6
What was the name of the act formed by Bernard Sumner and Johnny Marr whose first hit was called 'Getting Away With It'? Electroset, Electronicas, Electric Soft Parade, Electronic

QUESTION 7
Which singing comedian made the UK top forty in 1964 with a song called 'Eight By Ten'? Ken Dodd, Des O' Connor, Benny Hill, Mike Reid

QUESTION 8
What was the title of the only Top 10 hit achieved by American band, The Eels? Novacaine For The Soul, Mr E's Beautiful Blues, Susan's House, Last stop This Town

QUESTION 9
Can you name the group that in 1987 revived the classic song 'Ev'ry Time We Say Goodbye' taking it into the top twenty? Simple Minds, Simply Red, Simple Plan, Simplicous

QUESTION 10
Which of these titles was a top twenty hit for Boney M in 1979? El Capitan, El Nino, El Manana, El Lute

Answers

QUIZ 358

Q1 *Status Quo*

Q2 *Elvis Presley*

Q3 *Ed Sheeran*

Q4 *Iron Maiden*

Q5 *Gilbert O'Sullivan*

Q6 *Kate Bush*

Q7 *Oasis*

Q8 *Curiosity Killed the Cat*

Q9 *Mariah Carey*

Q10 *Boyzone*

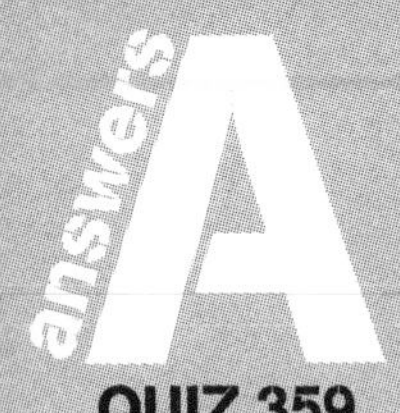

QUIZ 359

Q1 *Adam Ant*

Q2 *Pit Bull*

Q3 *Elkie Brooks*

Q4 *Marilyn*

Q5 *Bono*

Q6 *Macy Gray*

Q7 *Chris Farlowe*

Q8 *Jay-Z*

Q9 *Cozy Powell*

Q10 *David Soul*

QUIZ 361 POPMASTER

STOCK, AITKEN & WATERMAN

In this round you will be asked about the top production team of Mike Stock, Matt Aitken and Pete Waterman who have had hundred hits

QUESTION 1
'Whatever I Do (Wherever I Go)' became a Top 5 hit in 1984 for which of these singers? Princess, Haywoode, Hazell Dean, O'chi Brown

QUESTION 2
The only top twenty hit for this act was in 1984 with 'You Think You're A Man.'

QUESTION 3
Brilliant, Errol Brown, Divine, Yell!

QUESTION 4
From 1989, 'I Just Don't Have The Heart' became a Top 3 hit for which of these four acts? Edwin Starr, Cliff Richard, Boy Krazy, Pat & Mick

QUESTION 5
'Take Me To Your Heart' reached number 8 on the UK charts in 1988 for which singer? Rick Astley, Jason Donovan, Phil Fearon, Nick Straker

QUESTION 6
'I Can't Help It' scraped into the top twenty at number 20 in 1988 for which female act? Kylie Minogue, Bananarama, Mel & Kim, Mandy Smith

QUESTION 7
'You've Got A Friend' was released as a charity record for the Childline Foundation in 1990 and featured sax player, Gary Barnacle, but who recorded it? Jason Donovan & Kylie Minogue, Kylie Minogue & Keith

QUESTION 8
To which of these acts was the 1987 top twenty hit 'Roadblock' credited? Dead Or Alive, Dolly Dots, Stock, Aitken & Waterman, The Cool Notes

QUESTION 9
'All Of Me' was the second and final top forty hit in 1988 for which of these acts? Roland Rat, Big Fun, The Reynolds Girls, Sabrina

QUESTION 10
Taken from the album, 'Another Place And Time,' the song 'Love's About To Change My Heart' was a top twenty hit for whom? Donna Summer, Lonnie Gordon, La Toya Jackson, Samantha Fox

POPMASTER QUIZ 362

THE BEATLES

QUESTION 1
Which member of The Beatles composed the song 'Here Comes The Sun' originally on the album, 'Abbey Road' but later a 1976 hit for Steve Harley & Cockney Rebel? John Lennon, Paul McCartney,

QUESTION 2
Their 1966 No 1 hit, 'Yellow Submarine' was part of a double 'A' sided hit, what was the song on the other side of the record? We Can Work It Out, Eleanor Rigby, Penny Lane, Strawberry Fields

QUESTION 3
What was the title of The Beatles first American No 1 hit single? Please Please Me, From Me To You, She Loves You, I Want To Hold Your Hand

QUESTION 4
What late sixties single has a 'B' side called 'The Inner Light"? Get Back, Lady Madonna, Hey Jude, The Ballad of John & Yoko

QUESTION 5
Which member of The Beatles released a solo album in the seventies titled 'Goodnight Vienna'? John Lennon, Paul McCartney, George Harrison, Ringo Starr

QUESTION 6
In 1964, one of the group's early recordings from their Hamburg days made the top forty what was the title? When The Saints Go Marching In, Kansas City/Ain't She Sweet/Sweet Georgia Brown

QUESTION 7
On which of The Beatles albums did the song 'Michelle' first appear? Beatles For sale, Rubber Soul, Abbey Road, Revolver

QUESTION 8
Which of The Beatles' hits was the last to make No 1 on the UK singles charts? Hey Jude, Get Back, Let It Be, The Ballad Of John And Yoko

QUESTION 9
Which member of The Beatles released a solo album in the eighties titled 'Somewhere In England'? John Lennon, Paul McCartney, George Harrison, Ringo Starr

QUESTION 10
1What was the title of the first full length movie that was premiered on the 6th July, 1964 at the London Pavilion Theatre? Help, Yellow Submarine, A Hard Day's Night, Magical Mystery Tour

A answers

QUIZ 360

Q1 *Everly Brothers*

Q2 *Paul Young*

Q3 *Evelyn 'Champagne' King*

Q4 *Echo & The Bunnymen*

Q5 *Electronic*

Q6 *Ken Dodd*

Q7 *Susan's House*

Q8 *Simply Red*

Q9 *El Lute*

Q10 *Olivia Newton-John*

QUIZ 361

Q1
Hazell Dean

Q2
Divine

Q3
Cliff Richard

Q4
Rick Astley

Q5
Bananarama

Q6
Sonia & Big Fun

Q7
Stock, Aitken & Waterman

Q8
Sabrina

Q9
Donna Summer

Q10
WWF Superstars

QUIZ 363 POPMASTER

THE SONGS OF......

This round consists of ten songs that have been written or co-written by either Les Reed, Tony Macaulay, Bill Martin or Roger Greenaway.

QUESTION 1
THIS GOLDEN RING The Fortunes
Les Reed, Tony Macaulay, Bill Martin, Roger Greenaway

QUESTION 2
THERE'S A KIND OF HUSH, Herman's Hermits
Les Reed, Tony Macaulay, Bill Martin, Roger Greenaway

QUESTION 3
BACK HOME, England World Cup Squad
Les Reed, Tony Macaulay, Bill Martin, Roger Greenaway

QUESTION 4
MY BOY, Elvis Presley
Les Reed, Tony Macaulay, Bill Martin, Roger Greenaway

QUESTION 5
DOCTOR'S ORDERS, Sunny
Les Reed, Tony Macaulay, Bill Martin, Roger Greenaway

QUESTION 6
BABY MAKE IT SOON, Marmalade
Les Reed, Tony Macaulay, Bill Martin, Roger Greenaway

QUESTION 7
TELL ME WHEN, The Applejacks
Les Reed, Tony Macaulay, Bill Martin, Roger Greenaway

QUESTION 8
LOVE GROWS (WHERE MY ROSEMARY GOES), Edison Lighthouse
Les Reed, Tony Macaulay, Bill Martin, Roger Greenaway

QUESTION 9
SOMETHING'S GOTTEN HOLD OF MY HEART, Marc Almond & Gene Pitney
Les Reed, Tony Macaulay, Bill Martin, Roger Greenaway

QUESTION 10
SHANG-A-LANG, The Bay City Rollers
Les Reed, Tony Macaulay, Bill Martin, Roger Greenaway

POPMASTER QUIZ 364

TV ADS

A round especially for couch potatoes, can you name the products that the following ten songs have helped sell through television

QUESTION 1
'Jeans On' is a song recorded by David Dundas, the second son of The 3rd Marquess of Zetland but what was the product it helped advertise? Levi's, Nike, Brutus, Monsoon

QUESTION 2
The 2004 top twenty hit by The Strokes, 'Reptilia' was used to advertise which make of car? Ford, Fiat, Jaguar, Volkswagen

QUESTION 3
Rock band Boston helped the sales of which popular credit card with their hit 'More Than A Feeling'? American Express, MasterCard, Barclaycard, Capital One

QUESTION 4
'Get It On' by T-Rex topped the charts for four weeks in 1971 but what did it help promote in 2016? confused.com, google.com, eBay.com, hotels.com

QUESTION 5
This vintage track, 'A Nice Cup Of Tea' by Binnie Hale was used to promote a famous brand of tea, but which one? Twinings, Brooke Bond, Tetley, Lipton

QUESTION 6
You may have a sweet tooth for the hit by Queen called 'Don't Stop Me Now' but which brand of confectionery did it advertise? Nestlé, Mars, Cadbury, Ferrero

QUESTION 7
The backing track to 'Busy' the Olly Murs song was used by which leading chain store? John Lewis, Selfridge, House Of Frasier, Marks and Spencer

QUESTION 8
Another vintage hit and the only chart record by The Honeybus,' I Can't Let Maggie Go' helped sell which brand of bread? Mother's Pride, Nimble, Allinson's, Kingsmill

QUESTION 9
'Right Here, Right Now,' a 1999 No 2 hit by Fatboy Slim was used by which men's clothing stores? Topman, Calvin Klein, Armani, Adidas

QUESTION 10
1Finally, which hotel chain used Katie Melua's version of Black's song 'Wonderful Life' to promote their brand? Holiday Inn, Hilton Hotels, Sofitel, Premier Inn

QUIZ 362

Q1 *George Harrison*

Q2 *We Can Work it Out*

Q3 *I Want to Hold Your Hand*

Q4 *Lady Madonna*

Q5 *Ringo Starr*

Q6 *Ain't She Sweet*

Q7 *Rubber Soul*

Q8 *The Ballad of John & Yoko*

Q9 *George Harrison*

Q10 *A Hard Day's Night*

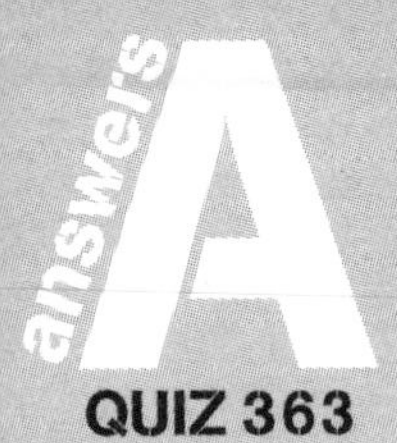

QUIZ 363

Q1
Roger Greenaway

Q2
Les Reed

Q3
Bill Martin

Q4
Bill Martin

Q5
Roger Greenaway

Q6
Tony Macaulay

Q7
Les Reed

Q8
Tony Macaulay

Q9
Roger Greenaway

Q10
Bill Martin

QUIZ 365 POPMASTER

RECORD LABEL LOGOS

Below are ten record label logos with the name of the company blotted out. How easy is it for you to name the labels?

1

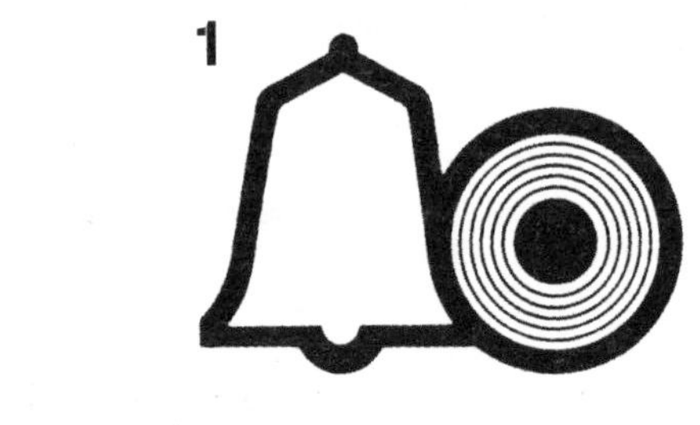

2

3

4

5

POPMASTER QUIZ 365

6

7

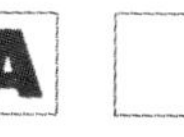

8

9

10

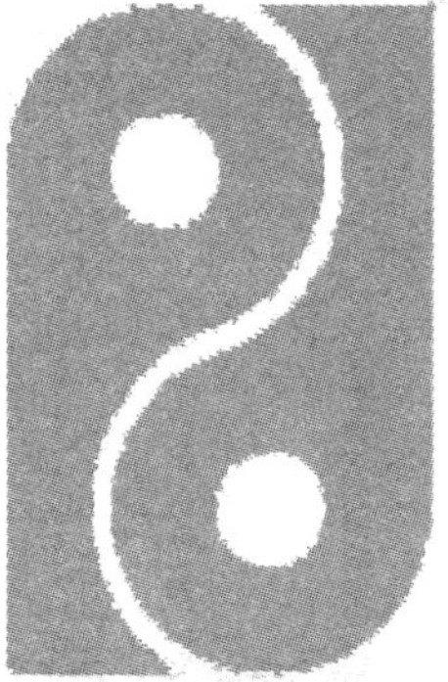

QUIZ 364

Q1
Brutus

Q2
Volkswagen

Q3
Barclaycard

Q4
Confused.com

Q5
Brooke Bond

Q6
Cadbury

Q7
Marks and Spencer

Q8
Nimble

Q9
Adidas

Q10
Premier Inn

QUIZ 365

Q1
Bell

Q2
Bronze

Q3
Dep International

Q4
Dekka

Q5
Elektra

Q6
Epic

Q7
Manhattan

Q8
Harvest

Q9
Parlophone

Q10
Philadelphia International

QUIZ 366 POPMASTER

Here are ten successful male singers – past and present. How many can you identify?

1

2

3

4

5

POPMASTER QUIZ 366

6

7

8

9

10

QUIZ 366

Q1
Rick Astley

Q2
Bryan Adams

Q3
Dickie Valentine

Q4
Craig David

Q5
Perry Como

Q6
Gary Numan

Q7
Peter Gabriel

Q8
Lonnie Donegan

Q9
James Blunt

Q10
Sam Cooke

QUIZ 367 POPMASTER

Here are ten successful female singers – past and present. How many can you identify?

1

2

3

4

5

POPMASTER QUIZ 367

6

7

8

9

10

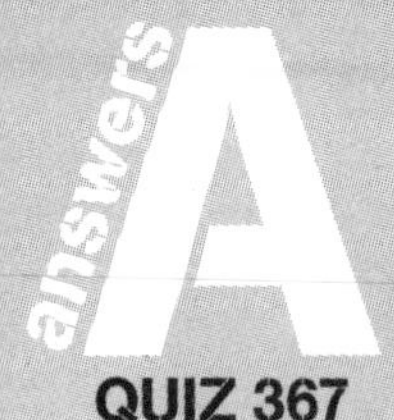

QUIZ 367

Q1
Susan Maughan

Q2
Mary Hopkin

Q3
Cyndi Lauper

Q4
Sia

Q5
Kim Syms

Q6
Roberta Flack

Q7
Jennifer Hudson

Q8
Amy Madconald

Q9
Kiki Dee

Q10
Joan Armatrading

QUIZ 368 POPMASTER

Here are ten successful hit duos – past and present. How many can you identify?

1

2

3

4

5

POPMASTER QUIZ 368

6

7

8

9

10

QUIZ 368

Q1
White Stripes

Q2
Everly Brothers

Q3
Sonny & Cher

Q4
Wendy & Lisa

Q5
Phats & Small

Q6
Shakespear's Sister

Q7
Hall & Oates

Q8
Robson & Jerome

Q9
Shampoo

Q10
The Allisons

QUIZ 369 POPMASTER

Here are ten well-known pop bands – past and present. Can you name them from their pictures?

1

2

3

4

5

POPMASTER QUIZ 369

6

8

7

9

10

QUIZ 369

Q1
The Verve

Q2
Manfred Mann

Q3
Little Mix

Q4
Kings of Leon

Q5
The O'Jays

Q6
Fine Young Cannibals

Q7
Westlife

Q8
Scooch

Q9
Black Eyed Peas

Q10
Heatwave

QUIZ 370 POPMASTER

CROSSMASTER 1

Fill the answer to each pop-themed clue into the crossword opposite.

Across

2. Razorlight's only No. 1 single (7)
9. Beatles manager (5,7)
10. Justin Bieber's middle name (4)
12. Kermit's nephew who sang 'Halfway Down The Stairs' (5)
13. Title of both act & song representing UK at Eurovision 1995 (4,4,6)
15. Elton's 'Eyes', The Orb's 'Room' & Erasure's 'Savannah' (4)
16. 'Joybringer' by Manfred Mann's Earthband is based on music by which composer? (6,5)
20. Seal, Patsy Cline & Gnarls Barkley have had different hits with this song title (5)
21. What Adele was 'Chasing' in 2008 (9)
25. 2016 number one album by Biffy Clyro (8)
28. Alphaville, The Scorpions & Nena all hail from this country (7)
29. Coldplay's fifth studio album (4,6)
32. 'You Get What You Give' was this chart act's only Top 40 hit (3,8)
33. The only Jackson brother younger than Michael (5)
34. Norah Jones' debut multi-million selling album (4,4,4,2)

Down

1. Different hit songs for Abba, Roxy Music and Wet Wet Wet (5,4)
3. Record label co-founded by Madonna in early 90s (8)
4. Edwyn Collins' band was full of Vitamin C (6,5)
5. European city Morrissey threw his arms around in 2009 (5)
6. Singer of 2009 number ones 'Mama Do' & 'Boys & Girls' (5,4)
7. Instrument played by Stevie Wonder on Chaka Khan's 'I Feel For You' (9)
8. Club Nouveau's Bill Withers' cover (4,2,2)
11. Daft Punk No. 1 featuring Pharrell Williams & Nile Rodgers (3,5)
14. Glenn Tilbrook's songwriting partner in Squeeze (5,7)
17. Motown Founder (5,5)
18. Surname of Ron & Russell from Sparks (4)
19. Girls Aloud cover of Pretenders' hit (3,5,2,3)
22. 1967 debut hit by The Move (5,2,4)
23. Released in 1979, the title of Violinski's only chart hit (4,5)
24. Bass player with The Police (5)
26. New Zealand act of 1996 Top 5 hit 'How Bizarre' (1,1,1)
27. David Bowie's real surname (5)
30. Tina Turner's 'We Don't Need Another Hero' featured in this movie franchise (3,3)
31. Instrument played by Cozy Powell (5)

POPMASTER QUIZ 370

CROSSMASTER 1

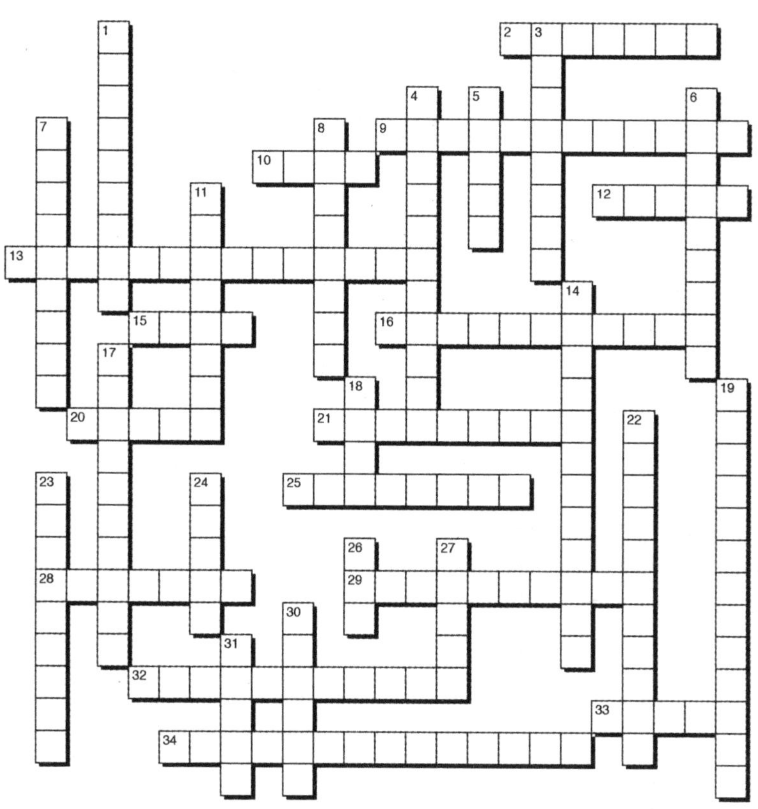

CROSSMASTER 1

POPMASTER QUIZ 371

POPSEARCH 1

Can you find 23 well-known artists and groups from the Seventies glam rock era?

GLAM ROCK ARTISTS POPSEARCH

Z N W U E X F S G D E L P O O H E H T T T O M A R
X E M S I A C L T B B C I N Z P I T Y R O C I H C
V W C K F Q O Z I Z M Z T A Z O R T A U Q I Z U S
L Y O R O X Y M U S I C S E A K G Z E G B M G J D
B O U Q N V S O M B R I A N E N O H B N A P N B P
R R S V R N K E Z T G D T J N W S U A R S I W R Z
C K N Y X X L L O Y E V O V S O S Y C Y D J U T C
O D F E Z D E D W Y T C M I I O S B I O C B M U L
A O R Q U T D E L T O N J O H N O N V D E N Q V Y
T L V P B J V L K M U D B U Q L F P O T J H R F G
W L I A P K I J N D H J Q B A G E M T R R E N X C
K S V S Q E I Y T R D X T N Y E V E Q F K Z J X Z
X D D H H L I I Z H B M Q S S M S J G P U C N U Z
N Y C U A X G B Q A E W T R U T B P Y K H E I V S
T O L S A N V P E O V R A B N D V V V T J A U M A
R L K O V J W U R W L M U N E G R X E H A I G S W
E I I F N I L Y I O M D Y J I D L A I W L Z M P S
X A O I J B N B Z O N J C O W D V Q T E P C R A L
P C R L Y K J H R A G P Q P O F M B L S D L F R G
B U M R B X Z F B O T K G N B V H W G R N A L K F
Z J R Y P Y S R S F Q I N K D V X D D F Q I L S E
U A K C H R E S O W V S X O I I O S E R A L V S H
B C R K E T D U K X Q W X O V H E L L O A B Q L Q
F H A D T P C E P T C O W T A B Z C W B U Z P T A
I O I I F V C Y A C D R Z B D M J Y T L C T Z O E
R P L J N L I D J T W R V B L P F P N A S T I I X
S G G A S J A N G R M A X N W H P F W R Q E G Q W

GLAM ROCK ARTISTS POPSEARCH

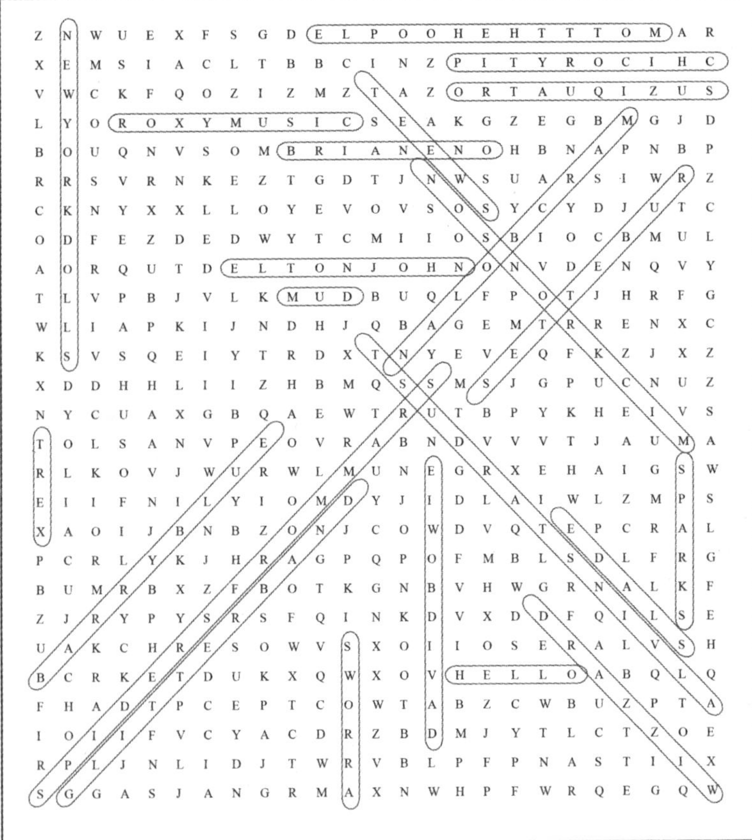

POPMASTER QUIZ 372

POPSEARCH 2

Hidden in the wordsearch below are 24 titles of albums by David Bowie. Can you find them all?

DAVID BOWIE STUDIO ALBUMS POPSEARCH

```
F K T S U D R A T S Y G G I Z A P Y I M N D L O J
N R N U B V X O P X Z A I F M P Z R Q B Y W Z Y W
A S M A A I J E S I O N E T I H W E I T K C A L B
B P T L S C B K B K M U H H X S E C Q T P J V C E
A A B A J W A H E N V L K E T H E N E X T D A Y N
G C A D L T V A Z U H O K A A G X A L O A R J E Y
X E V D L F F S T L Z U W T X G U O I A P P V H U
A O S I X O D Y S H N W N H D H O Z X H X E P G H
I D X N F E W T Q W T R T E Z U I Z M T R X A U T
W D C S H M N I Q L B V H N T W S S Y L Y Q N J D
S I K A L V Q L D A U X T S T L E S E P U K D X L
C T K N P N I A K E P D I Z C Q G T V F Y I O O R
A Y N E I O Z E N H T D F Z F D M H S D K F B D O
R N C D G I E R M G E A D S C E P K O R S V Z J W
Y S A M R T H G A X H H W O D K A R A N M R Z P E
M G J U H A O N O S E V I O K E Y T A Y S A N W H
O O M S D T N I U Q K N W F U N G C H F A C W B T
N D N X H S W L D O X N H C X J I D H G X K T X D
S D O Z T O D H N M S Y X A S R E E B R I Y I K L
T N J G H T S T W Y Y R J L E C X P A N U N E G O
E O C X E N J R Y P R V L M N Z Y T S C I Z O C S
R M T C R O W A X E Y R A A N W S Y P E R V M T O
S A S L O I W E Z A Q G D L C K S M U H E N G J H
U I H H E T I U H B N S G N C R V P N J G Q B I W
C D P H S A W H M U T B N A U F B K I Q D S K Y N
I D Z A K T S J O E M Z L O G P L A P D O P I H A
Q W U C T S Z Y L F U B H D P Y V K Z N L K Z P M
```

DAVID BOWIE STUDIO ALBUMS POPSEARCH

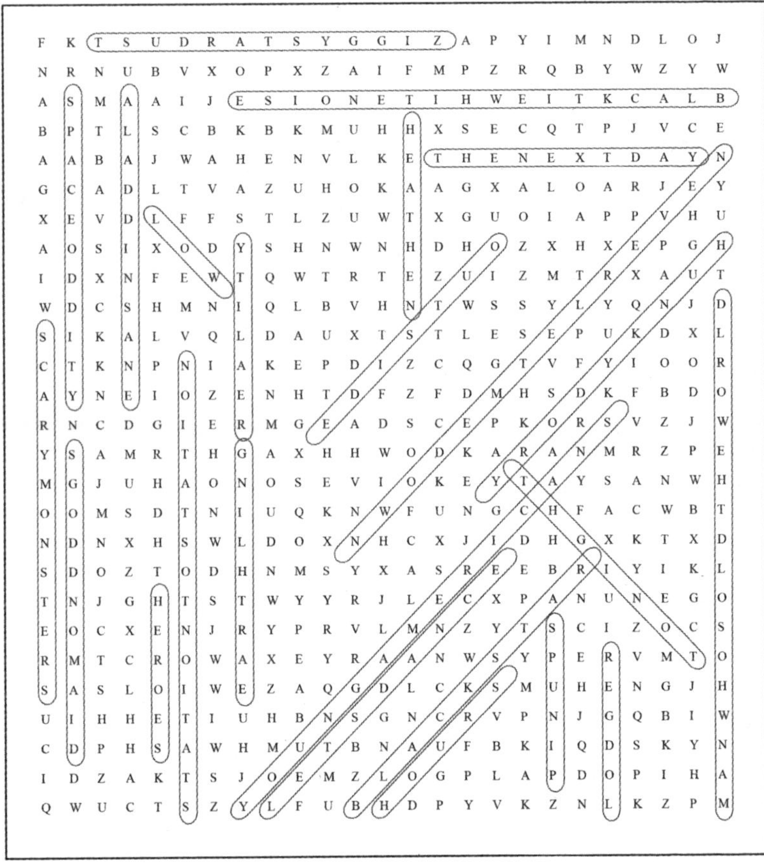
F K T S U D R A T S Y G G I Z A P Y I M N D L O J
N R N U B V X O P X Z A I F M P Z R Q B Y W Z Y W
A S M A A I J E S I O N E T I H W E I T K C A L B
B P T L S C B K B K M U H H X S E C Q T P J V C E
A A B A J W A H E N V L K E T H E N E X T D A Y N
G C A D L T V A Z U H O K A A G X A L O A R J E Y
X E V D L F F S T L Z U W T X G U O I A P P V H U
A O S I X O D Y S H N W N H D H O Z X H X E P G H
I D X N F E W T Q W T R T E Z U I Z M T R X A U T
W D C S H M N I Q L B V H N T W S S Y L Y Q N J D
S I K A L V Q L D A U X T S T L E S E P U K D X L
C T K N P N I A K E P D I Z C Q G T V F Y I O O R
A Y N E I O Z E N H T D F Z F D M H S D K F B D O
R N C D G I E R M G E A D S C E P K O R S V Z J W
Y S A M R T H G A X H H W O D K A R A N M R Z P E
M G J U H A O N O S E V I O K E Y T A Y S A N W H
O O M S D T N I U Q K N W F U N G C H F A C W B T
N D N X H S W L D O X N H C X J I D H G X K T X D
S D O Z T O D H N M S Y X A S R E E B R I Y I K L
T N J G H T S T W Y Y R J L E C X P A N U N E G O
E O C X E N J R Y P R V L M N Z Y T S C I Z O C S
R M T C R O W A X E Y R A A N W S Y P E R V M T O
S A S L O I W E Z A Q G D L C K S M U H E N G J H
U I H H E T I U H B N S G N C R V P N J G Q B I W
C D P H S A W H M U T B N A U F B K I Q D S K Y N
I D Z A K T S J O E M Z L O G P L A P D O P I H A
Q W U C T S Z Y L F U B H D P Y V K Z N L K Z P M

POPMASTER QUIZ 373

RECORD PRODUCERS

Can you name the record producer or production team at the controls of the following singles?

QUESTION 1
'Get Ready' by The Temptations, 'My Guy' by Mary Wells, 'Floy Joy' by The Supremes?

QUESTION 2
'Human' by Human League, 'Miss You Much' by Janet Jackson, 'Just Be Good To Me' by S.O.S. Band?

QUESTION 3
'Parklife' by Blur, 'Linger' by The Cranberries, 'I Predict A Riot' by Kaiser Chiefs?

QUESTION 4
'Watching The Detectives' by Elvis Costello, 'Stop Your Sobbing' by The Pretenders, 'New Rose' by The Damned?

QUESTION 5
'She's Gone' by Daryl Hall & John Oates, 'Waiting For A Star To Fall' by Boy Meets Girl, 'Wood Beez (Pray Like Aretha Franklin)' by Scritti Politti?

QUESTION 6
'Why' by Annie Lennox, 'Leave Right Now' by Will Young, 'It's Raining Men' by Geri Halliwell?

QUESTION 7
'Space Oddity' by David Bowie, 'Your Song' by Elton John, 'Streets Of London' by Ralph McTell?

QUESTION 8
'When Will I See You Again' by The Three Degrees, 'Me and Mrs Jones' by Billy Paul, 'Back Stabbers' by The O'Jays?

QUESTION 9
'Come On Eileen' by Dexy's Midnight Runners, 'Our House' by Madness, 'Reward' by The Teardrop Explodes?

QUESTION 10
'Sultans Of Swing' by Dire Straits, 'This Town Ain't Big Enough For Both Of Us' by Sparks, 'Love Me Like I Love You' by Bay City Rollers?

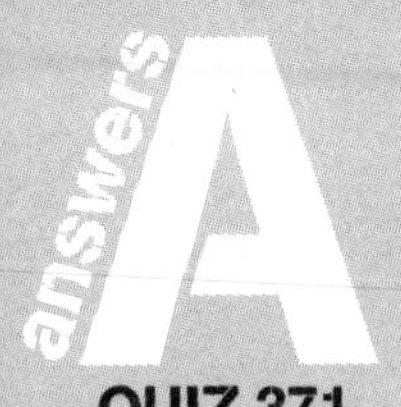

QUIZ 371

Q1
Smokey Robinson (billed just as "Smokey" on the original American releases)

Q2
Jimmy Jam & Terry Lewis

Q3
Stephen Street

Q4
Nick Lowe

Q5
Arif Mardin

Q6
Stephen Lipson

Q7
Gus Dudgeon

Q8
Kenny Gamble & Leon Huff

Q9
Clive Langer & Alan Winstanley

Q10
Muff Winwood

QUIZ 374 POPMASTER

CROSSMASTER 2

Fill the answer to each pop-themed clue into the crossword opposite.

Across

4. Sang 'Mockingbird' with Carly Simon in 1974 (5,6)
7. Group sounded eager to have hit with their 2004 chart debut 'Somewhere Only We Know' (5)
9. There's nothing unstable about this 1985 Ashford & Simpson hit (5)
12. Bruno's favourite planet? (4)
14. The most alliterative Police single (2,2,2,2,2,2,2,2)
16. Olivia Newton-John's character in 'Grease' (5)
22. Singer who made her Top 40 debut in 2010 with 'Starry Eyed' (5,8)
24. 1996 George Michael album that included 'Jesus To A Child' & 'Fastlove' (5)
26. Zayn, Louis, Harry, Niall…who? (4)
27. a-ha's Bond song (3,6,9)
30. Dr Feelgood's favourite libations (4,3,7)

Down

1. Bullets fired by 10cc (6)
2. McKee, Muldaur, Vidal…Blondie? (5)
3. Sang alongside Joe on the 2016 UK Eurovision song 'You're Not Alone' (4)
5. Greatest hits album by Bob Marley & The Wailers that has spent over 14 years on the Top 100 (6)
6. Band that sang both 'Masquerade' and 'Charade' in 1979 (5)
8. Animal that has brought Lulu, Survivor & Mud chart success (5)
10. Darn renumbers need a new order for group's singer (7,6)
11. Singer songwriter with hit albums 'Long Way Down' & 'Wrong Crowd' (3,5)
13. A number one Radiohead album you might have forgot (8)
15. According to The Sweet, love is like this (6)
17. East 17 cover of Pet Shop Boys (4,3,5)
18. Song title common to hits by both Kylie and Kate (3)
19. Animal featured in hit songs by Stone Roses, Boomtown Rats & Toy Dolls (8)
20. Mark Owen's 1997 solo single sounds a bit fruity (10)
21. Italian song that Elvis turned into 'It's Now Or Never' (1,4,3)
23. Colour of hits by D12, Jimi Hendrix Experience and Sheb Wooley (6)
25. Alice Cooper's only Top 10 hit of the eighties (6)
28. Acker Bilk's 1976 Top 5 instrumental (4)
29. 1983 Top 3 hit by Freeez (1,1,1)

CROSSMASTER 2

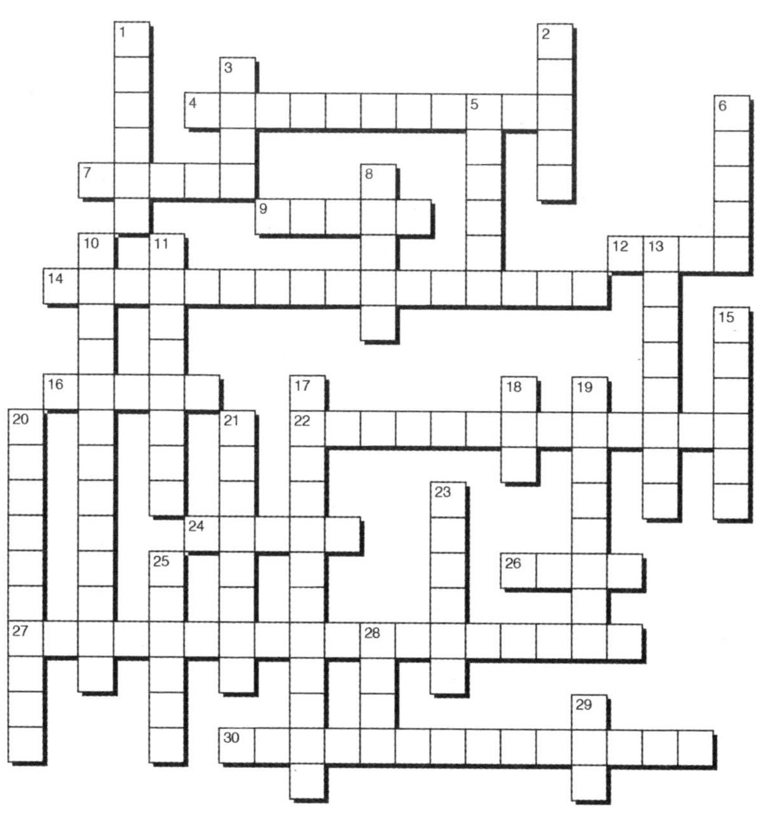

QUIZ 374 POPMASTER

CROSSMASTER 2

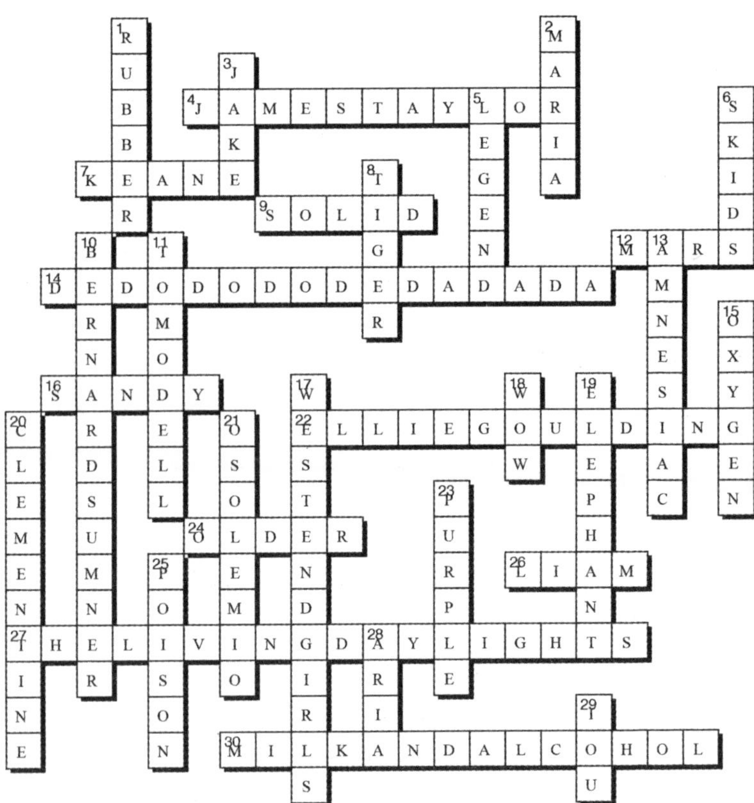

POPMASTER QUIZ 375

POPSEARCH 2

Hidden in the wordsearch below are 19 titles of albums by the Pet Shop Boys. Can you find them all?

PET SHOP BOYS ALBUMS POPSEARCH

C	F	A	H	V	V	H	S	X	C	U	U	A	K	F	L	X	Q	J	P
X	I	J	V	D	Z	G	D	Z	L	F	B	F	C	F	S	L	H	O	Q
N	E	Y	I	P	Q	C	K	T	K	S	I	U	D	C	N	Z	P	P	P
H	I	P	V	V	Q	O	I	J	C	J	L	N	E	B	Q	A	Y	X	W
X	Q	G	M	C	C	M	S	U	N	P	I	D	H	D	R	U	F	W	Q
B	Z	R	H	S	A	J	Q	D	Z	P	N	A	P	T	D	F	K	J	T
K	S	R	I	T	W	R	T	V	A	L	G	M	V	X	D	R	R	O	W
H	N	D	E	R	L	E	H	Z	E	E	U	E	N	Y	Y	X	I	X	J
S	U	P	E	R	H	I	C	B	V	A	A	N	J	C	J	Y	J	X	I
E	U	H	M	E	V	U	F	D	I	S	L	T	B	S	A	E	R	Y	Y
J	H	Y	U	V	G	R	F	E	T	E	G	A	M	A	Y	I	W	E	F
Y	Y	I	I	I	B	J	A	R	C	N	N	L	E	U	J	B	Y	N	V
Y	E	S	N	T	L	L	R	U	E	R	D	C	K	S	I	W	H	N	F
L	S	F	O	A	S	L	F	O	P	L	F	O	I	E	A	S	E	E	G
L	R	Q	M	N	I	A	P	I	S	V	I	K	C	R	M	E	Y	H	J
A	F	M	E	R	W	Z	P	V	O	R	G	Y	P	Y	T	Q	L	L	N
U	M	Z	D	E	X	G	R	A	R	T	A	M	R	O	F	C	G	E	E
T	T	D	N	T	S	T	T	H	T	Y	X	B	N	X	W	J	E	L	R
C	R	G	A	L	V	A	J	E	N	V	P	S	C	J	B	E	S	L	E
A	Y	M	P	A	R	F	E	B	I	R	X	C	P	E	L	T	M	C	E

QUIZ 375 POPMASTER

PET SHOP BOYS ALBUMS POPSEARCH

C	F	A	H	V	V	H	S	X	C	U	U	A	K	F	L	X	Q	J	P
X	I	J	V	D	Z	G	D	Z	L	F	B	F	C	F	S	L	H	O	Q
N	E	Y	I	P	Q	C	K	T	K	S	I	U	D	C	N	Z	P	P	P
H	I	P	V	V	Q	O	I	J	C	J	L	N	E	B	Q	A	Y	X	W
X	Q	G	M	C	C	M	S	U	N	P	I	D	H	D	R	U	F	W	Q
B	Z	R	H	S	A	J	Q	D	Z	P	N	A	P	T	D	F	K	J	T
K	S	R	I	T	W	R	T	V	A	L	G	M	V	X	D	R	R	O	W
H	N	D	E	R	L	E	H	Z	E	E	U	E	N	Y	Y	X	I	X	J
S	U	P	E	R	H	I	C	B	V	A	A	N	J	C	J	Y	J	X	I
E	U	H	M	E	V	U	F	D	I	S	L	T	B	S	A	E	R	Y	Y
J	H	Y	U	V	G	R	F	E	T	E	G	A	M	A	Y	I	W	E	F
Y	Y	I	I	I	B	J	A	R	C	N	N	L	E	U	J	B	Y	N	V
Y	E	S	N	T	L	L	R	U	E	R	D	C	K	S	I	W	H	N	F
L	S	F	O	A	S	L	F	O	P	L	F	O	I	E	A	S	E	E	G
L	R	Q	M	N	I	A	P	I	S	V	I	K	C	R	M	E	Y	H	J
A	F	M	E	R	W	Z	P	V	O	R	G	Y	P	Y	T	Q	L	L	N
U	M	Z	D	E	X	G	R	A	R	T	A	M	R	O	F	C	G	E	E
T	T	D	N	T	S	T	T	H	T	Y	X	B	N	X	W	J	E	L	R
C	R	G	A	L	V	A	J	E	N	V	P	S	C	J	B	E	S	L	E
A	Y	M	P	A	R	F	E	B	I	R	X	C	P	E	L	T	M	C	E

POPMASTER QUIZ 376

POPSEARCH 3

Here's a tricky one. Hidden in the wordsearch below are the names of 39 famous singers and musicians of the past and present. Some are solo acts, some are members of bands. All of the names they perform under are single words.

SINGLE NAME SINGERS POPSEARCH

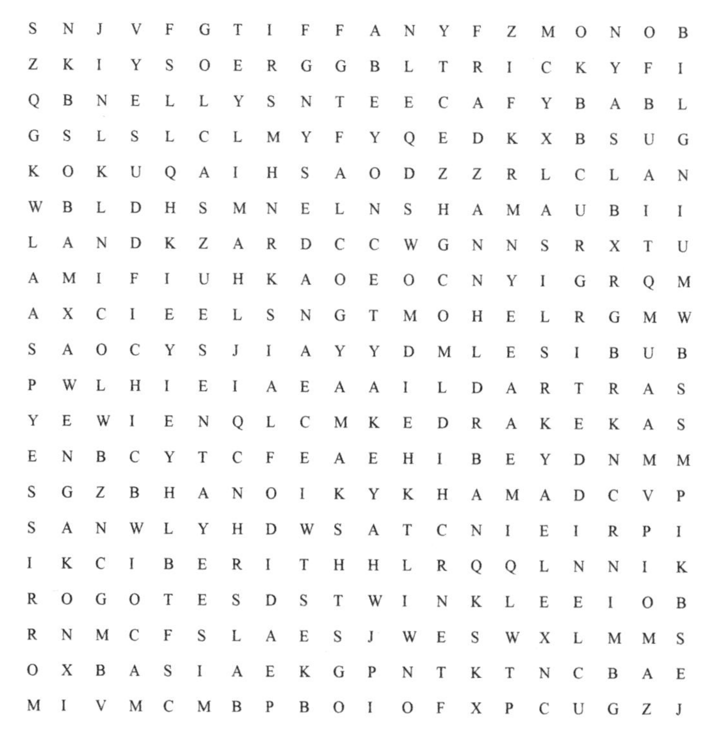

S	N	J	V	F	G	T	I	F	F	A	N	Y	F	Z	M	O	N	O	B
Z	K	I	Y	S	O	E	R	G	G	B	L	T	R	I	C	K	Y	F	I
Q	B	N	E	L	L	Y	S	N	T	E	E	C	A	F	Y	B	A	B	L
G	S	L	S	L	C	L	M	Y	F	Y	Q	E	D	K	X	B	S	U	G
K	O	K	U	Q	A	I	H	S	A	O	D	Z	Z	R	L	C	L	A	N
W	B	L	D	H	S	M	N	E	L	N	S	H	A	M	A	U	B	I	I
L	A	N	D	K	Z	A	R	D	C	C	W	G	N	N	S	R	X	T	U
A	M	I	F	I	U	H	K	A	O	E	O	C	N	Y	I	G	R	Q	M
A	X	C	I	E	E	L	S	N	G	T	M	O	H	E	L	R	G	M	W
S	A	O	C	Y	S	J	I	A	Y	Y	D	M	L	E	S	I	B	U	B
P	W	L	H	I	E	I	A	E	A	A	I	L	D	A	R	T	R	A	S
Y	E	W	I	E	N	Q	L	C	M	K	E	D	R	A	K	E	K	A	S
E	N	B	C	Y	T	C	F	E	A	E	H	I	B	E	Y	D	N	M	M
S	G	Z	B	H	A	N	O	I	K	Y	K	H	A	M	A	D	C	V	P
S	A	N	W	L	Y	H	D	W	S	A	T	C	N	I	E	I	R	P	I
I	K	C	I	B	E	R	I	T	H	H	L	R	Q	Q	L	N	N	I	K
R	O	G	O	T	E	S	D	S	T	W	I	N	K	L	E	E	I	O	B
R	N	M	C	F	S	L	A	E	S	J	W	E	S	W	X	L	M	M	S
O	X	B	A	S	I	A	E	K	G	P	N	T	K	T	N	C	B	A	E
M	I	V	M	C	M	B	P	B	O	I	O	F	X	P	C	U	G	Z	J

SINGLE NAME SINGERS POPSEARCH

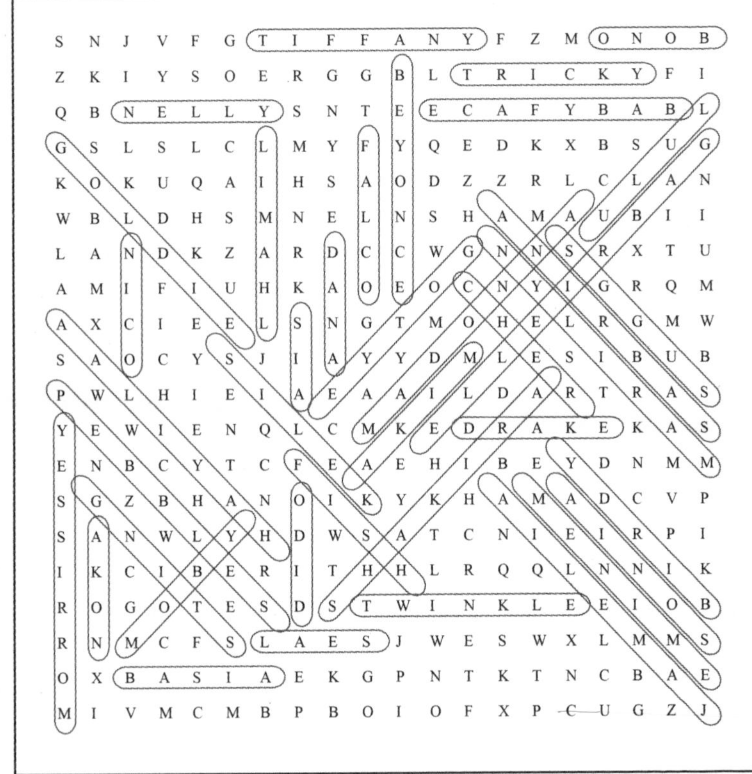

POPMASTER QUIZ 377

MISSING WORDS

Here is a list of ten song each with one word missing from the title, can you name the performer and fill in the blank?

A answers

QUESTION 1
The Importance Of Being--------‘? (From 2005)

QUESTION 2
‘One ---- Woman’ (from 1980)

QUESTION 3
‘Let The ------Control Your Body’? (From 1994)

QUESTION 4
‘My------Is Coming In’? (From 1965)

QUESTION 5
‘--- For The Weekend’? (From 2016)

QUESTION 6
‘I’ll Put You ---------Again’? (From 1979)

QUESTION 7
‘Have You Ever--------Loved A Woman’? (From 1995)

QUESTION 8
‘--- Of Our Lives’ (from 1999)

QUESTION 9
‘I Will Never Let You------‘? (From 2014)

QUESTION 10
‘Banana---’ (from 1975)

QUIZ 377

Q1
'Idle'
Oasis

Q2
'Man'
Sheena Easton

Q3
'Beat'
2 Unlimited

Q4
'Ship'
The Walker Brothers

Q5
'Hymn'
Coldplay feat. Beyonce (uncredited)

Q6
'Together'
Hot Chocolate

Q7
'Really'
Bryan Adams

Q8
'Summertime'
A1

Q9
'Down'
Rita Ora

Q10
'Rock'
The Wombles

QUIZ 378 POPMASTER

CROSSMASTER 3

Fill the answer to each pop-themed clue into the crossword opposite.

Across

1. Mr Mister's 'Wings', The Adventures' 'Land' and Alexandra Burke's 'Heels' (6)
3. Released 2006 No. 1 album 'Black Holes & Revelations' (4)
4. Early seventies Top 5 movie theme from Isaac Hayes (5)
7. Perrie, Jesy, Leigh-Anne & Jade (6,4)
9. Male name in Top 10 hits by Pat Boone, The Piglets and Fine Young Cannibals (6)
12. Reached Top 5 in 1991 with 'Sunshine On A Rainy Day (3)
14. Singer with Libertines & Babyshambles (5,7)
19. Singer who got more than a dollar for guest vocal on Avicii's No. 1 'Wake Me Up' (4,5)
21. Title of Alison Moyet's debut solo number one album (3)
22. Carly Simon, Annie Lennox, Bronski Beat, 3T (3)
23. Paul Weller's 'Wood', Maxi Priest's 'World', Susan Boyle's 'Horses' (4)
24. 1982 'Give Me Back My Heart' and 'Videoteque' duo (6)
25. Sang 'The Word Girl' and 'Absolute' in the mid-eighties (7,7)
27. Surname of chart singers Angie, Joss and R&J (5)
28. China Crisis 'found religion' on debut Top 40 hit (9)
29. Female name in seventies hits by Rolling Stones and Helen Reddy (5)
30. American singer Dan who wrote 'Relight My Fire' (7)

Down

1. 'More Than A Feeling' group and location of Sensational Alex Harvey Band's 'Tea Party' (6)
2. British singer with Top 20 cover version of 'Don't Dream It's Over' in 1991 (4,5)
5. Was Wizzard involved in a fracas on this playing field in 1972? (4,4,8)
6. Chic's 'Times', The Beach Boys' 'Vibrations' and Inner City's 'Life' (4)
8. Sinead O'Connor's 1988 Top 40 debut (8)
10. The No. 1 colour for The Beatles, Christie and Dawn featuring Tony Orlando (6)
11. Lead single from Dire Straits' 'Brothers In Arms' (2,3,4)
13. Reached No. 1 with 'Orinoco Flow' (4)
14. Late sixties hit by Judy Clay & William Bell (7,6)
15. City in song titles by Boney M & Simple Minds (7)
16. 'Unbelievable' hitmakers of the early nineties (1,1,1)
17. Sang the Top 10 hit 'Another Step (Closer To You)' with Kim Wilde in 1987 (6)
18. Crowded House singer and songwriter (4,4)
20. Liam Gallagher's post-Oasis group (5,3)
25. Favourite day of the week for Small Faces, Blondie and Oasis (6)
26. Germany's 'Da Da Da' band from 1982 (4)
27. 1978 Top 40 debut by Evelyn 'Champagne' King (5)

POPMASTER QUIZ 378

CROSSMASTER 3

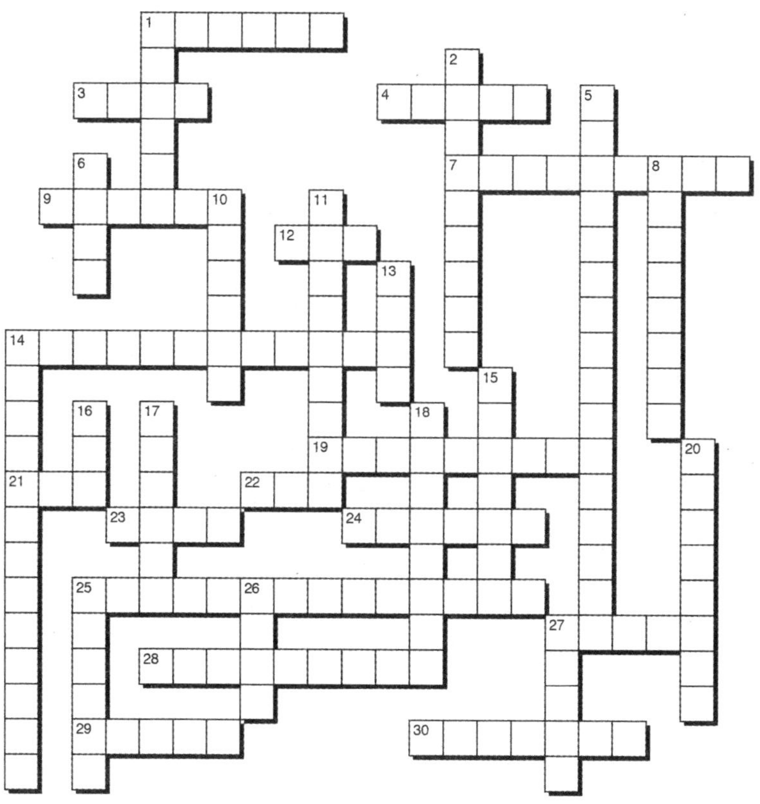

QUIZ 378 POPMASTER

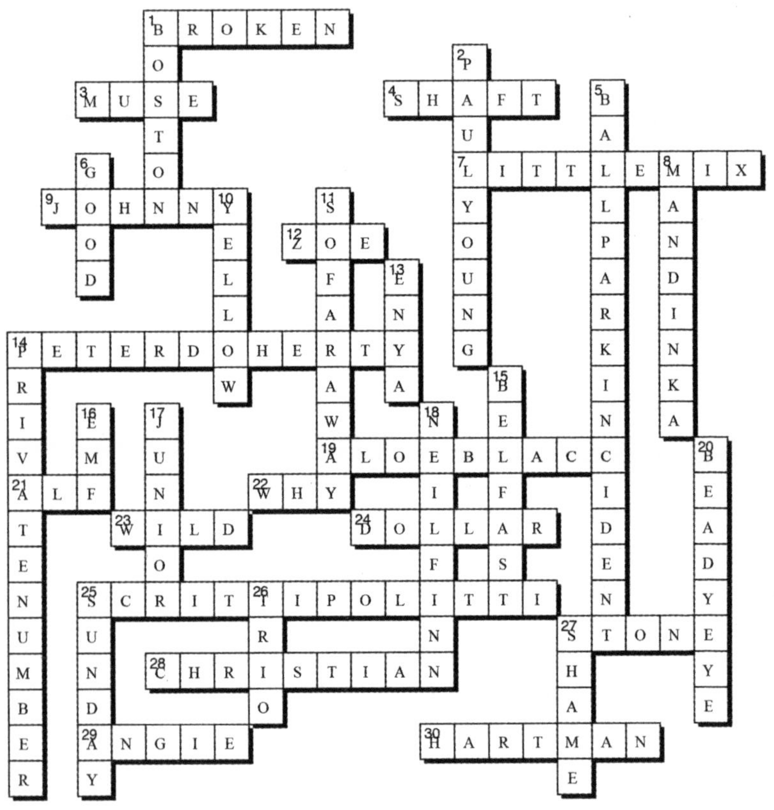

POPMASTER QUIZ 379

POPSEARCH 4

Here's a even trickier one. Hidden in the wordsearch below are the names of 17 chart hits, none of whose titles were in English.

FOREIGN LANGUAGE HITS POPSEARCH

C W O Y U X H V V O H T T G X P P X Q M M J Y F G
W B P C V A D O V I A E D A B Q H I Q H F I M U D
D Y G O B G Q M J M C M O E U Q M H F O S H A K J
V E K P T P D L R N A G A S B R D I J J R N N O R
L K D N G T M A A K M C W D A M O V J T T F E G D
F E Z A C E W R H X N W A J L M K F P A Q L D O M
U Y A F R I F N N L F E K R R Z K I N J E L M U B
G E P Z Z E S N J V I A F U E U K A P T B I X J P
F K R B D M K H V W F E O H V N M C A P N S E E A
P E X R H E Y B T R E P T E B E A X T I Z Y T E K
D P U V S Y D F J B E H P N R T I Z Q E S W R L T
V O S J Z K G J L N F A V A I F A U P U R J Y D Q
T B M D Z L N Y A C N I V A P D E T L X X A H O M
Q V J L L L U L F H C Q Y D F O A P X A F H L F C
W D N C P D P M X A C S F J U B N E J D N X A O Y
M E H D Z A D O X N Y A P P Y O I R T F U I S O V
H E C E C D N B W S W N G L N H A O N S H U N C S
E H D W I Q Z U H O S I R I B G Y I A J O E A M J
Q R A M K D V O M N O R O H C W O E F A L G I H I
R A D W A K X C N D M M U M Q L G N T U S D A W C
C H A P Y I D A L A E P M D H W R I H C V V P R R
W N B R I Y T P N M K W F I P T L I X A J T G M D
N P M S K X S W I O G K L E C O L M F P B E C Z I
Z B A T U G V A B U I M G A L P A D K C O O X N D
H X L B S N T B X R B Q M I Y N A T J Z H J T B G
D K H S F E M Q A K W M O T B J R E Z U F T I U G
K D B Z J Y F Q T B R M I M V Z P I Q S U K Z K A

QUIZ 379 POPMASTER

FOREIGN LANGUAGE HITS POPSEARCH

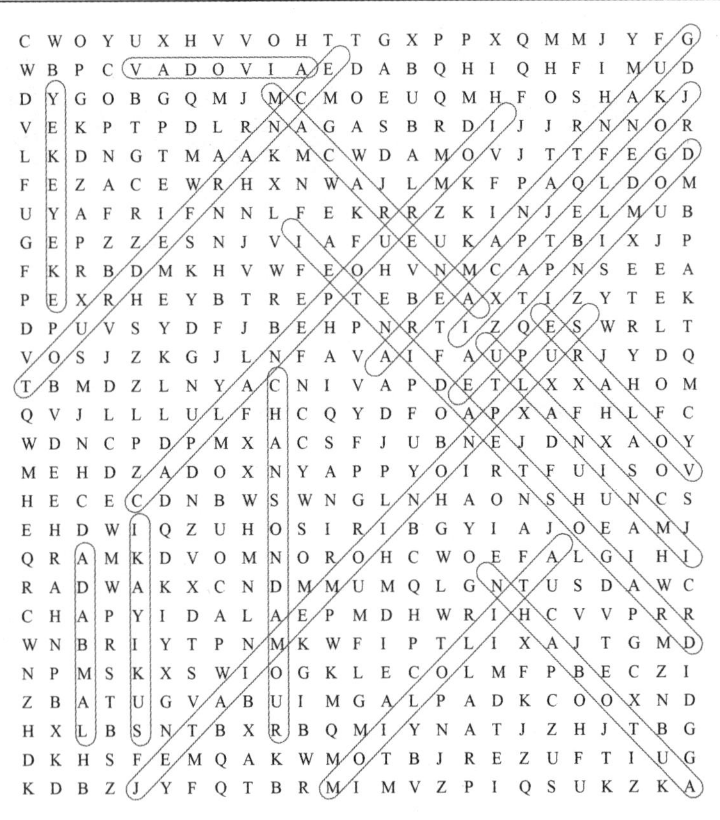

POPMASTER QUIZ 380

Here are twenty album sleeves with the words removed or obscured. Award yourself one point for correctly identifying the album and another for naming the act.

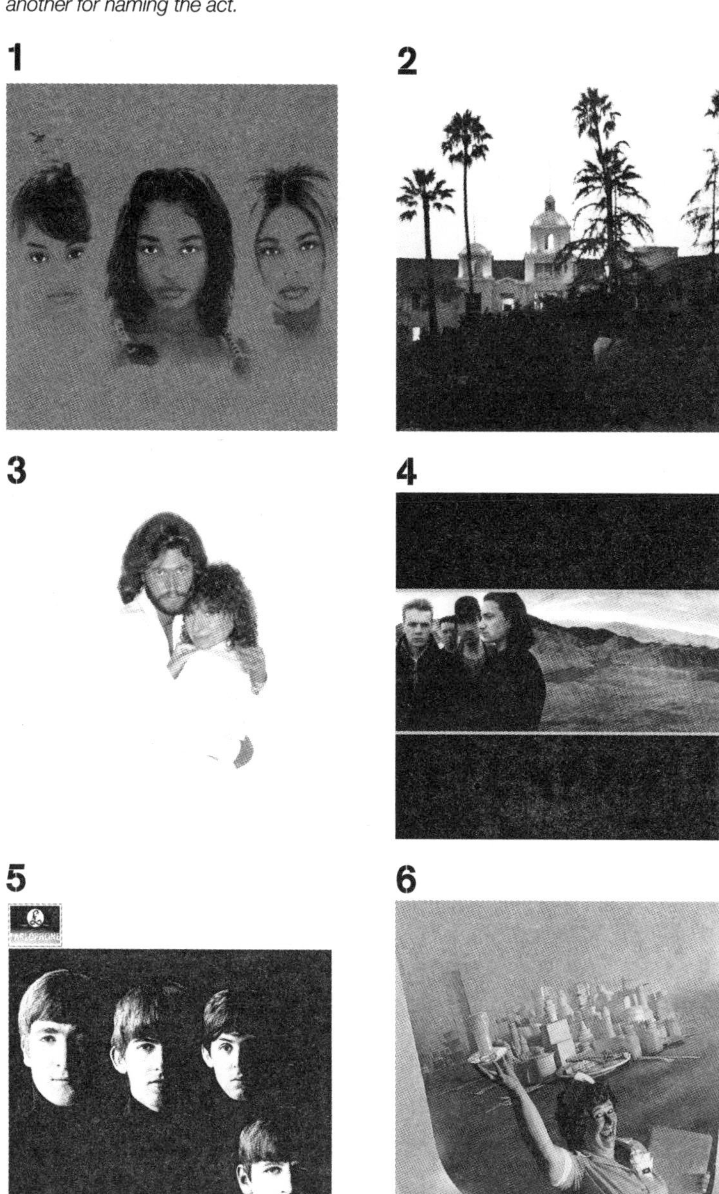

QUIZ 380 POPMASTER

7

8

9

10

11

12

13

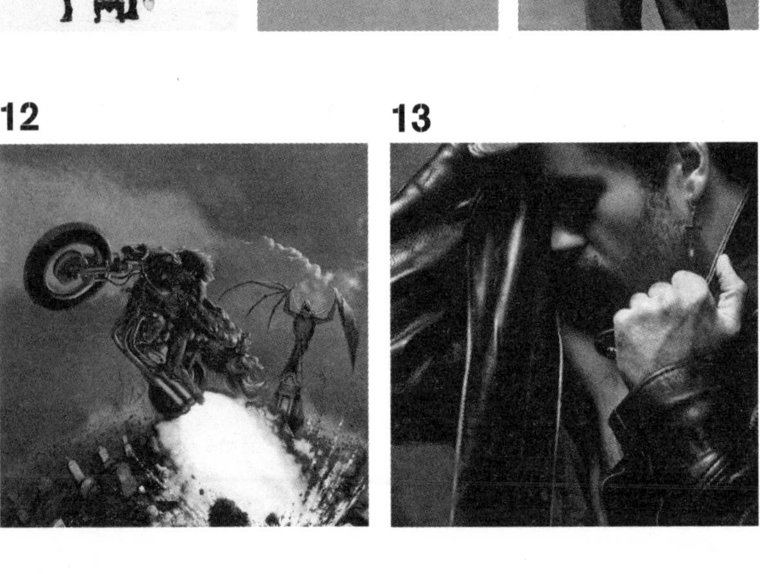

POPMASTER QUIZ 380

14

15

16

17

18

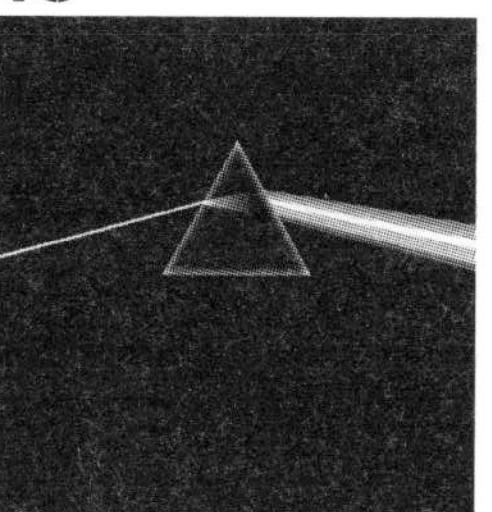

19

20

QUIZ 380

Q1
Crazysexycool – TLC

Q2
Hotel California – The Eagles

Q3
Guilty – Barbra Streisand

Q4
The Unforgettable Fire – U2

Q5
With The Beatles – The Beatles

Q6
Breakfast in America – Supertramp

Q7
The Marshall Mathers LP – Eminem

Q8
Tapestry – Carole King

Q9
Rumours – Fleetwood Mac

Q10
Brothers in Arms – Dire Straits

QUIZ 381 POPMASTER

Here's one for lovers of vinyl. Can you name the record labels who released the records that were housed in these inner sleeves?

1

2

3

4

5

POPMASTER QUIZ 381

6

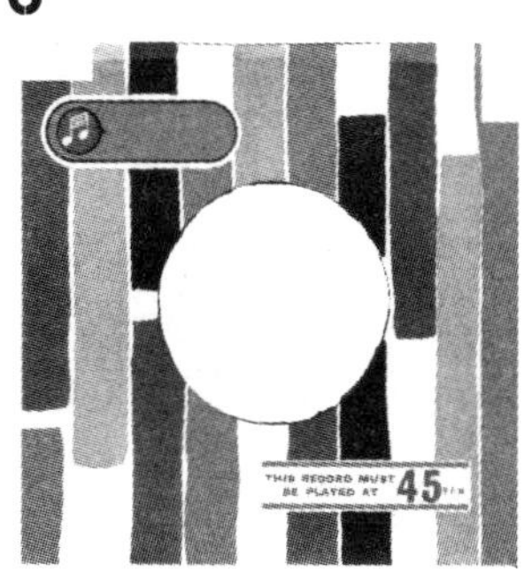

7

8

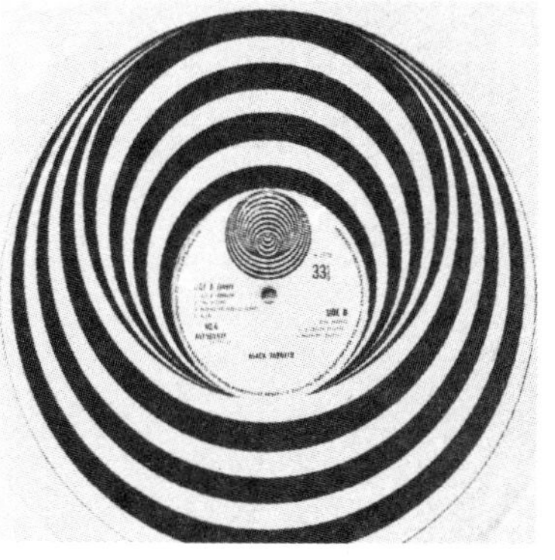

9

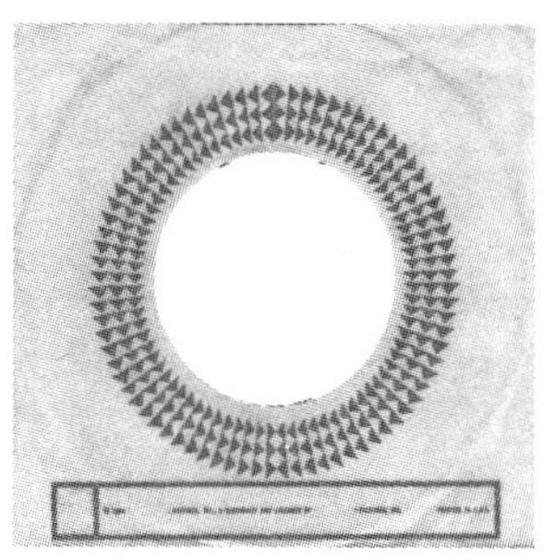

10

Answers

QUIZ 380

Q11
Born in the USA – Bruce Springsteen

Q12
Bat Out of Hell – Meatloaf

Q13
Faith – George Michael

Q14
IV (aka Four Symbols) – Led Zeppelin

Q15
Music Box – Mariah Carey

Q16
No Jacket Required – Phil Collins

Q17
What's the Story (Morning Glory) – Oasis

Q18
Dark Side of the Moon – Pink Floyd

Q19
Between the Buttons – The Rolling Stones

Q20
Private Dancer – Tina Turner

QUIZ 381

Q1
A&M

Q2
Berwick

Q3
Mercury

Q4
HMV

Q5
Fontana

Q6
Columbia

Q7
Tamla Motown

Q8
Vertigo

Q9

Q10
Pye

QUIZ 382 POPMASTER

Here are ten picture sleeves of hit singles from the Seventies - can you name both the hit song and the chart act?

1

2

3

4

5

POPMASTER QUIZ 382

6

7

8

9

10

QUIZ 382

Q1
'Picture This', Blondie

Q2
'Love's Gotta Hold on Me', Dollar

Q3
'Love will Tear us Apart', Joy Division

Q4
'Working for the Yankee Dollar, The Skids

Q5
'America', David Essex

Q6
'Listen to What the Main Said', Wings

Q7
'I Can't Stand Losing You', The Police

Q8
'Mr Blue Sky', ELO

Q9
'No More Heroes', The Stanglers

Q10
'We Are the Champions', Queen

QUIZ 383 POPMASTER

Here are ten picture sleeves of hit singles from the Eighties - can you name both the hit song and the chart act?

1

2

3

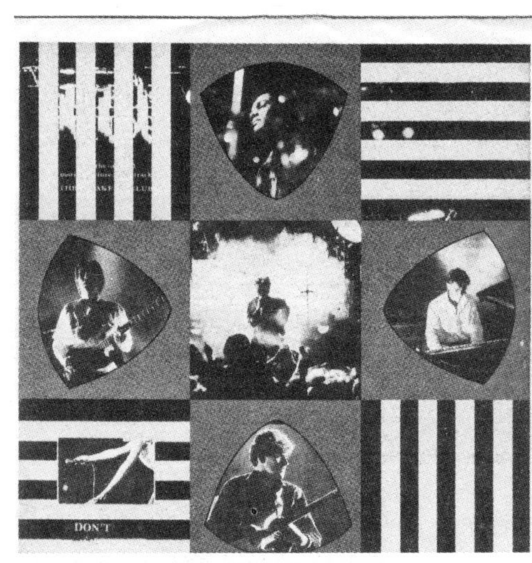

4

5

POPMASTER QUIZ 383

6

7

8

9

10

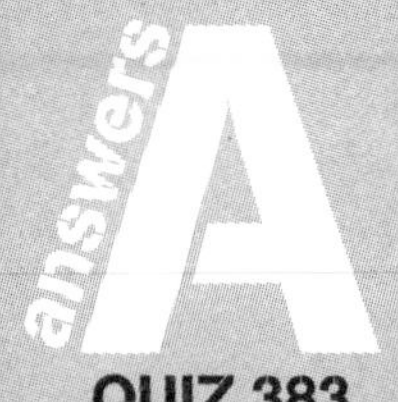

QUIZ 383

Q1
'Who's That Girl?', Eurythmics

Q2
'Respectable', Mel & Kim

Q3
'Don't You (Forget About Me)', Simple Minds

Q4
'Cloudbusting', Kate Bush

Q5
'Holding Back the Years', Simply Red

Q6
'Road to Nowhere', Talking Heads

Q7
'Don't Go', Yazoo

Q8
'Desire', U2

Q9
'Raspberry Beret', Prince

Q10
'Two Tribes', Frankie Goes to Hollywood

QUIZ 384 POPMASTER

CROSSMASTER 4

Fill the answer to each pop-themed clue into the crossword opposite.

Across

3. Pulp's '...People' (6)
6. Beyonce's album beverage (8)
8. Temptations' Eddie who kept on truckin' in 1973 (9)
10. American trio with 90s hits 'Waterfalls', 'Unpretty' and 'Creep' (1,1,1)
11. Vocal group who reached Top 40 in 1974 and 1982 with 'After The Goldrush' (7)
12. According to Scouting For Girls, this legendary singer '...Ain't Dead' (5)
15. Hue and Cry were looking for her in 1989 (5)
17. Hit group of 1980 double 'A' side 'A Lover's Holiday/The Glow of Love' (6)
19. Tall building loved by both Sam Bailey & Demi Levato (10)
21. Sugababes first No.1 single (5,4,2)
24. Surname of both Eagle-Eye and Neneh (6)
25. The only Top 40 single by Bruce Hornsby & The Range (3,3,2,2)
26. Spandau Ballet, East 17, TAFKAP, Beverley Knight (4)
31. 2004 Top 5 duet by Ronan Keating & LeAnn Rimes (4,5,2,2,4)
32. His only number one is 1999's 'Praise You' (6,4)
33. They were 'Worried About Ray' on their 2007 Top 5 hit (8)
34. 'Hold My Hand', 'Take Me Home' and 'Right Here' singer (4,6)
35. Michael & Emily of Glastonbury fame (5)

Down

1. Fat Les's 1998 curry (8)
2. Brother in both Hot Chocolate and Modern Talking hits (5)
3. Both 'On The Road Again' group and title of Jamiroquai hit (6,4)
4. Elton's partner on his 1976 No.1 duet (4,3)
5. 1972 Stylistics hit covered by Prince as 'The Artist' in 1996 (6,2,5,3)
7. 1971 and 2002 number one for George Harrison (2,5,4)
9. Did the Ramones' punk rocker go on to be a 'Modern Girl'? (6)
13. Australian singer who had 'Cheap Thrills' in 2016 (3)
14. The name of Free's brother according to the group's Top 5 hit (4)
16. Nirvana's album that includes 'In Bloom, 'Lithium' and 'Come As You Are' (9)
18. Latin-titled 1973 hit for Steeleye Span (7)
19. Billy Corgan's wonderful squash plant band! (8,8)
20. City favoured by Kenny Ball in 1961 and Michael Jackson in 1996 (6)
22. Younger Gibb brother who sang 'An Everlasting Love' in 1978 (4)
23. Liverpool band with 90s hits 'Walkaway', 'Free Me' and 'Flying (4)
27. Catatonia's motoring anger? (4,4)
28. Drumming sister of Richard Carpenter (5)
29. Elvis Costello, Devo, Lene Lovich and The Damned have all recorded for this label (5)
30. George Benson, Coldplay, Natalie Imbruglia (6)

POPMASTER QUIZ 384

CROSSMASTER 4

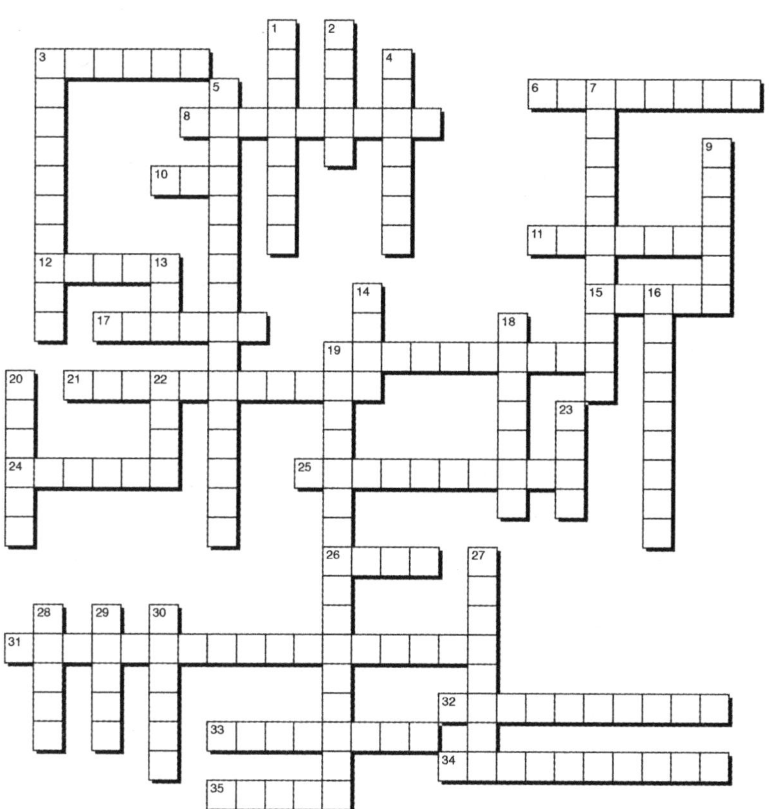

CROSSMASTER 4

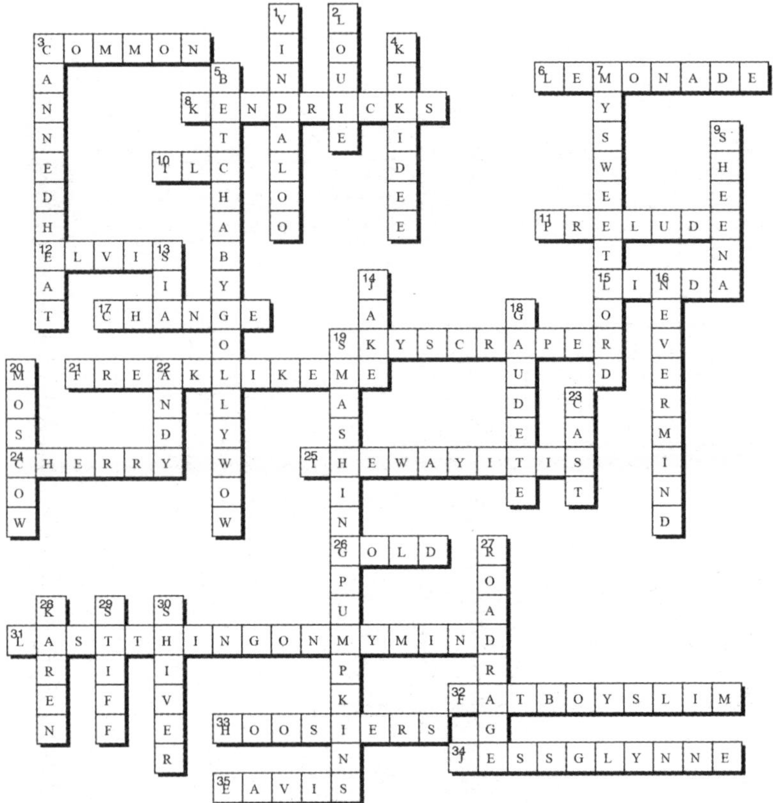

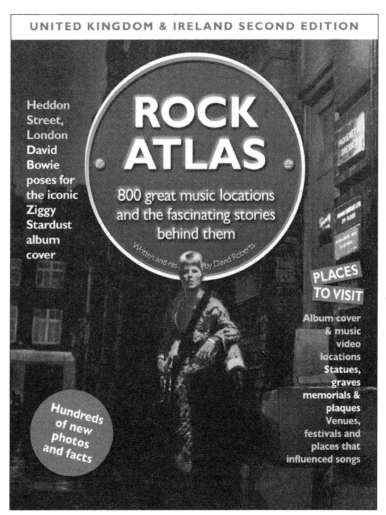

About the authors

Phil Swern on Neil Myners

When Ken Bruce and his producer at the time, Colin Martin, invited me to help develop a quiz for their new look Radio 2 show, we sat over an enjoyable lunch and a bottle or two of Merlot and devised PopMaster. It has now been running daily since 1996.

My job was to write all the questions, make up the music clips for the bonus rounds and deliver them a final package, which I continued to do for five years. But then I found it was taking up half my working week. So I decided to recruit a couple of colleagues – Shaun Greenfield to help with the questions and Simon Bray with the music clips. However, in 2003 Shaun realized he could no longer dedicate his time to the project, so I had the task of finding a new co-compiler.

My first thought was Neil Myners, as we had worked together on a number of various bank holiday specials for Radio 2. I was delighted when he agreed to take on the challenge and he has continued to work with me on the questions ever since.

When I suggested the idea of producing a PopMaster book to Red Planet, they were really enthusiastic about the concept and quickly commissioned it. I immediately invited Neil to co-write with me. This second volume was decided upon at quite short notice and it was only Neil who persuaded me that we could prepare it in time for the publication deadline. It's thanks to him that you are holding this edition of the PopMaster quiz book right now.

Neil Myners on Phil Swern

Paths cross in radio with alarming frequency. I've known Phil since the late Nineties, although it would be a few years before we began working together. He was producer of 'Pick Of The Pops' with Alan Freeman whilst I was working with 'Fluff' on his light classics show 'Their Greatest Bits'; we'd regularly chat at the weekly BBC Radio 2 playlist meetings; we both freelanced at the same production company.

Add to this a mutual love of record-collecting, albeit with vastly different sized libraries, meant working with 'Dr Pop' seemed a natural progression. That chance arose when Phil kindly asked if I'd like to work with him on ideas he had for Radio 2. We quickly found the best business and programme plotting was done over lunch at La Vigna, an excellent though now-defunct Italian restaurant.

Our first collaboration was a 2002 special celebrating the 50th anniversary of the charts. This was quickly followed by 'Twos On 2' – a show about the greatest songs to reach number two. A simple but very effective idea from the mind of Mr Swern, it led to a compilation album and many more special programmes. All our co-productions were Phil's ideas. I was just very pleased to be asked along for the ride.

In the spring of 2003, Phil asked if I'd join the Popmaster team. This request felt a bit surreal as, along with countless other radio listeners at home, I'd enjoyed my daily dose of being an armchair contestant since it started. Twelve years later and here we are with book number two. I'm still very grateful to him for the opportunity to work on this much-loved quiz.

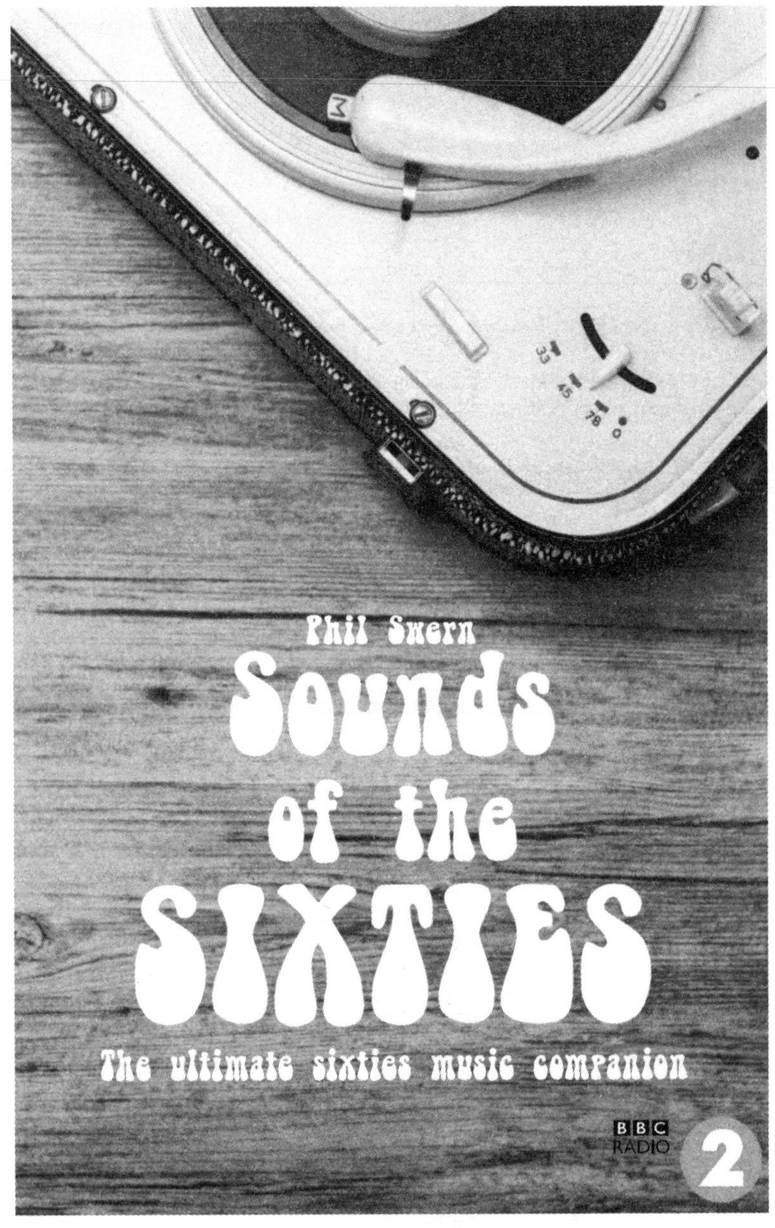
Phil Swern
Sounds of the SIXTIES
The ultimate sixties music companion
BBC RADIO 2